All the best
with love.
Shahla Shahmiri
06.28.19

TEARS OF
ONIONS

THE GIFT OF FINDING REFUGE
IN OUR OWN LIVES

BY SHAHLA SHAHMIRI

Inspired Forever Book Publishing
Dallas, Texas

Inspired Forever Book Publishing™
"Words with Lasting Impact"
Dallas, Texas
(888) 403-2727

Printed in the United States of America
Library of Congress Control Number: 2019935120

ISBN-13: 978-1-948903-01-1

TABLE OF CONTENTS

PROLOGUE

Why I Wrote *Tears of Onions*

There was a season in my life when I lost everything. Amid that period, and for years afterwards, my soul felt unfulfilled and empty. I lost all hope. All the while, I was longing to return to a point in life when I was joyful, a period when I was loved, and a time when I was amped up about life.

One day as I looked out my kitchen window feeling numb, even as tears rolled down my cheek, I shut my eyes and let my mind take me back to a time when life was simple and friendship meant everything. I had wanted to write this book for almost two decades but never had the courage to do so. Deep down, I was afraid to face my past. Nevertheless, at that moment, I felt like I had nothing left to lose. All that remained was an overwhelming need to find something beautiful to cling to before I drowned in an ocean of pain and hopelessness because there are no words to describe the pain and inner turmoil that result from facing the insurmountable fear of uncertainty that comes after being displaced from your homeland, separated from family and children, and experiencing the death of a loved one as a refugee.

Every word I wrote in this book saved me and rescued me from self-destruction, especially when I remembered the faces of other refugee women who shared personal stories I'd kept in my heart for years. Their stories are presented here in a fictional manner, with each one narrated by a different fictional character. Although it is hard to imagine, such true-to-life accounts do actually take place in the world. *Tears of Onions* is about life, love, struggles, fighting to survive, injustice, unfairness, and how we all share a common ground when it comes to our human nature. In the end, love and simple human compassion can save us all.

Mama Jee's story taught me to never give up. Eldana enabled herself to be free from the guilt of her past, which inspired me to face my own past. Anouk resuscitated my hope in humankind, and she helped me believe that there are still great individuals around. Her biography was a reminder that regardless of the difficulties we face, we still have tomorrow—a fresh new day—and it will be "green." Anouk had this peculiar conviction that green was the color of joy. Ray, who lived the vast majority of his life in the shadows of his dark past, at last discovered protective love in the arms of a stranger. This comfort helped him reach a place of peace that he had longed for all his life. Through Ray, I've discovered that all of us have our "evil spirits" somewhere within us, yet we must each make the choice to confine them and not let the darkness define us. Michael's story taught me how a compassionate coach could become a true giant in the life of a young man and save him from a life of confusion, anger, and pain.

Recalling their faces and stories influenced me to take a close look at myself as I peeled back my life like an onion, layer by layer, until my own truth was revealed. I cried until there were no more tears left. It was ameliorating when I unmasked myself, which led me to acknowledge that I had been alone all those years hiding my inner soul from the outer shell of a person I had become.

In the realization of this disconnect, I found the greatest disclosure of all: I am my own perfect partner and my own guardian angel. Through all the good and bad times I had endured, I remained deeply separated from everyone else. The internal child I found within saved me in the end, pushing me to continue forward and giving me the strength to move on. Frankly, I had never felt that inner power before. However, the acknowledgment and realization of my own strength helped me discover that there are no impediments to accomplishing any dreams that I have.

I owe my life to *Tears of Onions* for showing me that affection and empathy are essential to a more fulfilling life. Never again will I cut onions as a way to cover up the tears of hurt I was not allowed to freely shed. I know this book can save lives, change lives, and show each reader that we are all connected. It will uncover that there is no such mind-bending concept as dejection, particularly when you find the genuine you; there is no emptiness when you fill your heart with affection and seek loving people to surround you. There is no dim alleyway when you understand the path to your life. The power is before you—if you just look somewhat harder, the fog of uncertainty will vanish and the path will be brilliant and radiant for you to stroll through.

Thank you very much for reading and sharing in this journey with me!

Sincerely,

Shahla Shahmiri

THE QUILT
OF LIFE

There was a season in my life's journey when I dwelled in a refugee camp. For most people in such an environment, the number one goal is to get out of that place. It's rather an oxymoron, though. On one hand, I had been emancipated from an even worse situation and placed in the camp for my safety and well being. On the other hand, I had this strong desire to leave the camp. My mind was often preoccupied, dreaming about living far away in a Western country. In anticipation, I waited patiently for the realization of this dream. I was convinced that my life would change for the best. I believed I would find happiness the moment I left the confines of the camp. After all, it was a common understanding that once you left a refugee camp en route to a Western country, then all your worries were over. Overwhelmed with that misinformation, I could not wait to enjoy a worry-free life.

Oh, how wrong I was! In retrospect, the journey was far more exciting than actually reaching the destination. When I first arrived in America, the primary comfort I found was in a local park. There was always a lot of activity in the park; it was the perfect environment to de-stress, away from my busy routine. Have you ever noticed that park benches are placed in just the right spots? Sitting on a park bench, I watched the people around me. Some were running, some were reading, some were walking their dogs. The people who captured my attention most often were the couples or parents with strollers. They all seemed so happy in their little families, but maybe they had their own shattered dreams like me. It's comforting to know that you are not alone in this journey of painful encounters. Several feet away from me was this glowing lake, shimmering elegantly in the rays of sunlight. As time elapsed, I could still feel the kindness of the fading sun and the generous summer breeze on my skin.

For a moment, I closed my eyes and escaped, letting the memories of twenty years ago pull me in. As images flooded my mind, I was not surprised to see Mary's face—we fondly called her Mama Jee. At the refugee camp, her kitchen was our sanctuary, our safe haven. She had created this so-called cooking room to be our comfort place. Without any masks or fear, we could converse with her about any issues. It was also our therapy room because of the love she exuded toward all of us younger women. She was more advanced in her years, yet she had a strong heart like a young warrior. All of us refugees viewed her as our guardian angel. She devoted her life to helping others, as though she did not have issues of her own. Her house was filled with love, and her kitchen was my sacred place. She truly was Mama Jee, a name meaning "Dear Mama" in Urdu.

On one particular day, she invited us to come and make some samosas, which were fried pastries with fillings of one's choice. As we gathered around the kitchen, kneading the dough for the crust, she began to tell us her story. We listened intently.

"Girls!" She looked at each of us one by one, expressing the importance of what she was about to say. "Please listen carefully. All my life, I have been told to not even dare to dream. Not to mention the reminders to not dare to talk with anyone outside of our family circle. Yet I knew deep inside that one day I would dare to talk and dare to dream. You must realize that our dreams sometimes come true. The sky is the limit, no matter what your dreams may be. In this lifetime, we all have opportunities to live our dreams. I am a warrior, not a broken angel. I am a survivor, not a victim. I am a woman with a heart as deep and full of mysteries as an ocean."

Some of her remarks almost sounded like stand-up comedy, like a prelude to a joke. She was so tiny and fragile. I couldn't believe those powerful words were projecting from a seventy-eight-year-old woman. Nonetheless, I wanted to know more about her life. How did she end up in this refugee camp? How did the odd scar on her face end up there?

Watching her cook those samosas, I was deep in my own thoughts. Questions raced through my mind. As she talked, I was keenly tuned in to just her voice, barely realizing that the other girls were leaving the room. They had to go back to their family rooms. How could I just leave? I couldn't! I needed to know more of Mama Jee's story. I didn't know why, but people and their life stories fascinated me. Maybe by hearing what they had been through, I could find strength inside of me to believe that I wasn't alone.

Mama Jee turned to me. "May, would you like to know my story?"

"Yes, Mama Jee." She must have read my mind. "I would love to."

She continued, "I was eight years old when my mother died. My father and their three children survived her. Being the oldest child in my family, I naturally became the mother figure to my younger siblings. This unsolicited, dutiful role also involved taking care of my father. It was far easier stewarding even ten children than being responsible for my father. Thank goodness, I already knew how to cook despite my young age. I salute my mother for training me with basic household responsibilities. My mother had been ill for a long time, so she had prepared me to take care of my siblings. This had been my way of living for a while.

"It's tough as a child to learn how to be an adult; I had nobody to go to when I was tired and nobody to comfort me when I was sad and lonely. My father was an alcoholic with a violent temper. Usually, I would hide from him. On other occasions, I just avoided any kind of eye contact with him, because with his rage, he always found any reason to get me into trouble.

"After my mother died, my father began deteriorating. Each day, it got worse. He used to stay out and come home late. If my sister or brother made any noise while he was sleeping, all hell would break loose. Sometimes he would beat them up or punish me for any infraction of my daily chores. In the interest of maintaining peace and with the fear of being punished, we learned to make sure we were all in bed before he returned home from work. My responsibilities included making sure his dinner was ready, his clothes were folded and packed, and the tea was hot enough so that he wouldn't have any reason to lash out at me in the middle of the night.

"Years passed, and I forgot that I was a child. I started to believe that this kind of life was my destiny. All I wanted was to survive. After I put my brother and sister to bed and finished all my daily chores, I would sit by the window, watching people pass by. I would think to myself that maybe it wasn't just me—everything and everyone else looked miserable too. Or maybe it *was* just me? I would sit and watch the neighbors' kids playing in the street, wondering what it would be like if I could join them. How wonderful would it be if I was that free from any responsibility? I wished I could be a normal kid, but then I would remember my mother's face and how I had promised to take care of the family for her sake. I was her only hope. She used to tell me, 'Mehri, I know I can count on you, my darling daughter.' Any time I wanted to play, I would remember those words and her teary eyes. I would close my eyes and whisper to myself, 'I promise you, Mama, I promise.'

"It never dawned on me that life would ever change for me. Turning fourteen years old brought change to my life. One day, my father came home and asked me to clean up and get ready to meet our future mother. I thought that surely I hadn't heard him correctly, because otherwise, I wouldn't have dared to ask him to repeat what he had just said. I couldn't fathom him bringing a strange woman into our lives after my mother's death. There was no warning or preparation, and she soon arrived. She was a young woman. My dad had his arm over her shoulder.

"A rage seized me, and I just couldn't control myself. All the bottled-up emotions came out in one single exclamation, as I shouted at him, 'Our mother died a long time ago, and I am their mother now! That woman is not our mother!' This was a terrible mistake on my part, because the next thing I remember was a searing pain across my face. Unable to open my eyes, all I could do was cry on the inside. I didn't want my siblings to see my tears. Not knowing how long I had sat there in pain, I felt a tiny hand comforting me and telling me to be quiet because my dad could come back again. It seemed that I had passed out, and I had no idea how long he had beat me. My little sister was the one comforting me. I tried to get up and wash my face; it was then that I realized I was bleeding from my left ear. This was not the first time he'd beaten me, nor was it the first time I had passed out, but I knew I was not going to take it anymore. I think he felt that too, because for the first time, he ran out of the house after punishing me.

"He avoided talking to me for the next few days. I did not care to talk to him either and was happy he did not approach me. The first time he opened his mouth to talk to me, he just told me to cook something really nice for guests who were coming. He told me that they were special guests, and it would be a very special day. I was left with countless questions. Who were these people? This thought continued to recycle in my mind.

"Nonetheless, I managed to cook an amazing meal. Around six in the evening, there was a knock on the door. I opened the door, and three men and four women came into our home. I had never seen them before. They sat down and started to talk. Immediately, my father asked me to go to my bedroom and wait there until they called me. He gave me very specific instructions; he told me that when I was called, I must only answer 'yes' before walking back into the room. That seemed odd to me. As strange as it was, I didn't mind at all. Normally, I would be serving and waiting on my father and his guests, so I was glad to get a few minutes of freedom. The looks in those ladies' eyes were not welcoming at all. The men were all whispering and had creepy, suspicious looks on their faces. I was glad to get out of that room.

"Approximately an hour later, someone called my name, but it was not my father. I remembered the brief instructions from my father, so I shouted 'yes' in response. As I walked back toward the main room, everyone suddenly started to clap. A woman came to me before I could enter, and she led me into the other room. The atmosphere made my skin crawl, and I was besieged with a sinking feeling in my heart. Something was wrong; I wanted my mother back alive at that very moment. My heart sank deeper and deeper, and I was so scared. What was it? Why did I feel this way?

"As I was being buried by my fear, one woman came over and hugged me, saying, 'You are a woman now. You are getting married. You are a lucky girl. Be grateful to your father and your God.' The whole world seemed to spin around me in that moment. What had just happened? I looked at my father for answers, but he completely avoided looking in my direction. He looked ashamed, but it was as though he was trying not to show it. How could he sell me out like that? Was he chasing me away because he wanted to bring his girlfriend into our home? Had I failed to cook and clean properly? Was I not taking care of the kids well enough? Was it because I refused to be beaten by him any longer? Why was he doing this?

"A few hours later, everyone left our house. I couldn't sleep. My thoughts were full of questions—so many questions—and fear. Why did I have to get married? Who was my husband? What did I know about being married? I couldn't talk to my father, because it appeared he was in one of his bad moods. Even if he hadn't been in a bad mood, he was not going to explain himself to me. I knew I had to wait for the right moment.

"I do not remember falling asleep that night, but I woke up the next day feeling so scared. I rushed straight to the kitchen and made my dad his usual breakfast. Despite this heaviness in my heart, I prepared his favorite breakfast meal. At the same time, I made sure my siblings remained in their bedroom. The idea was to ensure they did not make any noises, lest they irritate him. This was not the day to fuel any kind of tensions in the air. Remaining calm and staying in a healthy mood was pretty challenging for me because I had so many questions from last night. What was the best way to initiate a conversation with him without it turning into a world war?

"To my surprise, he was in such a good mood. He told me to sit beside him. For the first time I could remember, he patted my hair gently, saying, 'You are such a big girl now, and it is not easy for me to have a beautiful young girl at home. It is not safe. That's why I decided you are going to get married.' As if he knew that would make me mad, his eyes suddenly narrowed, and he started to yell at me before I could even respond. That was usually how his good moods ended—as soon as they came, they were gone. He yelled, 'No more talking! I made up my mind, and I made my decision. Last night was your engagement party. No more arguments.'

"With tears in my eyes, I said, 'Father, what have I done? Didn't I keep the house clean? Didn't I take care of you and my brother and sister? What have I done wrong? Can you tell me, Father? Please don't do this to me. Please, I don't want to get married. I don't know those people. I promised Amma that I would take care of you all. Let me do it. Please, Appa!' I took his hand and started to kiss it, crying hysterically. He pulled his hand from mine and slapped my face.

"He shouted back, 'Stop nagging! I told you I made my decision, and you will be out of this house very soon. Get used to it, or face the consequences.' He just walked away, leaving me sitting there, alone and crying. I watched him as he left, with hatred for him building up in my heart. How could he make a decision for my future without talking to me? What would happen to my brother and sister?"

My own emotions were raging, and tears were flowing down my cheeks when I realized that I was so engrossed in Mama Jee's story. She interrupted the story by turning to gaze out the kitchen window. As I followed her eyes, I realized that it was getting dark outside. She kindly told me to go home, promising to continue the story.

"Come back tomorrow, May," she said, again with such kindness in her voice. I was still trying to return to reality after hearing the depths of the story.

I gave her a hug and I left, but I couldn't stop thinking about Mama Jee and her story. I couldn't wait for the next day to come. I could not wait to wake up the next morning. As soon as my daughter left for the playground, I quickly looked for an excuse to go to Mama Jee's kitchen. She was such a generous and warm-hearted person that you never even needed an excuse to go to her house. I felt no shame in knocking on her door so early in the morning. Before I could think of what to say, I found myself in her kitchen. The inviting aroma of fresh-baked bread reminded me that I should get a recipe from her. She looked at me with her kind eyes, evidently not surprised that I had returned so quickly. It seemed like her eyes could speak a thousand words without saying a single syllable. Every line and scar on her face repre-sented a story.

She offered me a cup of her famous tea, which I loved, and then very gently asked me what I had been waiting for. "Do you want to know what happened next?"

"Yes, Mama Jee," I replied hurriedly.

She sat down, clutching a cup of tea, and picked up right where she had left off yesterday. "After that, my father and I hardly spoke to each other until my wedding day. I became like a zombie in everything I did. I couldn't smile, couldn't play with my siblings, and couldn't even concentrate anymore. My mind had become a host of unanswered questions and fear. As for my siblings, I did not tell them anything. They were too young to understand, and I didn't want to scare them or make them anxious. I loved them so much. All I could think of was that I was betraying my mother and breaking my promise to her. Oh, I had no choice, no choice at all. I felt as though this was the river of my destiny, with many strong, angry currents rushing toward me. I was helpless, like I was letting go and allowing the angry river to take me away. No point fighting it. I had no adults to talk to or any friends to confide in. This river was too strong, and I was clearly a tiny feather drifting away in its current. This had to be a bad dream. I thought that at any minute, I would wake up from this torture, but this was my reality. My life was going to begin with a man whom I had never met before. All I knew was that I was getting married, which was supposed to be the happiest day of my life—yet I was nowhere near happy. How could I even begin to prepare for married life while in this state of mind?

"The day came. I wore the wedding gown given to me. It was a beautiful green dress with gold trim. How ironic—a very sad bride in a pretty wedding gown. As was custom, my face was covered with a long scarf, which I was thankful for so that no one would see me or my tears. I was adorned with expensive golden jewelry I had never seen before. My hands were painted with mehndi. My makeup was heavily applied, which felt strange since it was my first time even wearing makeup. I felt like a clown, not a bride. I could not even recognize myself in the mirror.

"Loud music and dancing were the customs of the day. I sat there on a beautiful chair while people walked all around me, kissing me and congratulating me, telling me how lucky I was. My mind raced. I wished for my mother. I wanted her to come and save me. I wanted my mother. I needed her that instant. I wanted to drown. There I was, denying who I was and losing myself. Who had I become? I was being pushed in a direction I did not want to go to. In the midst of all those emotions and questions, and in the midst of all that music, laughter, and singing, I promised myself I would not let anyone see how terrified I was. I promised myself I wouldn't cry. After what seemed like a never-ending wedding party, everyone eventually left. My father left without saying a word to me and didn't even let me say goodbye to my siblings.

"I was so scared. I had never slept anywhere other than my mother's house. I had never even had a sleepover anywhere. It was the first night I ever had to sleep at someone else's house. Everything was strange and new to me. This was a strange house with strange people, and strange things were about to happen to me in a stranger's bed. After the ceremony, I was led to a room.

A couple unfamiliar people told me this was my bedroom, the bride's bedroom. They told me to wait for my husband, who was coming to greet me for the first time. What was a bride to do, waiting for a husband to come and greet her? How does he greet a bride, by the way? Nobody was there to answer my questions.

"I chose to sit on the edge of the premade bed. My heart was pounding louder than the drums they had played during the wedding. The entire household could surely hear my heartbeat. Lost in my own thoughts, I suddenly felt a hand on my shoulder. I froze. I didn't know what to do. Should I look back? Should I stand up? Should I breathe, move, or just stay still? I prayed in my heart that God would tell me what to do. As I was struggling to figure out what to do, I chose to close my eyes tight, as though that would hide me. My new husband held me in his arms and carried me further up on the bed. I couldn't open my eyes. I didn't want to look at him, because I had no idea what I was supposed to do.

"With such a surprising gentleness, he said, 'Open your eyes, please.' I opened my eyes at that command. Instead of looking at him, I looked at the ceiling first. He was very patient as he repeated his request. For the first time, I saw my husband's face. For a moment, I thought this was a cruel joke. I couldn't believe how handsome he was. He was in his twenties, I guessed. Was I lovestruck? Nope, I was just genuinely surprised. I had imagined him to be an old, ugly man from hell. He interrupted my sidetracked thoughts, saying, 'I know you don't know me. You are so young, and you have no idea what is happening now. Let's just go to sleep, and I will tell my parents that you did your wifely duty and everything with you was perfect.'

"I couldn't believe what I was hearing. Was he for real? He just kissed my forehead and then left the room. For the first time in a while, my mind seemed to stop for ten seconds as I sat there in a state of shock. Then the questions came tumbling back. What just happened? Was he willing to protect me because he loved me? Was he willing to lie to his parents for my sake? Who was this man? Was this what husbands were supposed to do? Certainly, he was the first man who had ever spoken kindly to me. I tried to sleep but was scared that he might come back. I was also scared that his parents may come and ask me questions, so I just lay wide awake in bed, waiting for the next surprise to happen. In the early hours of the morning, he came back and just dumped himself on the bed without talking to me.

"That was my turning point. From that moment on, everything was different. For the next two years, I lived with my husband, his parents, and his two older brothers. My duties were clearly spelled out for me. My main duties were to help my mother-in-law around the house and just be obedient to anyone in the house who needed anything done. During those two years, my husband and I slept in the same room, but in reality, we had two separate lives. In those two years, not once did he try to touch me or even kiss me. Two years after our wedding, I had done some growing up, and I had also grown to love him. Every time I tried to get close to him or talk to him, I got rejected. His constant reminder was, 'You are too young. Just wait until you are older. I'm not attracted to you yet.' I was not sure which was worse, being forced to marry him and leave my siblings or accepting the rejection of my husband. My pride was hurt, but I tried to keep my anger and sadness inside.

"Sometimes, when he was in a good mood, he used to tell me, 'Don't say anything to my parents if they ask you why you aren't pregnant. Just tell them you have not started your monthly cycle yet.' That was a big lie, and if they asked, they would know I was lying. They would not have even arranged the marriage other-wise, since they came for me at the age of fourteen, right when my cycle kicked in. However, he was my husband and I had to listen to him. For some strange reason, his mom never asked me anything. He used to leave the house early in the afternoon and come back home at almost midnight, drunk. Sometimes, he came back home with a friend, and after eating dinner, they would sit and drink some more or play cards until morning.

"My favorite time was my monthly visit with my family. After I left my father's house, he wasted no time in getting married too. His wife's name was Najib. She was a widower and had one young daughter. Much to my relief, she was patient and kind to my siblings. She managed to put up with my father's moodiness and anger issues. Surprisingly, I felt sorry for her. However, in those days, she was considered lucky to find a husband. She was a 'secondhand,' as they used to call widowed or divorced women. I felt that my brother and sister were safe and in good hands. Every time I visited my family, my father would be there, doing his best to avoid and ignore me. He would create excuses to go to work. He could never be in the same house as me. I could never figure out if he was embarrassed, mean, or scared of me. Whatever the reason, he succeeded in creating a wider rift between us.

"With every visit, I could see how much Najib was suffering in that house. I was hurt by my own experience of being a woman in a house without much love, and I did not want Najib to go through the same. I had a soft spot for her because she took great care of my siblings. Once, I told her not to put up with my father's stupid demands and to learn to stand up for herself. Somehow, telling her that and encouraging her gave me some sort of confidence for my own cause. She took my encouragement seriously. To my surprise, I learned that she had listened to every word I told her, because on the next visit, she had a black eye. Oh, it made my heart sink, and when I asked her what had happened, I was confronted with a very angry man—my father.

"He stormed out from his bedroom, screaming, 'You are not allowed to put a foot in this house ever again! You are a bad influence in my wife's life. Did you tell her to disobey me? Who do you think you are? Look what you did to her. This is your fault, not mine. Get out of my house! This is not your house anymore, get out!' He proceeded to push me out the door.

"I was crying and could not believe what my father had just done. I wondered why I was surprised at this behavior, but I was finally done putting up with him. I asked, 'Is this my fault?'

"He scoffed at me, as though it should be obvious, and said, 'It is your fault. You are sick and deranged.'

"I stood in the middle of the street, shouting, 'I can come here if I want to! I'm coming to visit my family, not you. I hate you. I hate you!' Suddenly, he was running toward me with a belt in his hand. I ran away so fast, determined that he would not catch me. Where was my newfound confidence coming from? His days ruling over me were finished. After all, he had sent me off to get married, and I was not a kid anymore. Yes, he was my father, but I was not about to give him the joy of beating up another man's wife, so I didn't stop running. This was real drama and a treat for onlookers. He continued to chase me, and frankly speaking, I was surprised at his speed. He ran so fast that I believe it surprised even him. However, age must have started playing a part, as he suddenly stopped and bent over to catch his breath. As he gasped for air, he continued to curse me and yell insults between each huff and puff.

"I responded, 'Oh Appa, I hope you die! I hope I bury you soon, you ungrateful snake.' He waved his belt at me in anger. He was as shocked as I was. He had never heard me use that kind of language in response to his abuse or run away when he held the belt. I thought of the years when he took pleasure in beating me up and knocking me out with his fist.

"I felt a newfound freedom, and as he continued to curse, I could not help laughing. For the first time, I truly saw a deranged, sad man. His insults and threats from a distance meant nothing to me. That distance between us was a good safety measure for me. I had never run away from him. This was my first victory. I chose to taunt him, saying, 'Yeah, keep saying those words, you old man. Why don't you run and catch me? What's wrong? Getting old? All you can do is beat up a defenseless woman. Yes, what a man you are.'

"His face turned red with rage, and I could sense his desire to catch me and punish me, but he knew he couldn't—I was someone else's property now. I walked toward my husband's home, feeling so strong and good about myself. This was a victory for me. This was the first time he had been unable to quench his fury. I had just talked back to him, outran him, and laughed at him. I had to do it for my siblings and for Najib, and I could only hope she was happy I stood up to him.

"That was the last time I ever saw my father. He disowned me and banned me from going to his house. Frankly speaking, I didn't want to see him either. Every now and then, Najib would go to the bazaar so I could see the kids. I would visit with them at the bazaar and give them presents. I grew to love Najib. I would look forward to this bazaar day; every time, she would tell me that the best day of her life was when I showed my father that he was a coward. My father never laid a hand on her or the kids again.

"Najib was content with my father. She would tell me that even though she knew that he was just a miserable old man, she was grateful she had a husband providing a home and much-needed finances. She was oddly happy. My siblings called her Amma, or Mother, and to be honest, I didn't mind. She loved them like her own children. She told me once, 'Mehri dear, I know I'm not your mother, and I'll never claim to be your mother, but I want you to know I love you like my own child. I promise you and your mother's spirit that I will take care of your brother and sister like they are mine. I dreamt about your mother the first night I came to your father's house, and from that day on, I knew your mother's spirit was watching me.'

"I gave her a tight hug and thanked her. 'You are too good for my father,' I said. Certainly, he did not deserve her.

"She laughed and then surprised me by saying, 'He is not that bad a guy, you know. He just doesn't know how to handle himself when he is disappointed with himself. You know, when you are a sad, sorrowful person, you tend to make everyone around you miserable just by trying to make yourself happy.'

"Surprised by her words, I looked at her and realized how wise this tiny, abused woman was. I found a new respect for her. I still could not understand how my father was so cruel to her and everyone around him, yet she found a way to be happy and content.

"As years went by, I came to the conclusion that nothing would change in my life. I was lonely most of the time. All I knew was a life of daily chores, like that of an unappreciated maid. I spent much of my time in silence, keeping my mouth shut about everything I saw and witnessed. I could not even have a conversation with my own husband! If he did talk to me, it was usually an instruction, which I had to respond to with obedience. I was tired of it. I felt like a queen who had no access to her king. I decided I was going to end that. I was going to have a conversation with him, and he was going to hear what I had to say. I planned out the day. Each night, the opportunity just never seemed ripe enough. I had to make myself brave. I chose a specific night and stuck to my gut. That night, I stayed awake, waiting on him to come to the bedroom, if he even came at all. I prayed that he would show up and he did, after I stayed up very late.

"I had made myself look beautiful for him. I made his favorite dish for dinner and took it to our bedroom so he could see the effort and hopefully eat in private. I tried as much as I could to be presentable and set the atmosphere for my one night with the king. I was determined to start my own family. Surely a son or a daughter would make things better. The child would love me, and I would love my child. I was lonely and needed company. Oh, I started getting excited at what the future might hold. When he walked in, I gave him a huge hug, and as I tried to kiss him, he pushed me away without hesitation. In utter disgust, he asked, 'What is this? Why are you acting like a whore?'

"I was overcome with embarrassment, and I didn't know what to do. 'I did all this for you,' I said. 'Why does it make me a whore, when I am your wife?' I asked. 'All I want is your love, your affection. All I want is for you to look at me and want me. That's all I am asking. For the past five years, I have been so lonely. All I am is your servant and your roommate. Do you even see me as your wife? I want to be a mother—I want to have a family with you. Your brothers got married, and they have their families now. All I do here is help your mother. I am always sweeping, cleaning, washing, and gardening. There is never a word spoken between us. Your mother, whom you told me to respect, keeps asking me why I am not getting pregnant. She keeps asking why you don't give me a child. Because of your overnight outings and drinking habits, they say I'm a bad wife and that it's all my fault. Everyone is blaming me. All I want is for you to love me and be with me. I love you.' I reached for him.

"He pushed me away so hard that I lost my balance and fell to the floor. 'I never loved you,' he said. 'I never wanted you. This whole marriage business was my parents' idea, not mine. I am in love with someone else. For the past ten years, we have been in love, but we cannot be together because of the stupid culture and religion. I can't be true to myself; I can't stand to be with you in this house, let alone in this room. Your smell, your touch, your look—everything about you makes me sick. Do you understand what I'm telling you, Mehri?' With rage in his voice, he continued, 'All I do is pretend to be a perfect son and a perfect husband to you. Pretending is all it is, so why can't you pretend with me?'

"I sat there on the floor where I had fallen, weeping. 'You and I are victims in our own way.'

"He shook his head at me. 'You want a baby? Okay, I'll give you a baby.' Without any hesitation, he threw me on the bed, aggressively ripping off my clothes and pushing me down. Oh, what a nightmare—I kept begging him to stop. His face was so strange to me. I did not know this man anymore. There was no mercy in his eyes. I looked into his eyes, pleading for mercy, and he covered my face with a pillow as he forced himself on me. When he was done, he simply got up, got dressed, and walked out. I was so angry—not with him but with myself. Why did I fall in love with him? Why did I even tell him that, today of all days? Why did I want his child? What did I bring upon myself for loving him and telling him how I felt about him? It all made me so mad. I was in pain.

"Oh, how things changed. The longing for him disappeared; it was plain now that there was a sea of hatred inside me, running down to my heart. All I could feel during that time was emptiness and anger. I made a vow to myself that I was going to survive. Nothing was going to stop me. I did not come here to die."

Mamma Jee stopped for a second. I looked at her face, and for the first time, I noticed that her eyes were full of tears. She wiped her tears, and I put my hand on her shoulder to comfort her.

She looked at me and said, "Oh child, it's tears of onions." She was peeling onions while talking to me. We laughed, then she continued, "After nine months, I had a little boy. A year had hardly passed when one night, my husband came home drunk and decided to violently rape me again. He simply called it 'making Mama happy and proud' because his parents wanted another grandchild. To tell the truth, I didn't mind having another child. After the birth of my daughter, I decided I would never be a victim again. That was the last time—I made it clear to him that he would not touch me again.

"It was then that I decided to create happiness for myself and for my two kids. I knew there was no way out of that house, so I chose to live and make my world within that cage. I was trapped, but I had to survive. I definitely needed a hobby. I needed to find my passion and start doing something that would affirm me. I taught myself how to make quilts with beautiful silk patterns. I started making lovely quilts for my children's bedrooms. I was honestly surprised with what I produced. I made another quilt for myself and loved it. I felt different. I made myself busy, and once in a while, I would catch myself singing while I was sewing. I started to enjoy playing with my children in the backyard. I started taking good care of myself, for my benefit only.

"One day, my mother-in-law actually complimented me, saying that she had seen the change in me. She told me she was going to help me. One day, she called me from the backyard and asked me to come quickly. She told me she had a gift for me. She even had a playful glee on her face. She gave me a box full of cut-out cloths, all beautiful, bright colors, and she said to make a beautiful quilt for her and a nice dress for myself so they didn't have to see me in this black dress all the time. For the first time, she smiled at me, and I felt some connection between us. It was a good feeling. She then said the strangest and most surprising thing to me. 'I know you are trying to make a life for yourself. I see your efforts. I am happy for you. I know what you are going through, just hang in there.' She left me standing there with a blank look on my face. What had prompted her to say that?

"That was the beginning of a little freedom to be myself. As years went by, I grew in confidence. My children were growing. I became stronger, I became a better mother, and I was determined to start my own business. Of course, it wouldn't be a business outside of the house, but by that time, everybody in our neighborhood knew about my talent for making beautiful quilt covers and amazing wedding dresses. My business grew as women referred each other to me for wedding gowns or bridesmaid dresses. My mother-in-law kept telling me she was proud of what I had achieved for myself. Despite that, from time to time, if she deemed that I was not obedient or if my kids did something wrong, she would confiscate all my working materials as a punishment. I loved my work, and I was getting wiser; I knew how to keep the peace so I wouldn't lose my privileges. I made sure my children went to school. My daughter became my teacher, so to speak, as she came home and taught me to read and write and further my education.

"I enjoyed my relationship with my children. They were the best gift. God had answered my prayer. Soon enough, I earned the household's respect. Life was good, and I could feel it in my heart. These were the best days of my life. I was more independent. Meanwhile, my husband was his same mean self. Over the years, I had learned to just ignore him, but I continued to serve him, cook for him, and clean up after him—yet still I ignored him. He seemed to be getting weaker in his health and bitter toward everyone, including me and the kids.

"He continued to stay out late. Fights with his parents increased. He could not stand his brothers. After his father passed away, he lost all his sanity. He had not been close to his father, but the man had still been like a pillar to him. I think that in all his craziness, my husband lived under the impression that his father would always be there. Even though he used to go out late or even sleep away from home, he would come back the next day because he knew his father was home. When his father died, my husband started going out for two days, then three days, and then one time, it was a whole week, which eventually turned into weeks at a time. Every time he showed up back home, he was dirty and filthy. Well, by then we were sleeping in two separate bedrooms, and it was no longer a secret. The last time he ever touched me was the night he raped me and we conceived my daughter. It was like he was done with his duty. Frankly speaking, I was more than okay with that, as I had vowed I would never let him abuse me again.

"My son, Sina, turned twenty-one, and I was happy for him because he fell in love with the girl next door. Actually, she was his best friend's sister. He wanted to get married, and even though he was so young, I could sense that he wanted to start his own family. I think that deep down, he was sad and disappointed with his father, and I think that was a big motivation for him to have his own kids, so he could be the best father for them. I could understand that, which was why I didn't object to his request when he asked me if I gave him permission. I was happy for my boy. They got married, and it was a beautiful ceremony. I would have never imagined this day. The whole family got together, and people were genuinely happy for Sina. I wished my father was still alive to see true happiness. He had been gone for a few years at this point. All I could think of was his request that I not attend his funeral. Per his wish, I did not. He died angry with me for running away and not allowing him to beat me. To him, that was the utmost disrespect, but I wasn't going to be sad about it now, because this was a happy day for my son.

"Najib, my father's widow, and my siblings were there. My husband did not show up for his son's wedding. We just couldn't find him. He left for his usual outings and did not come back. In our culture, it was unheard of for the father of the groom to be missing. A huge lie was purported to save my son's reputation and pride; we just told everyone he was out of the country on urgent business. It was so hard to lie because everyone knew it was a lie, but nobody talked about it any further.

"I was so happy that I didn't care at all. My daughter-in-law was a beautiful bride. I had the privilege and honor of making her wedding dress. She wanted it to be a beautiful, bright red dress with a delicate silver border, accompanied by a long silver and red shawl to go over her head. Her wedding fabric and jewelry were imported from India. The fabric was pure silk, and her jewelry was handmade. She was the most beautiful bride I had ever seen. My son was so happy, and everyone could see the joy. As I looked at him, I realized that he had inherited his father's good looks—despite that, his heart and mannerisms were nothing like his father's. My son was a gentle, smart, and hardworking man. He was helping his uncle with the family business, and because he was good with numbers and was a smart businessman, they let him control one of the businesses himself.

"My son was only twenty-one, but his uncle respected him so much that he always sought Sina's opinion on big business ventures and deals. Sina had grown up to be an admired and well-respected groom. I was very proud of him. His wedding ceremony lasted for three nights, and by the third night, he was ready to leave the house.

"My husband's side of the family was very wealthy, and as a wedding present, my son's uncles and grandmother gave him the key to a brand-new house. I was astonished because no one had told me anything about it. I had thought that he and my daughter-in-law would come live with us; however, my mother-in-law surprised us both that night. Sina was so happy and grateful. After everyone was gone, I went to my room to get his special present. It was a quilt—the best quilt I had ever made for him. Every piece of material that I used was from his childhood memories. It was made up of a combination of memories, including the first jacket I had made for him, his first blanket, his first pillowcase, and a piece of my wedding dress. I wanted him to always remember that I loved him from the moment I gave birth to him. It was not an ordinary quilt. It took me years to prepare it, because I wanted it to be special. It was the 'quilt of our life.'

"I wrapped it in green velvet with a holy book beside it for protection and a long life of peace and faithfulness. Before he left, he came to my room looking for me, and I sat him down for few minutes. He took my hand and kissed it. 'Amma,' he said, 'I will never forget the sacrifices that you made for us. I am the oldest child, and I know exactly what you went through. I know you did your best to hide it from us, but I saw it all, Amma. I saw your strength and endurance. I am proud to have such a strong woman in my life, and it is my honor to call you my mother.'

"I took his hand and told him, 'Sina, my handsome prince, all I'm asking is that you do your best. I am sorry you did not see it modeled in this house, but I want you to go and be the best husband and a kind father to your children. Faith and compassion are what I want from God for you.' I gave him my present and told him, 'Every stitch of this quilt is made with the love that I have for you. May this quilt always cover you and your bride in love, safety, and happiness.' We hugged and both shed some parting tears.

"That was the best night of impartation to my son, and I will never forget it. We talked for longer than expected, then his lovely bride came to bid farewell, and they left. My beautiful daughter got engaged the following year. She actually got married three months after her engagement. Her wedding was just as beautiful as her brother's wedding. Before I could blink, I had an empty nest. Suddenly, the house was too big and quiet. It was business as usual but without the children. It was indeed an empty nest. My husband continued with his foolishness. I continued with my sewing business.

"One day, my mother-in-law got sick. She had actually been sick for a long time, but she was not the sort of woman to show weakness by letting sickness get her down. She was the family backbone, the pillar of the family. She was the great 'mama bear.' She took care of her family and her children; no matter how wrong or right they were, she always took their side and never mine. She was good to me, but not even once did she ask if I was happy or what was going on with her son. She never could admit that her son was unfair to me, and when he abused me, she never intervened or tried to help me. Not even once did she ask why I was crying. Even though I learned to stay with her and serve her, I had a deeply buried pain, wondering why she never tried to help me. Now she was sick and hopeless, and there was no one else to take care of her except me. One morning, I went to her room to serve her breakfast as always, but she wasn't in her bed. I went to her bathroom, where I found her on the floor, fighting for her life.

"It was the scariest sight I had seen since my mother died. I ran to the neighbor's house and asked for help. My mother-in-law was taken to the hospital, and we were informed she had suffered a stroke. She survived it and came back home from the hospital; however, she was paralyzed on one side of her body. Oh, she was so helpless and needed my constant assistance. She needed someone to feed her, change her sheets, give her baths, and be with her like a nurse. There were three of us sisters-in-law, but her two other boys told me that their wives were too busy with their children to care for their mother. They wanted me to find a caregiver, which they would pay for. She was paralyzed, but her mind was sharp, and she could feel and understand everything. I think it broke her heart when she found out her kids didn't want to take care of their own mother. Now all she had was me, the daughter-in-law she was always hard on.

"Destiny is a funny thing. What you do in life will always come back to you if you just have faith and be patient. It saddened me to see her suffering, but deep down I was angry and hurt by her actions toward me when they took me from my father's house at the age of fourteen. No matter what, though, she was so fragile and helpless now. I had to help her. I wasn't going to let a stranger come and take care of her, because I knew how proud of a woman she was. I knew that she would rather die than have a strange caregiver take her to the bathroom or give her a bath. Even in her sickness, she still had a reputation she wanted to keep up.

"After all she had done to me for almost three decades, it was now my turn to treat her exactly how she had treated me. But when I looked at her face and saw how helpless she was, all that anger and rage suddenly vanished from my heart. I knew better. I made a decision to give her the best care. I gave her love and treated her like she was my mother. My faith was being tested. I was going to take care of her myself. It was sad that in all these years, I had been holding on to something in my heart, but I never knew that by just forgiving her, I was helping myself more than I was helping her. I felt free. I remember one night after bath time, when I had just finished feeding her dinner and cleaning her face, I felt a pull as she gently took my hand. She slowly pulled my hand toward her heart. I realized she was trying to speak to me. I told her it was okay, but she was determined to tell me something.

With a broken voice and broken words, she forced herself to say a few words. 'Forgive me, please,' she said. I looked at her and kissed her forehead.

"I leaned forward and whispered in her ear, 'I forgave you a long time ago, Mama. I forgave you a long time ago.' Her face became so peaceful, and her eyes filled with tears that ran down her face. I wiped her tears away, a smile on my face. We both cried, and I hugged her for the very first time, laying my head down on her chest as she started to gently pat my hair. At that moment, I remembered that I had longed for that touch in my father's house. That night, for the first time, she started telling me family secrets. I listened quietly as she spoke. Then she told me she had the biggest secret of all time. I was all ears and eager to hear. It was about a family secret that they'd kept from me all these years.

"She told me it was about Raj, my husband. She said, 'Raj, my oldest son, was fifteen years old when he came home and told us that he was in love with his classmate. He told us that he had never been interested in girls and did not want to marry one.' This was the most shameful thing that could happen to a well-to-do family. This information was never to be repeated to anyone, as it was very disgraceful. They still loved their son, though they thought he was going to hell. It was against their religious beliefs, and it could have destroyed their family's reputation. He could even be killed if anyone ever found out, so they kept it a secret and swore him to secrecy as well. Still, they had to fix it. It had to look all right. They had to come up with a plan, and the first step was to find him a girl. Then he would forget about the whole thing. Once he had a wife and his own family, everything would work out. They went hunting for a beautiful girl who would take his mind off boys. His father threatened to disown him and banish him from the family if he did not comply.

"His mother continued, 'So he promised his father that he would do as he was told and be the good son for his parents. Well, after we found you and the two of you got married, we found out that he had started seeing his lover again. But what could we do? He was our son. We loved him, even if he brought shame to our family. We had tried. You were our last hope. We thought that once he settled down with a beautiful girl, he would be okay, but even that didn't change him. All we could do was ignore the situation and be hard on you for not making him happy. We wanted you to try your best to make him happy. For years, I was mean to you. In my eyes, you had failed your assignment. I never looked you in the eyes, because deep down I knew you did nothing wrong. My love for my child blinded my judgment, and I let you and my grandchildren suffer. If only we'd had the courage to set him free and accept him as he was—if only I could understand him the way he wants me to understand him—perhaps it could have set you free too. Can you find it in your heart to forgive me, my dear girl? I need your forgiveness before I leave this life, please.'

"This had to be the most shocking news of all news. I told her, 'For so long, I wanted to know why he couldn't love me.' What was wrong with me? Why wasn't I good enough for him? Was I not presentable enough? What had I done? As if I suddenly had all the answers, I felt so light, like a huge burden had been removed from me and I could fly like a bird. I was free from all that anger and pain.

"I felt nothing but pity for Raj. Not even in my wildest dreams would I have come to this conclusion. I thought he was in love with another woman. I always thought the woman was perhaps from a different religion or race. It would have made sense that his family didn't want him to be with someone who wasn't from their culture. This news, though, was a total shock to me. In our culture, men like Raj had no place in society. I could understand how challenging it must have been for his family to know this and disguise their shame for all those years. However, I put myself in his mother's shoes and asked myself what I would do if my son, Sina, was like Raj—would I abandon him or want him to be happy? That was not an easy question to answer, given the circumstances of our culture.

"She unloaded all the secrets and everything she wanted to say to me. A few days later, she passed away. The funeral was at home. After the funeral, I saw my husband. He looked so pale and skinny. He looked at me for the first time after such a long time. I didn't love him, but somehow, after all those years, something still moved inside my heart. Those beautiful eyes, which used to melt my heart each time he looked at me, and those lips, which I used to dream about—it was all so cold, so empty. I was seeing him with different eyes.

"He approached me, saying, 'I need to talk to you, okay?'

"I wondered what he could possibly want to say. 'About what?' I replied, not particularly wanting to look at him.

"He surprised me by taking my arm and saying, 'Tonight, after everyone is gone.' I pulled my arm out of his hand and walked away to the kitchen. He waited until everyone was gone. I watched him the whole time. He did not talk to any of his children or his brothers. My son tried to strike a conversation with him, but Raj ignored him and said, 'You look just like your mother. I don't see anything from me in you.' Then he walked away, leaving my son in deep hurt. I decided I would not react to his games, maybe because I knew where all that anger was coming from. In a way, I actually felt sorry for him. Everyone helped me clean up the kitchen and the house after the funeral, and then everyone left.

"My son invited me to his house that night; I think he was worried when he noticed his father wasn't leaving. I told him to go on, as I had to take care of more business at home. I knew my son was scared, but I was more concerned with what would happen to me now that my mother in-law was gone. Would my brothers-in-law want me to leave the house? To me, it had become my home, but since my mother-in-law was dead and my kids were gone, I knew my days there were numbered. I practically grew up in this house, but I knew it was time to use my savings to go and find a place to stay.

"A few days before my mother-in-law passed, she had sent me to the basement to collect a special box. She told me to bring it upstairs right away, before her sons could take ownership of it. The box was full of money. She told me it was my money. Every time I found a customer for a quilt or outfit, she always took some of the money. She would tell me she was saving it for a rainy day, and I never believed her. I chose to painfully forget about that money, because I believed I would never get it. She never touched a penny of that money, though, and it was all in that box in the basement.

"That money provided me with possibilities. I was excited, but first, I had business to take care of. I was getting ready to go to bed after the funeral, when Raj showed up in my doorway. He seemed jittery and on edge. I asked him what he wanted to talk to me about. He scoffed and shook his head, as though that question was wrong of me to ask. I could see his anger rising. I tried to calm him down by asking how he was doing.

"I wanted him out of my room. I said, 'Raj, you should go visit your kids. I am sure they would be happy to see their father.' He did not respond. He just stared me down. I stared back at him and didn't know what else to say except to offer my condolences for his mom. 'She told me everything, and I don't blame you for abandoning me and the kids or whatever happened in our life.' Before I could finish my sentence, I felt a slap to my face. It knocked me off balance, and I hit my head so hard on the door that I was dizzy for a few seconds.

"He started screaming at me and kept hitting me on the head. I was in so much pain and just didn't know what do. While beating me, he repeatedly yelled, 'What did she tell you? I will kill you tonight, okay?' As if he was asking for my permission. 'You think you are so much better than me? You think that now you are independent and can live your life freely? Not a chance. You are not free. Tell me what she told you—that old witch!' He screamed, 'I hate you all! All I came here for was to get my share of the wealth and to spit on her grave.'

"I found strength somehow to stand up and face him. I was not going to let him kill me. I promised myself years back that I would not allow any man abuse me again. I found the boldness to tell him that he did not scare me anymore, confessing, 'I loved you for so long, and all you did was break my heart. The only reason I stayed in this house was for my kids, and because I thought that maybe I could somehow find a spot in your heart. Maybe someday you could love me. That stupid girl doesn't live here anymore. You could never break me, Raj. I'm still standing, and

I will stand no matter what. Yes, I know why you didn't want to be with me, and I know about the promise that you made to your father. I know about your lover and how much of an abomination it is. I know your big secret. You don't scare me.'

"I took a breath, but I wasn't finished. 'You are nothing but a coward. I pity you, and the only reason I am still talking to you is for my kids and your mother. She loved you—both your parents loved you—but you were so selfish and ignorant that you never noticed anything but your own selfish needs. Go away and never come back. You have no place in my heart anymore. I am leaving you this time. I am the one leaving this house this time. I don't need you or your house anymore. I raised my children, and I'm going to live my life just the way I want, free from you, free from the past, and free from your selfish need that has hindered you from success.' I had no idea where all that boldness came from. Words were just pouring out from my gut. I guess everything I had ever wanted to tell him poured out in that very minute.

"I turned around to leave the room, but he yanked my hand and threw me on the bed. He pulled out a flask that reeked of a strong odor, and he dumped the contents all over me. My heart pounded quickly—it smelled like gasoline—and before I could make a move, he lit a match. My whole body was instantly on fire, and I screamed from pain. The lessons I once learned about dropping and rolling were distant memories, but I kept rolling over the bed, trying to help myself. I kept telling myself I would live through this and not die. I would not let him do this to me.

"I woke up in a strange room, unable to see very well. He was not there. I was not burning. Where was I? Was I dead? All I remember were the people around me, trying to help. I seemed to have passed out again, because the next time I opened my eyes, I could hear soft sobs. I was in the hospital. My daughter and my son were beside my bed. They were crying. I tried to turn, but all I could feel was so much pain. I was not sure what to focus on, the fact that I was alive and not dead or the fact that I was in pain and so were my children. Raj had set out to completely destroy me. I reminded him of what he could not have in life, so he had planned all along to pour gasoline over me and start a fire. After he had done that and I started screaming, he ran out, likely scared that the neighbors would see him. They did see him, and in the chaos that ensued, he ran off and shot himself in the head.

"What a horror for my children. They had just buried their grandmother. Their mother was now in the hospital, barely hanging on to life, and their father just died. Life has a way of turning out ugly, but I knew I had to survive. My children would not be able to handle my death. This was not how the story of my life was going to end.

"The hospital became my home for the next two months. It was surgery after surgery on my face and body. Despite all the excellent work they did, I remained scarred on my face and body and especially in my heart. I was mad at myself for letting him get close to me. Why did I trust myself to be alone with him? Why did I not go with my son when he asked? I was mad at everything. The whole family tried to help me, but I wasn't in the right mind to accept their help. I didn't want to see any visitors, even my own children. Who had I become? When I was released from the hospital, I really had nowhere to go but to that same house, the house I thought I would never go back to. Funny how it was the house I had been so desperate to leave, then it became the house that was almost my place of death, and now it was my only place to stay. Everyone wanted that house for their inheritance. They let me stay, though, out of guilt, I suppose. No one bothered me about it again.

"At the back of the property, there was a guest house with two bedrooms, and it had been empty for years. It was a fully furnished house, not too far from the main house, with everything I might possibly need. It was in my mother-in-law's will to let me have this place, as long as I did not marry again. It was a private house, which gave me the privacy and freedom to be by myself. My son hired a caregiver for me. I asked my children not to visit because I needed some time to adjust and be by myself for a while, and they understood and accepted my wishes.

"All the dreams that I once had for myself were gone. I was miserable. Days turned into weeks and weeks into months, and I was still very angry at myself and at everyone else. I couldn't look at my face in the mirror. I knew I would not recognize myself. Here I was, a forty-year-old woman with a large scar on my face and a body that was half-grilled and disfigured. For what? Who would ever look at me again? I hated myself for letting this happen to me. Blaming myself over and over, I would repeat the story in my head daily, reliving what I did and what I could have avoided. But none of that helped me get better. My body and face were healing as much as they were going to, but my spirit was being torn apart. I was in the darkest place you could ever imagine.

"It had been eight months, and I had not left the house. I felt no need to face the outside world. I was constantly screaming on the inside. The pressure and the pain in my soul were killing me minute by minute, and I just couldn't handle it any longer. One afternoon, when my window was slightly open, I looked outside, and the outside world seemed to be calling me. I took off running and just kept going. The people I passed as I ran did not seem to exist in my own little world. I kept running with no clue where I was going, but running seemed to fan the fire inside of me. I did not even care about the dark clouds forming above me. Normally, I would fear being caught in a heavy storm, but nothing was about to stop me. My mother's grave was two miles from my house, and I found myself standing right in front of it. The rain was now pouring down, and I looked up to let the rain fall on my face. I wanted to feel the rain pounding on my face and on my scars—I just wanted to feel something. I wanted to feel alive. I have no clue how long I stood by the graveside. All I remember is that I had left the house early in the afternoon, but when I looked around the graveyard, it was dark outside. It was nighttime, and the graveyard was silent and peaceful.

"A soft wind blew through the autumn leaves, and the sound of the rustling leaves brought peace I had not felt in months. I could feel the breeze on my skin, and I savored it. Looking around, I saw nothing but old graves, trees, and some flowers over a few graves. In that instant, I could almost hear a voice inside of me, asking, 'What on earth are you doing here? You are not dead, Mehri. You are alive. You are still breathing, and you have so much to see, so much to do. You may have lost your beauty on the outside, but you are much more than a pretty face, and there is a reason you didn't die. Find your reason in life.'

"In a place of death, I found myself! We are all here for something more than just breathing, eating, and repeating. That confirmation was music and good food to my soul. At last, I had something to look forward to. I had hope, and I just wanted to be alive. I wanted to get home as fast as I could, so I took off running again, but this time with a direction, determination, and sense of purpose. My trek back home left me wondering how I had passed over all those roads without noticing anything; nevertheless, I still made it home, and I lay down on the grass in the front yard. The earth beneath my body was real, and it felt so good. I was soaking wet, but I didn't care. Excitement burst out of me, and I just didn't know how to control it any longer. I rolled on the green grass, literally rolling in laughter. That laughter was so welcomed by my whole being, even though I could not figure out why I was laughing. Whatever it was, I felt so alive and happy to be on that grass.

"The lesson I learned that day was that life goes on with or without me. I had wasted precious time and part of my life by closing myself in. I had allowed sadness to win. What was a scar on my face? My face might have been disfigured, but my spirit and soul were still invincible and stronger than before. Oh, I was glad to be alive!

"From that day on, everything changed in me. I wasn't going to let Raj get the best of me. I wasn't going to let the hard times bring me to my knees. I was a survivor, and now I was going to be a warrior. I developed a big plan for my life from that day forward. My first stop was going to school to get a diploma. I then started the first-ever women's sewing school in that region. My main goal was to eventually buy the main house from my brothers-in-law. Eventually, I bought the main house from them and changed it to a women's shelter and education center. I never got married again. I never felt like I needed to marry to be happy. To be honest, even though I lost my so-called beauty, I saw myself as more beautiful than ever. That part of me that thought I would one day find a man who would love me just disappeared because I figured out I didn't need anyone to love me. I was the one who should love me, first and foremost. All I needed was me!

"Also, deep inside, I couldn't forget my first love, even if it was only a one-way street. However, I'm the happiest I have ever been because I found my destiny, helping other women find themselves and believe in their spirits. Everything happens for a reason, May. If you can find hope and determination, you can survive anything."

I was so mesmerized by her story that I couldn't even see the scars on her face anymore. All I could see was an angel full of hope and determination.

Even though she had been through a lot, her heart was amazing. She was an incredible human being. I couldn't believe that I got to benefit from her life journey of pain and hope. It was for people like me that she never gave up. I could now understand why all the refugee women called her house a safe haven. Her house was always full of young women and mothers with their kids. This strong woman was always cooking and praying that each woman would find a safe place for restoration then go out and make a life. She worked tirelessly and never asked for a penny from any of the women.

Mama Jee paused, then asked, "Well, are you going to tell the world about my story some day?" She had the biggest smile on her face.

"I don't know how, Mama Jee," I quickly answered. "I'm not good at telling stories or writing." I distanced myself from the idea. "I don't think I will have it in me," I told her, with regretful tears in my eyes.

She took my hand and looked into my eyes for a few seconds without saying a word, then she said, "Listen here, May, you are much more than this fragile girl that people see. I see the strength of a warrior in you. You just don't know it yet. But you will. Someday, when you are far away from this place, when you find your true destiny, you will remember me." She spoke with such certainty. "Remember this moment, and when you do, remember to pick up a pen and a piece of paper and begin to write. My child, you are going to write everything, because through those words pouring out of you, you will discover your strength, your inner power, and yourself."

Years have gone by, but I will always be grateful for that moment and for those days in the shelter. If my whole reason for being there was to meet this woman who shaped my life, then I am so grateful. In that shelter, I had the opportunity to meet many wonderful people. What amazes me is that we all come from different backgrounds, cultures, pains, unknown roads, races, and costumes, but food and cooking unite people. Sharing a meal made us open our hearts to each other.

For a while, we became each other's family, confidantes, and shoulders to rest our heads on. We took off our daily masks, which we usually had no choice but to wear. In such an environment, we found life. We had no money and no wealthy lifestyles, but we were rich in our hearts and souls, and we were full of faith and determination imparted by one victorious woman. We cried together, laughed together, and watched our babies' first steps together. That time was full of joyful moments like watching my daughter take her first steps on that muddy road, with no money to buy her a pair of shoes, but with cheers of joy from all the women who made life worths celebrating. Life was real.

These simple words from Mama Jee that follow were framed and hanging on her kitchen wall, and I will never forget these words.

"Quilt of Life"

Life is a quilt to be made by your hands.
The choice is yours.
Make it colorful or make it to enhance.
Tell the story the way you want.
With every line and every point,
Each pattern tells your life.
Stich by stich, corner to corner,
Pour your heart into the design.
Make it beautiful, just the way you want.
Life is a quilt to be made by your hands.
Your life is a quilt to be made by your heart.
Make it colorful, make a new start.

The End

A ROAD TO
REDEMPTION

The clear blue sky enveloped the day. The cool breeze gently caressed my face as I took my occasional walk within the women's shelter for refugees in the heart of Australia. I walked the route that passed by the kitchen. Unexpectedly, the inviting aroma of food overtook my sense of smell. Well, as one might have guessed, I took a detour from my walk and stepped into the kitchen. This was the first time I saw her. During that initial encounter, she was in the middle of cooking something.

Her eyes stared intently outside through the small kitchen window. It appeared as though something at a distance had captured her bluish lavender eyes. Despite her physical presence in the kitchen, I could tell that her mind was a million miles away. At that moment, whatever she was cooking began to boil out of control. My instinct was to alert her immediately, while also being cautious to not startle her.

Gently, I said, "Be careful, it's boiling."

Her eyes darted quickly to me and she said, "I'm so sorry, I was—ah, somewhere else." We exchanged warm smiles. From then on, we had an instant connection.

As the days progressed, Eldana became one of my closest friends. I genuinely enjoyed our friendship. Nevertheless, even as we grew closer, there was just something amiss, as though there was a space, an eerie silence, a mystery between us. I could feel the eeriness in our interactions, but I never had the guts to confront her or ask her what it was. Her laughter and attitude were just not consistent with her aura, in my opinion. There was a subtle aloofness and sadness about her that I couldn't figure out. Even when she was laughing, her eyes had tears in them, as though she felt guilty for being happy or she didn't deserve to smile for even a minute.

Oh my goodness, she was a beautiful woman! She was tall, with a slender body, wavy black hair, olive skin, and almond-shaped lavender eyes. Later on, when we became close friends, all of us at the women's shelter used to give her a hard time about her beauty. At times, we would joke around with her, saying that if only she could make it in a modeling career, her success would remove all of us from the confinement of the shelter and move us into a rich neighborhood.

She had a little boy who was around six or seven years old. Her late husband was from North China, whereas she was from Turkistan. They'd had a unique marriage union, especially since there was a disparity between their customs and culture. No wonder her actions and mannerisms seemed oddly mixed at times. She had left her homeland and became a refugee. Regardless of our refugee status and the challenges we faced in the village, we were all impressed by her unique skills. She was an amazing cook! Memories of her cooking just make my mouth water. We all loved the meals she cooked, and whenever she cooked, the room was packed with women and children waiting in anticipation just to savor and devour her meals.

As weeks became months, Eldana and I grew very close emotionally. She started opening up to me bit by bit. I found out that she had been previously married, and the result of that union was a son, whom she left behind. She carried the guilt, shame, and regret of that decision throughout her entire life. I was not sure what exactly happened and why she was so weighed down by shame, but I knew it was only a matter of time until she filled me in on the details. I didn't want to push her to tell me the story, not with the likelihood that she would pull away from me and close herself in if I were to press on, asking questions about her situation. After spending many months together, I understood that Eldana just had to fully trust someone first. Once she felt secure, then she would be ready to share her story.

Our favorite evenings were spent on a bench in the local park reserved for refugees. We would take our children to play, then we would sit and talk for long periods of time. With our kids playing in the park as she and I made conversation, we formed a sort of ritual, a special club. We came to love and cherish this place and the conversations on that bench. This time in the park was a good break from our small apartments and daily chores. We shared so many things in common, which we uncovered during our regular discussions. We were both new to this country, and everything felt so strange to us. Sometimes, we felt like fish out of water, the kind of feelings that make you believe you don't belong. We struggled with the pain of needing to express ourselves, yet we faced a language barrier with the people around us. The culture in Australia was hard for us to digest. Without much effort, we were soon isolated like aliens. Our accents were very hard for our Australian hosts to understand. Some were intrigued by our skin texture and tone. There was this perception that us refugees were all one people or from one part of the world, and some of our hosts had never heard of our countries of origin. To most of them, Iran, Iraq, Pakistan, Tajikistan, Syria, Afghanistan, and Turkey were all one country combined. They thought we all spoke the same language. Some of the refugees could not understand this and easily took offense, which led to homesickness. I remember having a different take to all this; because I had come to their country as a refugee, my approach was to be grateful for the help. This fueled my determination to learn their language and culture, with the hopes of building healthy relationships in this new country. I would have opportunities to engage in dialogue and make them aware of my country and culture too. However, the differences didn't really matter to me. I grew up believing that the same God created all of us. The earth was my home, and we were all citizens of this planet. It didn't matter which part of it I was from or what color skin I had or what language I spoke. All that mattered to me were the connections with other human beings who could feel my heart and understand the journey and struggles that I faced.

The park bench was the center of our universe in those moments when we had our conversations. We shared our pain and our tears, yet it was still our happy place. There was one particular afternoon when we sat on the bench; it was only the two of us while our kids played at a distant. There was an awkward silence, which was constantly interrupted by deep breaths and loud exhales. Eldana rocked herself back and forth, causing the bench to make an annoying sound. I could sense that something was wrong. I sat in silence, patting her back and looking at her with concern. It appeared she was going down memory lane, judging by the look in her eyes.

"Mahtab, how can you heal a broken heart?" she asked. Her voice was shaky as tears started streaming down her beautiful cheeks.

Such personal moments are so beautiful yet can also be so nerve-racking. Within a split second, I repeated her question a dozen times in my mind. I was speechless, and I just decided to put my hand on her shoulder and gently rest her head on mine. There are no words to describe the mixed emotions raging in my heart during that friendly moment.

She was unique, and her looks were very different from the rest of the Asian women in the camp. We had never seen an Asian woman with such blue eyes and distinctly wavy hair before. She told me that her original family was from a Turkistan tribe and her ancestors came from Turkey. They had migrated, traveling along the Silk Road, and ended up in Turkistan. She did indicate that she also had some European blood in her ancestry tree. Unbeknown to me, she explained that some people in North China had different customs, culture, and even looks compared to the rest of the Chinese people. A majority of them were Muslim, and they celebrated their New Year just like the Persians. Politically minded people from that part of China always had trouble with the government.

Eldana told me, "All the time, my brothers or the neighborhood kids teased me for my looks. However, my father would tell me, 'Eldana, my beautiful flower, you look just like your great grand-mother, and she was the most beautiful woman in her whole village. So be proud of your looks, and don't let anyone tell you any less.' Then he would hug me and tell me, 'In a big rose garden, do you know which flower always stands out?' I would look up at him and ask, 'Which one, Baba?' He'd respond, 'The unconventional rose with lots of thorns, a beautiful lavender color, and a fresh, amazing scent. The butterflies and bees tend to choose to sit on her delicate leaves over the rest of the flowers. You are my beautiful lavender rose.' He would continue to uplift me and remind me to not be ashamed of my looks, because they were a part of my heritage and story."

She continued with her recollections about how she and her father shared such a special bond. She paused a moment, then admitted, "I never really felt that close to my mother. I'm not sure what caused the relationship to break down between us. It's possible that it was because she was always bragging about my brothers and never had anything good to say about me. It's really unfortunate, the power that words have to engrave pain in your heart. My mother always told me that I was a difficult child. She would tell me that no one would want to marry me. One of her favorite questions that she often asked me was 'Why don't you conduct yourself and look more like your brothers?' This was a question I could never answer.

"My looks and appearance were often the cause of my tears. My father was an amazing man. He would always fish me out of my hidden crying place and take me to the garden to talk. He kept reassuring me that my mother loved me. He'd say, 'Don't worry, my lavender eyes, you are going to grow up and do many amazing things with your life, so be happy and go kiss your mother now!' I'd say, 'Yes, Baba,' then I would grudgingly go to my mother just to obey my father.

"One day, I came home from school to the most terrifying news of my life. My father had been arrested. We had no idea that all along, my father was a hero. He was a secret freedom fighter, fighting for human rights. The government never tolerated anyone who opposed the oppressive policies in place.

"When my father got out of jail, he wasn't the same anymore. His time in jail had a negative impact on his life. He became paranoid, and, in the middle of the night, he used to wake us up and tell us to go to the basement and hide because they were coming to arrest us. We used to ask him, 'Who, Baba? Who's coming to get us?'

"He would just look at us with fearful eyes and say, 'Go hide. They are coming.' Everyone thought he'd gone mad, but I think he knew his family was in danger. I truly believe he knew something but could not tell us. He knew for sure 'they' were coming one day. He was sick for a while and never recovered. He passed away very soon after and left me with thousands of questions. After my father passed away, my life was never the same again.

"Our mother had to find a way to take us out of the country, for reasons best known to her. Maybe she knew what Baba had been worried about after all. She was looking for an escape plan for her and the boys. As for me, the solution was simple to her—marriage. That was her solution. Frankly, at that point, I didn't even care. I was happy to separate myself from the tension between my mother and my brothers. The pillar of my family had been my father, who encouraged all of us often. With him having passed on, I was not inclined to stay with my family anymore. My mother insisted that I had to get married, as it would be easier for her to function, and it would be an easier transition for me. She told me that her escape plan made it difficult to bring me along, because she feared I may be raped. She also expressed that I was the weakest link and may thwart her escape plan, should I be caught.

"Well, she could go, and I would be left to survive by myself. I didn't want to leave my country. My father was buried in that country and had been willing to stay. It was my home. I was more than happy to get out of my mother's life and start my own. In no time, she found a young man to marry me. I was so young and naïve, only sixteen years old. He was our neighbor, so I already knew him. He was a good-looking eighteen-year-old stud with charming mannerisms. He was everything any girl could want. The problem was that I was not in love with him. But how could I argue with my mother? He was from a good family. She thought I would be happy. In no time, we were engaged. As soon as the wedding and honeymoon were over, his mask came off. Everything changed.

"Even though I wasn't in love with this man, I had come to like him during that honeymoon phase. He was very gentle and sensitive. He was really very sweet to me. So when the drinking started, I realized that it had been a problem before I even came into the picture. He'd only hidden it for a short time until we were married. He would answer my questions by saying, 'Don't worry, my wife, I only drink to have fun, and I gamble for the excitement and thrill. I'm an adult and know when to stop.' Of course, I believed him. A year passed, and the dangerous habits did not change for the better but for the worse. On top of it all, I was pregnant! How could I have let that happen? I knew this was no environment to raise a child in, so I decided to have an abortion. While I was in the clinic, my husband showed up and dragged me all the way home, yelling at me. When we got home, all I remember is the punching and yelling. I ended up covered in bruises and aching pain throughout my body.

"My husband paced back and forth, fuming with anger, and he scolded me, 'You are not going to get rid of my child. You are going to love and cherish my baby until the day you die. He is going to be a boy—I know it—and you are going to love him, feed him, and take care of him. Do you understand me?' That was our last fight. Nine months later, I had a little boy. How on earth my husband knew it was going to be a boy, I have no idea.

"I did not feel the joys of motherhood. I was so overwhelmed by the pain. I never felt a love for pregnancy and never enjoyed carrying this tiny creature inside me, not even once throughout the whole nine months. My husband was watching me like a hawk to make sure I wouldn't do anything to harm his precious child inside of me. The child was born, and there was nothing in me to show that I could love him. I was empty. All I felt instead was rage toward this tiny human being. Nursing him was a chore, and with hate in my heart, I felt like he should be grateful that he was even being nursed. The anger I felt for my husband was being transferred to my son. Deep down, I knew it was wrong, but the feeling was too strong, and it overpowered me. I just couldn't help myself, or maybe I didn't want to fight the urge. My mother and the rest of my family didn't even care to come visit me or the newborn baby, and that isolation only created more hatred toward my husband and everyone else in my life. This child represented everything that should not be and yet he was everything I had—an innocent child. Watching him grow to look like his father did not help the demon inside of me. My hate was so strong that unimaginable things ran through my mind. Oh, Mahtab, I regret what I did."

Eldana stopped abruptly and covered her face; underneath her hands, her whole face was red. She was crying. I didn't know how to calm her down. I didn't know what to say, so instead I just silently processed her horrible past. How could this angelic woman be so cruel to an infant child? I had to remind myself not to judge, as I didn't know the whole story and hadn't been in her shoes. How could I jump to conclusions and just hate her for what she was telling me? I felt pain for her, for I knew it had to be a demon like she said.

I sat in silence as she continued. "I never asked my family for help, and they never wanted to know anything about my life. My mother and my two brothers moved to the capital city in search of their freedom. Their freedom led them to drugs, as they got involved in smuggling deals. No help would come from there. My mother got sick and very quickly passed away. My brothers had a funeral for her and buried her. I received the news of her passing after the funeral and burial. It hurt to even wonder why her burial place was a huge secret. I was left conflicted as to whether my brothers even knew where she was buried or how she had passed. Maybe they didn't even know the truth. I mourned my mother. We'd never had a great relationship, but she was my mother, after all. She had carried me in her womb for nine months, and, especially now that I had become a mother myself, I wanted to see her and ask her why she never gave me the same love that she gave to my brothers. Why was I such a big disappointment in her eyes? It was no hidden secret that she didn't like me, but I longed for her regardless. I longed for my father the most; I longed for his gentle words and touches, his kindness and love that were always there for me. I knew that if he were alive, our family would never have been separated and destroyed like this. He was the rock and the pillar of strength in my life. How I wanted his love right then—if only words could express those feelings. He would know what to do and say in times like that. His heart's desire was always for me to reconcile with my mother."

Eldana wiped her face with the corner of her sleeve. She looked at me with her red, tearful eyes. "Are you tired, Mahtab? You must be tired of me talking and talking nonstop. Do you want me to stop talking?" she asked, then quickly answered herself, saying, "Yes, let's just not talk anymore. It's getting late, and you have to get back to your family. We can get together some other time."

I looked out over the park, trying to bring myself back to reality, and replied, "I would like to meet up again, if you want to."

She didn't seem to be waiting for my response, as though she had only been talking to herself. She took a deep breath, stood up, straightened her skirt, and walked away. She beckoned for me to catch up, as I remained stunned on the bench. I ran toward her as we walked toward the playset to gather our children. She asked if we could meet again the following day after all our chores were done.

She told me, "I think that through all these years, I just needed to talk to somebody. Someone I could trust. For years, I bottled up everything inside of me. I trust you. Thank you for being such a good listener, Mahtab." Finally, I saw that smile spread across her face. I was glad to know that she felt so much better after talking to me.

I smiled back at her. "You can trust me with all your heart. I will never betray our friendship. I promise."

She looked at me with those bright lavender-blue eyes, nodded, and said, "I know."

The following day could not come fast enough. That night, as I lay in bed, I wondered how it was possible that one person could go through life in so many dimensions. I replayed her life story in my head and was glad when morning came.

The park offered much-needed peacefulness, and I was ready for the story to continue. This time, she came ready, and we shared a snack as she continued. "My son, Elham, grew up to be a handsome boy like his father. Unfortunately, he also inherited his father's bad temper and anger. He became a complete reminder of his father. His father was in and out of our lives, until he finally decided to just leave. However, once in a blue moon, he would show up at the door just to look at his son then disappear again. I know he loved his precious boy. Elham loved his dad, and every time they were together, I could see how happy he was. His father knew how to make the boy happy when he was around. He acted like a child with his son. Elham's father was like an oversized ten-year-old boy, and of course every kid would enjoy that kind of parent. I was always consumed with the future—bills, routine, discipline—and I guess I was busy being the adult parent. I used to think that was why Elham loved his father more and was closer to him. I wasn't as much fun as his dad. But when I look back now, I see that it was more than that. I was a distant parent, despite being the one who was always around. I had my own fears. I knew that getting closer to my son would mean pain, as he would go away with his father eventually or, even worse, end up just like him. So I kept my distance emotionally and never gave him the love that he really deserved from me. His father never offered any child support, and frankly, I never asked for it. He was busy being a drunk and an addict. If he couldn't realize for himself that the child needed money, then I was determined to not ask and to instead succeed on my own for once in my life, for the sake of my child.

"Watching my husband play with his son on those rare days was amazing yet piercing. They would have fun all right, and I would see my son laugh with joy. His father would never shy away from rolling on the dirt road just to make him laugh. I would smile, but

I hated it. Jealousy of their bond overwhelmed me. I was determined to end that perfect picture. I did the unthinkable and told my son that his father was a loser and a drug addict, and if he were not careful, he would end up just like him. With his innocent eyes, my son just looked up at me and then hid in his room from fear. I was in no way a good mother. Sometimes, I would feel guilty, and after punishing him, I would give him a hug and blame it on his naughtiness. But deep down, I knew it was all a lie. My anger really wasn't my son's fault, in any way.

"I desperately needed a job to take care of my son and myself. With no other choice, we moved to a big city called Dongguan. It was a city full of crime and corruption, but for me, it was the big opportunity to find a well-paying job. My passion for cooking finally got me a job as a chef in a very famous restaurant. Oddly enough, I owed all this success to my mother. We'd never had much to say to each other, but I loved the way she used to cook. From an early age, I knew I wanted to be a chef and own a restaurant. The idea of creating recipes had me daydreaming about being famous. I believed in that dream. I never told anyone about it except my father. He would listen with interest as I told him my fantasy. He loved it and would encourage me often. 'Go to the kitchen and watch your mother cook. Learn from her,' he would whisper. 'Your mother is the best cook in the whole village.' My father used to encourage me with such pride in his voice, rubbing his already big stomach.

"Within a few short months, I was promoted to head chef. I gained approval and admiration from my employers and patrons. I enjoyed this newfound success. I became so engrossed in my work, and it satisfied me. I had no time for my son. I had to work. My son walked home from school and pretty much learned to take care of himself. Nightly, when I got home, I would find him in bed already. Such were our days. I covered this negligence with work hours. In my mind, my obligation was to offer shelter. The child raised himself. I was glad when his father followed us to the city to be closer to his son. He started seeing him every day, much to my great relief. I was actually glad he did that, because then I didn't have to feel guilty about pursuing my dream and working longer hours.

"All this worked well because Elham was just a child. Then he turned thirteen, and everything changed. He had a mind of his own. I could not just tell him what to do and expect that he would do it. He would talk back to me and disobey every word that came out of my mouth. He demanded that he go stay with his father. I would not hear of that, and it made me so angry to hear that request. I knew he was getting older and stronger each day. He was soon taller than me. One day, we started our usual arguing. He raised his voice at me, and I went to slap him as usual. This time was different and rather shocking. He grabbed my wrist, looked straight into my eyes, and demanded, 'No more! You torture me with your words, with your hand, with your belt, all my life. Why? All for your own selfish reasons. Telling me every day that I'm worthless, stupid, and good for nothing, just like my father. I loved you, and I thought that if I just kept trying to be a good son, you would one day love me.'

"Nothing had prepared me for this. He continued, 'Sometimes, in the middle of the night, I used to go to your room. I'd watch you while you were in a deep sleep, and I'd gently touch your face. I used to lay down and sleep beside you, putting my head on your chest. I'd wrap my arms around you and pull your arm around my body. I would do this in the pretense that you were hugging me, loving me. Now I don't want to beg for your love anymore. I don't want to stay with you. Be happy, Mother, have your own life. Find a man and have ten children. I'm sure you will be a good mother for them. Maybe even love them. Hopefully you will be capable of loving someone someday. I'm thirteen. I already spoke to my father, and he wants me. He has always loved me. Even though you see him as a loser, at least he knows how to love me. I'm leaving tomorrow morning.' With that, he walked toward his tiny room in the basement. I stood still, speechless for the first time. I had nothing to say and didn't know how to feel. He was right about everything, but I was too arrogant, angry, and revengeful toward him to see the truth.

"The next morning, I woke up and was getting ready to go to work. Elham was in the kitchen, making breakfast for me. He had set some flowers on the table, along with my special tea that he knew I loved. As I took a sip of my tea, I looked around and noticed his suitcase by the door. He stood in front of me, looking down at his shaking hands. 'Mom, I'm sorry for last night,' he said. 'Please forgive me.' His voice trembled, and tears rolled down his pale cheeks. Did he think I would react to that? Did he think those tears melted my heart? I said nothing. I couldn't even look at my son. The day I had feared but at the same time looked forward to had arrived. I had no idea how to react. I didn't eat the breakfast he made for me. He moved closer to hug me, and I pulled back. I took my bag, passed his suitcase by the door, and left for work.

"I could hear the sound of him crying and calling me gently, 'Mom, I'm sorry. Let's not separate like this.' I couldn't look back. I kept walking and left without a word. That was the last time I saw my son. That was the last time I heard his voice."

I came back to the present when I heard my own daughter saying, "Mommy, I'm hungry."

We had been talking for the past two hours. Eldana was devastated by her memories, and I was shocked to hear of such cruelty from the person I thought to be the most loving and caring mother in the world. She had the face of an angel but the cruelest heart I could ever know. My mouth hung open in disbelief. I just didn't know what to say.

All I could do was take a deep breath and tell Eldana, "I'm sorry, I have to get home. My daughter is hungry, and it's getting late."

She hugged me, and we promised to talk again soon. She again told me that her outpour to me left her feeling so much better. She said that it was a wonderful feeling to be able to trust someone and open up.

She had no idea that she was not just telling a story but was helping me too. I was finding myself through her life. How? I had no idea, but it was changing me too. At that moment, I just wanted to go home and be the best mother for my daughter, Luna. It was time for me to cook the best meal for her. I wanted to go home, hug her, and make sure that she knew how much I loved her.

The next day, I returned to our usual bench, but Eldana did not come. Worried about her, I went to her apartment, wanting to know if she was okay or not. I found out that her son was sick, and she didn't want to expose him to the outside until he felt better. Unfortunately, for the next several days, we could not continue our conversation.

She told me, "Let's just wait a couple of days. I'll let you know." She was such a caring and affectionate mother toward her son that it was almost like the story of her past was based on lies. I mean, how could a woman who was so kind and caring toward this little boy be so cruel and evil back then? It just didn't make any sense in my mind, and I became determined to know everything about her past. Maybe there was something I hadn't heard yet that could justify everything. I had to know more.

After that, each time we wanted to sit and talk privately somewhere, someone else would show up at wherever we were. Another lady would graciously join us. More ladies seeking company would come to just sit and talk. We enjoyed their company, but oh, how painful it was, waiting to hear what the next part of the story might hold. I decided to be patient and wait for the perfect timing. I wanted destiny to create a perfect moment.

My patience did not last very long. I wanted to know what happened to her son, Elham. As much as I did not want to judge her, I couldn't wrap my head around how someone could be so cruel to her own flesh and blood. What made her heart that hard? I wanted to know more, to know everything. Those answers could come from her and only her.

After many days of waiting, I gave up on going to the bench for the day. When I answered a knock at my door, there she was. She wanted to know if I was free to take the kids to the park since her boy had fully recovered from the illness, and we could finally be alone. Without hesitation and with much joy, I was soon heading out the door with my daughter. I had missed my time with just Eldana so much, especially our conversations.

Actually, with everything else happening in my own life, it was a nice break to get away. My marriage wasn't perfect, and I just didn't know what to do, so I just kept living my life, hoping everything would work out somehow. Eldana's friendship and life story created some sort of hope for my own life, and I was grateful for that.

I took my usual picnic basket with my special saffron tea. Everyone loved my saffron tea. It also happened to be Eldana's favorite. I poured her a cup of tea and one for myself. In absolute silence, we watched our kids play. The only sound you could hear between us was the sipping of the hot tea. It was a beautiful spring afternoon. She looked different this time. There was a confusing peace about her, but I knew that she was not peaceful inside. The children were having fun, and their laughter helped us enjoy the moment, but I still wanted to know her story, and I couldn't wait any longer while she looked off into the distance. I was determined to be brave and just start the conversation.

"Eldana, what happened to your son after that day?"

She didn't even turn her head to look at me. She inhaled deeply, as though she had been holding her breath, waiting on me.

Then she continued her story, "I was full of anger and rage toward my husband, so much that all I could see in my son's eyes was my husband looking back at me. I didn't care what was going to happen to my son next. I left him in the doorway and didn't look back. After that, I was happy because I lived alone and worked long hours, with no responsibility toward anyone except myself. I was finally a free woman. The last reminder of my past and my husband was out of my life. As if my son never existed, I erased my past completely. I threw all of his belongings into the garbage bin and burned every baby picture of him that I had around the house. As if he and his father had never existed, as if I had never made the mistake of marrying that loser, as if I had never carried Elham in my body at all. That part of my life never happened—or, at least, I thought I could erase it from my story. All I wanted was to start fresh. I worked from early in the morning till late at night, and my goal was to save enough money to start my own business someday. I had no time for another relationship and no time for thinking about the past or anything but my future. No matter how hard I tried to erase the past, from time to time I used to dream about Elham and see his innocent eyes looking for me. There was guilt buried somewhere deep inside of me, but the ambition I held was much stronger, preventing me from stopping for a single moment to think about what I had done to my child.

"Everyone was so impressed by my work ethic and my self-discipline that they used to call me 'Ms. Machine' because I worked nonstop and never complained about too much work. I never associated with any of my coworkers outside of work or invited anyone to my place. My whole life was a mystery to everyone since I never got close enough to anyone for them to ask me any personal questions.

"Five years passed by so quickly. I was in charge of the whole restaurant and had gained the respect of every single employee. One day, there was an unusual buzz about the restaurant—they had found out it was my birthday, so they surprised me with a special birthday cake made by the best pastry chef in town. It was a great evening. No one knew who I really was, but in their minds, I was a hardworking woman with my past neatly buried inside of me. When my shift was almost over and I was getting ready to leave, I noticed one of our regular customers watching me. This man was quite well-known around our restaurant, and most of our female employees were crazy about him. He had a reputation as a powerful man in our society, and he was known for his wealth. He was an incredibly ambitious politician; particularly, he was a freedom fighter and had many followers. I respected his quest in fighting for freedom because my father had also committed his life to it. This customer was a regular, and when he dined with us, his regular choice was my special dish. We all knew that after he enjoyed the dish, he would always send a note to the kitchen that said, 'My compliments to the chef for an excellent dish.'

"But that night, the night of my birthday, was very different. I think he noticed the big commotion in the restaurant and found out it was my birthday. He asked for me to come out of the kitchen and introduce myself at his table. Although I could easily recognize him, I had never really looked at him closely. Our eyes met for the first time.

"He complimented me profoundly. 'You are an excellent chef, and I am in love with your food.' No one had ever been so complimentary of my food before. I considered it an odd compliment, but the other people sitting around the table all clapped and laughed. I just didn't know what to say but let out a simple 'Thank you.'

"He looked somewhat astonished, as if he'd expected more, and said, 'That's it? Young lady, I just put my heart on a plate for you, and that's all you can say?' Everyone around the table fell quiet, and they looked my way to see what my response might be to such a question. I wasn't sure what was happening, but he continued to talk, saying, 'We thought to see the dessert menu, but instead, we would love a piece of your birthday cake—if that's okay with you—as well as the pleasure of your good company at our table, Chef.' Everyone remained quiet. He looked at me with clear anticipation and such a cheeky smile on his face. I don't know why, but instead of making me feel good about myself, he just made me mad and annoyed about the whole situation.

"Without expressing any excitement, I bluntly replied, 'I will tell your server to bring your dessert.' I thanked him for the compliments and request for my company, but I declined his request, saying that I was busy in the kitchen. I wished them the best time and walked off in relief.

"He called after me, 'Well happy birthday, Ms. . . . ?'

"I looked back and said, 'Eldana, Ms. Eldana.'

"Although I did not ask his name, he started to introduce himself with far too many details. 'My name is Heng. My mother was Chinese, and my father was from Turkistan.'

"I responded cordially, 'Nice meeting you, Mr. Heng.' I met his gaze with a look as cold as ice, and then I walked away. Everyone else at his table was listening and began chuckling as I left. I could feel his eyes following me as I entered my kitchen.

"That was a significant conversation; I knew it, and so did everyone in the kitchen. I was greeted back in the kitchen with jokes and claps. I knew in my heart that something significant had happened in that conversation. I couldn't understand the sudden warmth in my heart when I dwelled on the conversation. I didn't want to get involved with anyone. I had paved my own path, and all I wanted was to get to the destination that I had set for myself, but I guess you can't argue with destiny. I liked him, no questions asked, and, inexplicably, I knew he liked me. It was so obvious to me and everyone else. It was as though a connection had already been made before I ever had this conversation with him. The more the kitchen staff talked about the incident, the more I wanted to go back and talk to him. I was proud of myself, though, for refusing his offer. Later, my staff laughed at me, because although my words said no to him, my actions were somehow saying yes.

"It was not surprising to anyone that from that day on, he made our restaurant his place of choice for dinner every day. Our conversations were no different from the first one; he would invite me to sit down with him, and I would politely decline. It took him a while to actually figure out that I was really working and could not just sit down and talk to him. Once he figured this out, he asked me out on a date for my day off. Finally, I said yes! And that was the first date I had ever gone on in my whole life. Things moved in the fast lane for us. We grew closer with each date, as he shared his dreams and how he hoped to change our country for the better. He was so ambitious, just like me, but his dreams were so dissimilar to my own goals and dreams. His whole existence was centered on his fellow men, humanity, and kindness, and mine was all about getting what I wanted just for myself.

"I never told him about my past because I didn't think he could have looked at me the same way if he knew. In his eyes, I was a beautiful, single woman who was hardworking and had class and style. I felt guilty from time to time and wanted to open up to him and let him know who I really was, but I never had the guts. I couldn't bear to think that he might leave me or hate me. I hated myself deep, deep down when the lights were off and I was without any mask. That was the time when I could see the real me, and I didn't like it. As a result, I hid myself completely and chose to ignore my inner voice. After a while, Heng introduced me to his family. A firm relationship started to develop. He came from a great family of wealth and education. I somewhat felt that I did not fit in, but he was very kind toward me. He would talk to me about politics, current events, history, and news, and I would listen in awe. I enjoyed his company. He was so passionate about helping people. He was a dreamer all right; he would tell me how he would make me happy in the new world he dreamed of.

"We had been seeing each other for eight months, and I wanted him to ask me to marry him. I was ready. I was crazy about him, and I was afraid that any day, at any minute, something could ruin our relationship or something bad would happen. One day, finally, he dropped on one knee and asked me to marry him. I said yes without any hesitation and we were engaged. I wanted to tell him the truth about myself before we got married. I just couldn't keep my dark secrets in the closet any longer. He had every right to know the real me. What was the worst that could happen? Would he leave me? I thought I should just tell him and see what happened. I wanted to start fresh and clean, and this time I wanted to have a loving and honest marriage if we were going to make it work. He was the one for me, I knew it in my heart, so I told him we needed to talk. I told him that after our conversation, he could leave at any time without any words being necessary, and I would never bother him, though I would still love him forever.

"He shook his head and said, 'You're scaring me, Eldana. Please tell me what it is that you want to talk about.' I was unbelievably nervous and didn't know where or how to start. He took both of my hands, sat me down, and said, with gentleness in his voice, 'Just know that I love you. Your past, whatever it might be, will never change my feelings toward you, okay?'

"I couldn't even look into his eyes, so I looked down, avoiding eye contact, and started to tell him everything. In my quest to be honest with him, I told him about my past marriage, leaving out the part about mistreating my son. How could I tell him that? I couldn't even forgive myself for treating Elham the way I did, so how could Heng? All I told him was that I had a son who lived with his father. After that, Heng always told me that if I missed my son, I could go visit him, or he could even come live with us. He would say, 'I love you, and I will love your son too.' In the end, I couldn't bear to be purely and totally honest with him. I told myself that maybe I would tell him later on, or perhaps he would never need to find out the whole truth. Soon after, we got married at the restaurant where I worked. It was a simple yet beautiful ceremony with his family and friends wishing us all the health and happiness. As for my dark secret, I buried it so deep that I never thought anyone could dig it up.

"After a year, I became pregnant with twin girls. The day we found out was the most beautiful day of our lives. I felt so blessed and extremely happy. I had finally found a man whom I could call my husband. He loved me and loved our twin girls. Deep inside, I missed Elham and thought about him often. I justified myself with the fact that he was with his father and they loved each other. Besides, it was better for him to be with his father since we had never been that close to begin with. Those thoughts and justifications were the only way I could stay calm and avoid feelings of guilt.

"Heng was a kind and generous man. From time to time, he would notice when I was feeling strange and was deep in my own thoughts, but every time he asked me what was wrong, I always told him I missed my father or my mother. He believed me. I knew he wanted to help me in any way he could, and I knew how helpless he felt whenever I was down, but the truth was something I could not tell him, so I used to just reassure him that I would be fine. He was a great provider, and we never lacked anything. Our life was wonderful. This was my new life. There was no need to look back and feel guilty. At least, that's what I told myself. Life is a mystery, and such things like happiness are temporary and can't last forever.

"The stability in China started to change. It was a crazy time. A civil war erupted. The country was filled with freedom fighters, different parties and groups, and demonstrations in the streets. A curfew was enforced, and everything changed. I was afraid for my husband. His activism could put his life in danger. Instead of scaling back, he got more involved. He joined the demonstrations and was often out late into the night. Our house was now a house full of followers. They were either running away or seeking shelter, and they wanted him to be their leader. They clearly loved him and his leadership. Our house turned into a workshop of people making posters and flyers. It became a boardroom of endless meetings, and I soon saw Heng turn into a man I did not know. He was so passionate about the cause, and every time I complained, he would remind me that it was not for us but for the country and our children. His favorite saying was, 'I would rather die for something I believe in than live a long life of no purpose.'

"I could only laugh painfully at what my life had become. I think life knew how to make me feel like a second choice. With my mother, I couldn't measure up or compete with my brothers. With my first marriage, the drugs and alcohol came before me. Now, with my true love Heng, his love for his country came first. I was mad at him and at myself, but I had to think about the twins and their well-being. I could not fail again. Daily, we were on red alert as the city became unsafe. The scariest part was hearing gunshots, sirens, and screams in the middle of the night. I was scared in my own home, as Heng was rarely there to protect us. What I feared the most was separation from Heng—and you know, it's true when they say the thing you are most afraid of will eventually happen, because it did. I was so fearful of losing my family and losing Heng, and finally the day came when he told me that we had been compromised and it was no longer safe to stay in our house. We had to move. We had built our house just a few blocks from my dream restaurant, which I had purchased with my own savings. I had to leave behind everything I had worked so hard for all those years. Once again, I had to lose everything. I didn't want to leave. He begged me to agree with him for the sake of our twins. He said he couldn't imagine what he would do if something bad happened to us. He wanted to stay behind until everything was safe, then he would join us. Until late that night, he held me in his arms as I cried and imagined that maybe I deserved this. Maybe this was my punishment for my past.

"Finally, the day of separation arrived. I was silent most of the day. Words didn't mean anything, and there was no way to express my pain, because I had this feeling that I would never see him again. Something inside of me was telling me that this was it, and I should make my last goodbye. He took my hands, looked into my eyes, and said to me, 'Listen, Eldana, my love, I just cannot abandon these people. I cannot. Now that we are so close to our freedom, I have to be with them. Please understand. This is much bigger than you and me and our girls. You have to go now, because I will never forgive myself if something happens to you all.'

"With the twins and just one suitcase full of clothes, I said goodbye. If I'd had a choice, I would have never ended that goodbye hug. He seemed to feel the same as well, as we both cried. 'You will be okay, my love,' he said. 'Be brave for our girls and for us.' That was our parting conversation. This time, I was the one looking back with tears in my eyes; this time, it was me with a heart full of sorrow and pain. There was no ego, no pride, no selfish desire. It was simply me with an open heart full of regret and sorrow. We left, and as I watched him from the moving vehicle, his image became smaller and smaller until I could see him no more. I turned around and took my twins in my arms, facing our unknown future.

"We were taken to an old house in a part of town I had never been to. We were stuck inside that house for days, as they had asked me to not let the girls go outside. Somehow I had to entertain them, and it wasn't an easy task during the day. Three days passed, which felt like a week, until late one night when two men showed up at the door and gave me a few minutes to pack up. They wanted us to leave the house with them and move to a new location. They had a written order from my husband, letting me know to trust them and do whatever they asked, but I had many questions. I asked them why we were moving. What went so wrong that we had to leave right that second? All they told me was that it wasn't safe anymore and our lives could be in danger.

"We left in the darkness of the night. I had no idea what was happening. All I knew from the note was that I had no choice. For the first time in my adult life, I wasn't in control, and I felt very vulnerable and scared. I had two young kids to think about now, and ensuring their safety gave me strength.

"As the large black van drove through the dark night, all I could hear were the whispers of urgency from the driver and the other two male passengers. The girls were fast asleep in the midst of this commotion. There were no streetlights or street signs to give me a hint of where we were going. I had no idea where they were taking us. Feeling helpless, I sat back and let life take its course. There was no point in asking or fighting. After a few hours of uncertainty, the van stopped in front of a very small house. The men told me that they would be back for me as soon as it was safe. They told me to get inside the house quickly, then they left.

"The house was very small and smelled of mold, which made it hard to breathe. It was also dark inside, and I could hardly see in front of me. I heard a voice telling me to watch my step and just walk forward, and finally my eyes adjusted to the light. I could see a person standing in front of me. It was an old woman holding a candle to light the hallway. She was very kind and just guided me to a room without asking me any questions. She seemed to know exactly what was going on. I asked her if there was any food in the house so I could feed my children. She went to another room and came back with some rice noodles and steamed vegetables that had no taste, but I didn't care; all I wanted was to feed the girls and let them get some rest.

"I was just sitting in a corner, looking around, trying to make some sense out of the situation, when the woman came back in and told me to get some rest. How could I? How does one sleep when you don't even know what the next minute might hold? I looked around. There was nothing to cover my girls with. There was no bed, pillow, or even a blanket. All I had were some extra clothes, and I used those to cover the girls' tiny bodies so they wouldn't catch a cold. The old lady offered me homemade tea, assuring me it would calm my nerves and help me sleep. Even today, I have no idea what kind of tea it was, but it made me feel so relaxed. All I remember after drinking the tea was someone shaking me and telling me, 'Get up, get up, we have to leave now!'

"I didn't know what time it was, but within a few minutes, I was all packed. The same men picked the three of us up again. This time, we climbed into a small bus full of men, women, and kids. We all had the same look on our faces, a fear of the unknown. No one talked, but our eyes darted around in constant communication. The bus stopped at the harbor after a few hours. This was no place to be with children in stormy weather. It was cold, and lightning lit up the dark sky. There was a small boat nearby, and the men instructed us to get in quickly. There were about twice as many people as should be trying to fit in such a small boat. Looking at the leaders, I wondered if they could not see that the boat was too small, but I guess it was survival time. They told us to get in fast because we had to leave very quickly, before the patrol guards showed up. We piled in. Before we could even start sailing, the water turned rough and choppy, and I wanted to be out of the boat. I refused to stay in, and I told them I would wait for the next boat. One of the leaders grabbed my arm and shouted, 'You will get in this boat right now, lady! There *is* no other boat!' Then he just pushed me back in.

"No one spoke on the boat, as everyone was clinging to any part of the boat they could reach. People were literally hanging on for their lives, trying not to fall out. My girls were crying from confusion and fright. My attempt to hold them, one in each arm, and try to simultaneously hold on to the boat scared the girls. They were screaming. One man told me to shut them up and threatened to throw them into the water if they did not keep quiet. I remember telling them we were going to see their daddy soon, then I covered their mouths. In total, there were probably about thirty humans on that boat. The leaders told everyone to not make a sound, and anyone who did could cause the Border Patrol to find us and kill us. They took a thick, dark, tent-like blanket and covered us. I could hear people muttering prayers.

"Everybody hugged each other so we could all fit under the blanket and stay in the boat. For a few minutes of sailing, everyone was quiet from fear. It was getting hot under the heavy cover, and everyone was breathing hard. The heat was so intense that I imagined someone giving up and pulling off the cover for fresh air. Suddenly, gunshots filled the night, and in no time, I was immersed in cold water.

"The fears I had been dwelling on could not have prepared me for this kind of terror. Our small boat was sinking; people broke the silence and began screaming and pushing each other to stay above the water and survive. I started moving my legs, while at the same time holding my girls tight in my arms. I knew how to swim, but the current was too strong, and it was freezing cold. My arms were full, so I tried using my elbows to swim and save my children. I screaming for help from someone, anyone to help me with one child so I could maneuver in the water easier. The more I screamed, the more everyone screamed. Everyone was trying to take care of his or her own children. No one could hear me, and even if they did, it was survival time. Someone even shouted that I should let go and the girls would float. I knew that such a thing would not happen, especially if I was having so much trouble staying afloat myself. I quickly accepted the fact that all three of us would sink and die before I would let go. I knew I could never let go of either of my girls, so I decided to just surrender myself to destiny. I took a deep breath, pulled my girls toward my heart, and looked into the dark sky.

"I could feel the cold water in every fiber of my body. We were drowning. I couldn't choose to let go of one child to save the other. I looked up and begged God for his help. 'Please, God, don't make me choose, don't make me choose.' My whole body grew numb, and I couldn't hear the twins crying anymore. I think they had given up too, but I kept holding on to them. The strength of the cold water was too overwhelming, so I held on to my children and closed my eyes, letting the waves take me. I decided to stop fighting and let it happen; I had done my best, and now I could stop fighting and let it be. In the distance, I saw my father's face looking at me with such love as he called my name, 'Eldana, hold on, my daughter. Hold on. It's going to be okay; just hold on. Don't give up.'

"I have no idea what happened next. All I remember was that my father's voice brought me back to the present. As I came to, I could hear faint noises, which gradually grew louder and louder.

I opened my eyes to see people walking around. There was such commotion all around me. I tried to turn my head to see what was happening and where I was, but my whole body ached. My palms were bleeding from where my nails had dug into my own flesh, clasped in a tight fist. A huge, artificial light made it look like it was daytime, but it couldn't be daytime already. What was this place? After a moment, I came to the conclusion that we were on a ship.

"Then, I realized that I did not have my children. I questioned the man who was offering me something to drink, and he told me that I had just been rescued from the water, so perhaps my children had been rescued too. I jumped up, forgetting the pain coursing through my body. I ran like a maniac, looking for my children. Everybody was calling their loved ones' names, so my yells got lost in the confusion. I fell several times because it was difficult to walk, but that was irrelevant—I just wanted my children. I must have asked everyone I came across, and no one responded. People were speaking different languages. I started crying, calling out the girls' names with no response. Finally, an English woman shook my shoulders and told me with a broken accent, 'We could only save one child. A doctor is looking at her now. Let me take you to her.' She must have been a part of my rescue if she knew who my children were. I just sat down on the floor. This was the worst day of my life. What had I done? Only one child? There had to be a mistake. I did not let go, I know I didn't—or did I?

"The American woman helped me stand up, then she led the way to a makeshift children's medical center. There was my daughter, wrapped in a blanket. My baby looked so pale. The doctor quickly told me that my daughter had hypothermia and wasn't guaranteed to survive, but I could hold her if I wanted to. I took her into my arms and vowed never to leave her again. I begged her to open her eyes, but a part of me knew she was already gone; her face was as white as porcelain. There was no life left in her tiny body. I was screaming from the deepest part of my soul, but no one could hear me. My scream was silent. Only God could hear it and see my guilty soul.

"I didn't know what to say or what to feel. I stared at her innocent face, and all I could feel was hollowness, darkness, emptiness. There was nothing more I could say or do but accept the painful truth. I looked at the doctor and told him, 'You should have let me die too. Why did you save me?'

"With a gentle tone, he responded, 'I'm so sorry. I wish I could say something or do something to ease your pain, but there isn't anything I can do.' The kind English lady did not leave me. She took me to a corner of the ship where some women were gathered. Some were crying, and others had blank looks on their faces, just like me. No one was talking. They just stared into the distance, searching the dark waters, hoping for a miracle.

"My mind was paralyzed, or maybe I was too exhausted to function. I curled up in an isolated corner and let myself fall asleep. I woke up to the loud blow of the ship's horn. Morning had come, and the hard truth of last night's reality sank deeper. The morning did not bring me joy, as I visited the empty mattress where my child had died. They had taken her body, as simple as that. Maybe we should have stayed and searched a little bit longer to find my other girl's body, but for what? She was gone. What was the point of searching? But still, I was a mother, and even her cold, lifeless body could have eased my pain. I could have held her in my arms and given her a proper burial. I wanted to ask someone to help me, but I just didn't know how or whom to speak to.

"It was morning when we reached the shore of Hong Kong. I was left alone to deal with the loss of my two beautiful angels and the sudden arrival in this strange land where no one could understand me. I felt so empty and angry with myself for trusting my husband, who had only abandoned us. Once again, a man ruined my life and destroyed everything that took me years to build. Nothing was the same after that. Depression paired with grief and guilt overtook me. I had so many regrets. They felt like a dark blanket covering me. What was I supposed to do now? In spite of it all, I knew that life would go on, and there was nothing I could do to change anything. Days turned to nights and nights to weeks. We were all shipped to a refugee camp.

"I thought that I would only be there for a few weeks, but those turned into months. I still had no place to go. Those days and nights forced me to think about my son and my girls. I would daydream, watching them play together. I wondered what they might have looked like by now. I'd never get to see them grow up. No news ever came about my husband or his whereabouts. As time passed, I would feel sorry for him and start to forgive him a little. Underneath the forgiveness, though, I still blamed him for everything that happened to us.

"Every now and then, I would go to the main office in the hopes of receiving a letter addressed to me. Every time, I left empty-handed. It seemed as though everybody was getting letters except for me and perhaps a few other people. Gradually, I gave up, believing that he must have been killed or imprisoned. I tried not to think about it. I accepted the fact that I was in a refugee camp and could not change that fact. The only way I could survive was to keep my mind busy. Everyone was doing some sort of work at the camp to stay busy and also make some money to buy personal things for themselves and their families. I was the only one who would just sit in a corner and do nothing. A few times, I was asked if I wanted to do something, but I never talked to anyone, so after a while, I think they gave up on me. Besides, they knew I had lost my children, so I think they just let me be until I was ready. One day, out of the blue, I decided that I had to push myself to move on and stay busy, so I asked someone in charge to let me work in the kitchen. My food spoke for itself, and they welcomed the idea of marrying me to the kitchen.

"The kitchen became my refuge and oasis. Cooking was my savior. Chopping onions was the only way I could cry freely. I could hide my sorrow, guilt, and regrets without being noticed. In a way, onions became my freedom to be without a mask in public, even if it was for just a few minutes. I could let myself go and be free.

"Time passed me by while I was cooking and stirring with the wooden spoon and diving into my deep thoughts. I don't know exactly how long it was before the managers of the refugee camp finally decided to send some of us to a country that accepted refugees from China. I didn't want to go, but it was their policy. Even if they didn't want me to go, they had to follow the rules and find a safe country for me in order to give my space to the newcomers. They chose Australia, which was one of the most humanitarian countries and used to accept refugees from all around the world. After they told our group that we were accepted to go to Australia, nearly everyone in the refugee camp gave me big smiles and shook my hand, congratulating me for being so lucky to leave this place and go live in the best country in the world. I would simply smile and nod my head in response, saying, 'Yes, it is so wonderful,' but deep down, I wasn't excited at all. The ambitious dreamer that I used to be was long gone, and now all I wanted was to let the days pass me by, one after another. Besides, in here, I was closer to my children, to my homeland, and to my family. Every afternoon, I would watch the ocean from far away and imagine my twins' faces as they lay motionless in the deepest and darkest part of the ocean. Always, their eyes were open in hope that I could save them. That was my daydream and that was my nightmare every single night, but even those horrible nightmares used to comfort me because at least I knew I could see their faces. What if I left this place and the nightmares stopped and I never saw their faces again? Those were desperate fears from my broken heart, and I had nothing to look forward to.

"Unfortunately, the time came sooner than I expected, and we had to pack our belongings and leave the camp behind to journey to our new home. Everyone else was overjoyed, singing songs and clapping, talking to one another about what they wanted to do when we got to the mainland. An old lady sat beside me on the boat, and with such excitement in her voice, she proclaimed, 'Eldana, you should get a job in the biggest hotel or something—you are the best cook I've ever known!'

"I smiled back at her and, without saying a word, turned my head toward the ocean and gazed far away into the blue ocean, hoping, just hoping I might see something or hear a whisper calling my name. I wished I had the guts to jump into the dark water and drown before anyone could save me. Such thoughts filled my mind and soul so pervasively that time passed me by very quickly. Before I knew it, we arrived in Australia. Since we arrived at another refugee center, we had to get medical examinations, then after that, we had to stay for at least three to six months to get used to the new country, language, and culture. They told us that everyone should rest, then after a few days, we would each have an interview so they could learn more about who we were and what our professions were back in our homeland, which could help them locate a job for us later on. Then we would be able to start our new lives. As for me, all I wanted was to get into their kitchen and hide myself in my cooking. My life had no purpose, no direction at all. All I had to do was breathe and do mundane, everyday tasks like the others. I was filled with anger, sadness, and guilt, to the point that nothing really mattered to me. After my interview, I was hired in the camp's kitchen with no hesitation, and after only a week, everyone knew who I was, and my cooking became a topic of many conversations. It seemed that once again, the kitchen saved me.

"They say time heals everything. I don't know about that, because no matter how busy I made myself, the painful memories of my past were still as fresh as if it had all just happened yesterday. But in time, I once again learned how to hide my pain and sorrow behind a happy mask. I'd smile and pretend everything was okay. It was so easy to pretend that I was happy and everything was cheery—all you have to do is smile and act like you're excited about life. People love the happy story with a happy ending, and of course, no one has time to look deep into your eyes, because if they did, they would have noticed how fake my happiness was."

Eldana paused her story now and looked at me. "Eyes never lie if you look deep enough." Then she stopped talking, took a deep breath, and said to me, "We should go. I don't want the kids to get sick, and it's a bit chilly now."

Puzzled and intrigued by what she had told me so far, I was curious to know the rest of her story. I hadn't even noticed the time or the fact that it was getting cold. I looked up at the sky, which looked like it could dump rain on us at any moment.

Eldana smiled as she stood. "If you'd like, we can go to my place for a cup of hot tea and continue our conversation, or we can meet some other time."

Before she could even finish her sentence, I jumped in and said, "Yes! Now, please. Let's go to your place!" I quickly realized how impatient I must have sounded, and, in embarrassment, I told her, "I'm so sorry, Eldana. I'm just intrigued, and I have so many questions to ask you. I mean, if—"

She stopped me and told me, "Mahtab, just be patient. In the end, all your questions will be answered." With a beautiful smile and sparkling eyes, she said, "Trust me."

We walked toward her apartment. At the women's shelter, we were all given one bedroom unless someone had more than three kids, in which case they got a two-bedroom apartment with a separate kitchen and a bathroom for the whole family. To us refugees, it was pure luxury to have our own kitchen, bathroom, and bedroom while staying in this shelter. It was amazing. Once at Eldana's apartment, we fed our kids and put them in bed for an afternoon nap, then I offered to make Eldana a chai, which was my specialty.

I told her, "You just go relax. I know your kitchen, and I know how organized you are. Besides, you love the way I make tea, so you go sit and let me do my magic. After all, I'm okay in the kitchen too, you know?" We both laughed.

As we drank our tea and sat in her small apartment, Eldana continued her story. "Everything was working just the way I wanted. Working in the kitchen and being invisible was my way of life. Still, from time to time, I would think about my homeland and my lost family, but I was sure that Heng had been killed. As for my brothers, I was sure they must have been thrown in jail by now. I hoped they were at least alive, even though we had never had any kind of relationship with each other. They were still my brothers, and I wanted them to be safe. Maybe one day we could even see each other. As for my beautiful Elham, I just couldn't think about him without crying and feeling extremely guilty and ashamed. I never wanted him to see me, because I had no idea how to face him after everything that had happened between us. Every night, all I could do was pray for him, and all I wanted for him was health and happiness.

"Life was the same day after day, and one by one, new faces entered the camp and old faces disappeared in the crowd; as for me, I was still in my own little world. One day, as I was working in the kitchen, I was asked to go to the main office. I remember my heart beating so fast. As much as I had waited for this day to come, I wasn't ready. I knew it had to either be news about someone from my family or the camp leadership getting ready to send me out to the real world, which I wasn't ready for yet. I walked in, and a man I had never seen before handed me an envelope. He had tears in his eyes yet apparent relief in handing it to me. He told me that the letter had gone through a lot to get to me. 'Your husband was a great man, and he gave his life for his country and his people. His last wish was for me to find you and hand you this letter personally.' He bowed politely and left the room.

"The head manager of the refugee camp was a middle-aged man, and he put his hand on my shoulder and told me, 'Take your time, as much as you want, Eldana. You don't have to go anywhere, so just sit here if you want to and no one will bother you.' He asked everyone to leave me alone. One remarkable quality about the Australian people is their extreme compassion toward refugees and people who fled to their country after going through so much. I will never forget their kindness, humanity, and generosity, to the day I die."

Eldana spoke with such gratitude in her voice, and I agreed with her. I had also escaped from my homeland because my country wasn't safe to live in and my whole family was being persecuted, and this strange land and the people whose language and culture we didn't even know offered me shelter, hope, and a chance to build a better future for my children and myself.

Eldana continued, "As I sat there, speechless, my heart was crying out, but I had no real tears. I had no more tears left in me at all. I was angry at Heng, but I loved him too. Tears wouldn't change anything. I looked at the envelope and recognized his handwriting. I put the letter in my pocket, stood up, and excused myself. I needed to be alone with my thoughts, and I wanted to get back to work.

"The manager told me, 'Do whatever you would like, just remember that you don't have to go back to the kitchen, Eldana. It's okay if you need to take a day or two for yourself. We understand. We are here for you if you need us.' I bowed and thanked him, but I knew that right then, I didn't have the guts to open that letter. I just couldn't bring myself to read Heng's last words yet. I walked back to the kitchen and started to cook, as if nothing was wrong and that day was just like any other day. The kitchen staff all watched me, no doubt with a thousand questions, and I could hear their whispers all around me, but no one wanted to say anything to me. I avoided any eye contact so they would leave me alone until my shift was over, then I immediately ran to my room.

"I wanted to open the envelope, but I didn't know how. Was I scared? What else could be stopping me? Questions flooded my mind. I was visibly shaking, my fingers were weak, and I didn't have the power to open the envelope. I was screaming on the inside, but I had to keep it contained since I shared the room with two other women. I didn't want to disturb anyone, so I pulled my curtain divider to create privacy for myself, then I opened the envelope. As I unfolded the pages, my heart pounded out of control. I started to read the letter."

Eldana paused and reached over to open a drawer in the side table. She pulled out a small, worn stack of papers and handed them to me.

"Is this . . . ?"

Eldana nodded. I was holding the letter from her husband, Heng. I began to read.

My love, my beautiful lavender eyes, Eldana, as I am sitting in my jail cell, I know with all my heart that I will never be able to see you again. I am sorry for everything I put you through. You sacrificed so much, and everything I did meant nothing. I am so sorry for all the pain and suffering I caused. I am sorry for letting you go through everything all by yourself. I had no idea what happened to our girls until tonight. I can never forgive myself for losing our girls. When I found out about our girls and how we lost them, I wasn't thinking about the pain I was going through as a father. I was in pain because I could only imagine what you must have been feeling in that moment, what you were going through all by yourself. I wish I was the one who sacrificed my life that night instead of our beautiful girls.

My selfish ambition cost us dearly. Trying to save my country and restore democracy for our people led me to destroy my own family, and for that I will never forgive myself, and I will never ask for your forgiveness. I do not deserve to be forgiven, my love. Tomorrow is my execution day. I will be shot with ten other young men who worked beside me. My beautiful Eldana, your son Elham is one of those men.

As I flipped the page, Eldana explained, "At this point, I dropped the letter, my eyes wide open in disbelief. My heart stopped for a second. I thought I had stopped breathing. I closed my eyes and imagined Elham's face. The last time I saw him was at the kitchen door when he was begging me to forgive him. I had chills all over my body. I couldn't stop shaking and crying. The pain of losing my son and my husband was just unbearable. Thoughts of their execution filled my mind—how could I continue to read? But I had to continue reading, so I picked up the pages from the floor, and with eyes full of tears, continued reading his words."

My love, destiny works in mysterious ways. I met him after he was arrested eight months ago. He was my cellmate. He was arrested for smuggling drugs. The first time I saw him, I couldn't stop looking at him. Something about him reminded me of you. He was very young, and I wanted to help him and educate him about politics. I wanted to show him how drugs could destroy his life. I wanted him to see how our country could benefit from a smart young man like him. I wanted him to fight for democracy, freedom of speech, liberty, and human rights. I could see every day that something was changing in him. I became like a father figure for him, and he became like a son I never had. He was a sad young man. I knew he had a past. I gave him his space so he wouldn't feel any pressure to talk to me until he wanted to. He was getting better, and he started reading books and asking me questions. I could see that he wanted to know and learn more.

He reminded me so much of you, and I didn't know why. Finally, one night after our routine chores, we went to our cell. The lights shut off, and we were supposed to get shut-eye, but in jail, most of our conversations occurred after the lights were off. If anyone had any news from outside about anyone's family or how the movement was progressing, we discussed after lights out. All the guards would go to the main building to play cards or watch TV. This was our safe time.

That night, I gathered enough guts to ask him which city he was from. He told me his mother was from Turkistan. He told me how beautiful his mother was and that she had lavender-blue eyes. My dear Eldana, my heart stopped. He was describing you, and I just couldn't believe what I was hearing.

He told me his mother married when she was very young. Her family wanted to move to a big city, and they didn't want her to marry someone outside of their culture, so they found a man for her who could preserve their bloodline. She was from a very wealthy family, but after his grandpa was imprisoned and then passed away, the government confiscated everything. They had nothing but their reputation to be saved. He told me that his mother's family sacrificed their only daughter to save their precious name and reputation by forcing her to marry a man whom she never loved to begin with. They married, but after a short while, his father left his mother. He said that his father had his own demon to struggle with and that he was a weak man. His mother reminded him of this fact every day.

My dear Eldana, Elham was an angry young man, and that night, I think he needed to talk to someone, so he talked nonstop. I could not believe my ears. I was glad he could not see my shocked expression in the darkness.

He continued by telling me how his mother never loved him, and through the years, she used to punish on account of his father. How he wanted so desperately to be loved by his mom. In that dark room, I couldn't see his face, but I could sense that his voice was quivering as he talked about his childhood. He was punished for his mother's hate for his father. She punished him for looking like his father, and as she said, he reminded her of the pain and hate that she had for his father. He never had a birthday celebration or any words of encouragement. In her eyes, he was his father.

My Eldana, my head was spinning with confusion and my heart was full of sadness for this young man. From his voice alone, I could sense deep pain inside of him. He was still that scared little boy who suffered tremendous pain inflicted by the one person who was supposed to believe in him, protect him, and love him all his life. He told me that when he was thirteen years old, he decided to go live with his father. I asked him what happened to his mother.

He said that she disappeared from his life without a word. She refused to talk to him when he left. But she never disappeared from his mind. She never vanished from his heart. He thought about her all the time and wondered what she was doing, even right then as we spoke. She must have married, he said. She is and always would be his mother, and deep down in his soul, he would always love her. But he just couldn't handle her abuse any longer, which is why he packed his stuff and decided to go live with his father. His father lived nearby in the city. Elham knew that no matter what his mother had told him about his father for years, at least his father would love him and want him. His father had an addiction to drugs and gambling, but he still welcomed his son with open arms. Elham told himself he would take care of his father from then on.

His father worked during the day, then spent all his money at night, feeding his demons. Gambling and getting high was his everyday routine. Once again, Elham was alone at home by himself. But when his father was around, he loved Elham. The only thing that Elham craved all his life, his father gave unconditionally. He tried so hard to forget about his mother and what she put him through. He wanted to have his revenge by being just like his dad. He wanted to hate her too. He decided to try drugs and alcohol, knowing it was wrong, but it was the only way he could forget the pain and also get closer to his dad or perhaps understand his world better. Drowning himself in drugs was the only way Elham could find peace of mind. His father did nothing to stop him. He became his father's best friend and his confidant. It made Elham feel important, made him feel like he was needed in someone's life. One time, after getting drunk and high together, his father told him something he had never known. He told Elham the truth about his mother, and how he used to upset her or beat her up just because she was a strong woman and he felt so insecure in front of her. How he was so jealous of her drive to be someone, and he always knew that she was going to be successful and leave his lazy ass behind. How he never took any responsibility as a father or a husband when they were living as a family. He took all the savings that she had reserved for buying a house and gambled with it and lost it all. He betrayed her trust and broke her heart over and over again.

Elham found out that she had dreams of attaining a higher education, but his father didn't let her because she had to work to support his addiction. That night, his father opened Elham's eyes to the reality of their marriage. He told Elham that his mother was forced to marry him, and he had broken his promise to love and cherish her. Here it was, the real truth about his parents' lives, which he wasn't aware of until then. He knew why his mother hated him so much, and such a revelation crushed his heart. His mother had been through so much with his father; however, he still couldn't forgive her for treating her own child the way she did.

From that moment, Elham didn't want to follow in his father's footsteps. He wanted to turn his life around. He started to doubt everything, including the path he had chosen for himself. He was a long way down the wrong road and didn't know how to pull himself out of this darkness. All he knew how to do was run away from his father and everything else. Before he left, he wanted to write his father a letter and let him know how he felt about the whole thing and why he had to leave him. Elham knew his father would be sleeping till noon, and by the time he woke up, Elham would be gone. He went to his room and took a piece of paper and a pen, then tried to explain his reasons for leaving his father without breaking his father's heart.

He wrote the following: *My dear father, let me tell you that no matter what you have done or said to me, I will always love you. But last night, you opened my eyes to reality and you showed me what my future will be if I stay with you. I will become your mirror, and I'd rather break that reflection right now and never see myself in your shoes in the future. I have a chance to change my life for better. I know I cannot change you, but by leaving you, I have a shot to change myself. Forever your son, Elham.*

He placed the letter beside his father's bed, kissed his forehead, and left. He had no place to go, but he was willing to take a risk, so he found a shelter for homeless youth. It wasn't easy to get rid of his addiction. It was a long and hard road in front of him, so after a couple of days with no money and no one to take care of him or protect him, he just gave up. His body was hurting, and he was hungry. He hated himself for being weak and giving up so quickly, but he didn't want to go back either. He told himself that just a little bit more to keep him straight wouldn't hurt, then he'd give up the addiction.

He had to make money to buy drugs, so he got involved with the wrong people and started making some fast cash. He became a prostitute, selling his body for cash. He was open to anyone who wanted to give him money and abuse him in any way they liked. After a while, he forgot about the promise he'd made to himself, the promise to quit. He didn't care. All he wanted was to get high enough so he wouldn't be able to think, and then he could forget the past and put an end to this pain he was feeling deep inside. He started to believe that he was not worthy of living. He was at his lowest point. He couldn't stay sober for long periods of time. He was searching for something—maybe it was love—but he was looking for it in the entirely wrong place. The self-hate inside him was getting stronger each day. He wanted to kill himself but didn't have the courage to go through with it. Instead, he let his lifestyle do the job for him.

Elham came to the conclusion that his mother was right. He was a worthless loser just like his father. Those words that she used to tell him all the time were dancing in his head every day, every second, and he was starting to believe her every word.

Nothing was changing. He was sinking deeper and deeper in the dark water of his addiction, and years passed without any progress in his life. During that time, he met a girl. Her name was Chunhua, meaning "spring flower." She worked in a hair salon next to a shelter where Elham used to crash every now and then. She looked like an angel from far away and even more so up close. Every time Elham passed her shop, she would look out the window and smile at him. And every time he saw her, everything moved in slow motion—her every move, her smile, the way she looked at him.

One day, he realized he was addicted to her, but it was the best addiction he could ever give in to. His new routine began to include passing her shop every day, often a few times a day, for no reason at all. All to see her turn her head to look his way and smile at him. He didn't know why. It made him feel something pure and innocent.

Finally, he found the courage to go inside and say something to her. They said hello to each other, then he sat in the corner while she finished cutting a customer's hair. She told him, "I finish my shift in ten minutes. Stay, okay?" Her sweet voice melted his heart, but it scared him too. He stormed out of the shop and didn't go back for a few days. He hated himself for doing that to her, but in that moment he saw himself in his father's skin, with Chunhua becoming like his mother. She likely had a thousand hopes and dreams for her future; would he destroy her whole life with his selfishness and weakness, just like his father did to his mother? No way. He'd rather walk away from her right now and never see a single tear in her beautiful eyes. Her sweet smile was more than enough for him, even from far away. He was satisfied just to have her attention from a distance and see her happy. He regretted storming out of her shop the way he did, but he didn't have the courage to go back and apologize to her.

One day, when he was sitting outside of the shelter, he saw her walking toward him. He panicked and wanted to run, but she called his name, and he couldn't move. How could he? She knew his name. He wanted to hear her say his name a million times with that angelic voice. No one had ever called his name with that much tenderness and love in their voice.

As she approached him, she asked, "Why didn't you stay that day? I wanted to give you the best haircut." And then she laughed, and Elham questioned whether or not she was even real. This beautiful creature was full of life and joy.

He told her, "Look, you don't know me. I'm not good for you. I'm bad news, and believe me, you don't want to get to know me or even give me a haircut. Walk away from me while you can." He turned around in an attempt to walk away from her.

Then he heard her voice, softly saying, "Elham, I can't. I like you too much to let you go that easily. You think I don't know you, but I do. We all have our pasts, good or bad; we all have our baggage. But I also know we all deserve to be loved by someone. Let me love you; let me show you how words can be true and make you feel pure and honest. How long do you want to run? Where will you run? Somewhere, somehow, you have to stop. Why not right here, right now? Let me make up my own mind, and don't leave without knowing that if you stayed, things could be different."

He turned around and looked at her. There she was, in front of him, standing tall and full of hopes and dreams. She was fresh air in his toxic life, she was like an early morning spring breeze, she was everything that he wasn't, and she wanted him. How could he say no? He walked toward her and got so close to her that he could feel and smell her beautiful skin.

She took his hand and said, with a cheeky smile, "Let's go in my shop so I can give you a decent haircut." They both laughed, and that was the beginning of his new life. She told him that if he trusted himself and allowed her to help, she would help him. She saw beyond his demons. For the first time in his life, he genuinely felt close to someone, enough to open his heart completely. He wanted to be honest with her about everything, and she felt close enough to him to talk about her life too.

She told him that she grew up with her grandmother, who was a hairdresser, and when her grandmother passed away, Chunhua received an inheritance of her house and the beauty salon, which was in front of the house. She had learned the skill from her grandmother. Elham was so impressed that at the age of twenty-three, she had her own house and her own business. She worked every day to pay for dance school. It was her dream to become a folk dancer. In some ways, she reminded him of his hardworking, ambitious mother.

Elham and Chunhua moved in together, and he promised Chunhua that he would clean up his act and become the man he always knew he could be. He knew he had her love and support. He was determined to make a change, and the change had to be drastic. He asked her to let him stay in the basement of the house for some time, and, no matter what, she shouldn't open the door for him. He wanted to kill the demon inside him all by himself. He knew he could do it. Now he had a reason, a light at the end of the tunnel to look forward to. He knew he could give up his addiction to drugs. It wasn't going to be easy, and he told her that no matter what, she shouldn't give up or feel sorry for him or open the door. All he needed was for her to leave food and water by the door and go back to work each day. He begged her to let him go through the process on his own. He had to prove to himself that he was worthy of change and that he could do it. It was tough, but he made up his mind because he loved her and knew she would encourage him. He had a reason to live and succeed.

Every morning, he could hear her voice from behind the door, telling him how much she loved him, praying for him every night before she went to bed. Her voice, her soft, loving voice was the only thing that kept him going. He stayed in that basement for almost a month. It wasn't only drugs that he had to defeat—it was all those painful memories and humiliations he had suffered. The physical and emotional pain was almost unbearable, but he knew there was an angel who loved him sleeping upstairs. He was not alone in this journey, and that kept him going; she was his strength and inner power, which helped him deal with all the physical pain he was going through. Every day, he would only open the door to get his food. Oh, how grateful he was for everything. It was usually a simple tray of soup, bread, and a single red rose with an encouraging note. Chunhua's notes were full of love and words of kindness. She was the one who kept him going. After the month was over, he left his dark cave, looking like a jungle man. He was so skinny that when he looked at himself in the mirror, he had the shock of his life.

He had to surprise Chunhua. He cleaned up and waited for her to come back to the house after work. He could still recall the screams of joy as she greeted him. It was a good surprise. He knew that he still wasn't over the addiction entirely, but he was committed to succeed. He had Chunhua beside him, and that was the most important reason to stay strong. He wasn't alone anymore. Mentally and physically, he felt great. He got a part-time job repairing bicycles. He had always been good at repairing things. This shop was close to Chunhua's hair salon, and they ate lunch together every day. He took up night school, and she helped him with his homework. He'd never had a chance to finish high school, but now, with her help, he finally got his diploma. For the first time, he felt truly happy and fulfilled, all because of Chunhua.

There was so much love in that small house, love that could fill the whole world. After two years, they finally decided it was time to get married. Elham just wanted to be sure that he was strong enough and wouldn't let the demon back in his life again. He wanted to make sure that he could hold a steady job to support Chunhua and let her achieve her dream of becoming a folk dancer. They got married at the local court-house; the only attendees were the young couple and three of Chunhua's best friends. It was such a small but beautiful ceremony, and they didn't care that it wasn't a fancy wedding at all. She became his best friend, his lover, everything that he never imagined he could have, and he was so grateful to God for sending one of his angels. He was in love. They created a little haven and made so many memories.

Two years flew by so fast. She came home one day with a shaky voice and darting eyes, and all sorts of possibilities as to why she was so nervous ran through Elham's mind, the worst and the best. Nothing could have prepared him for the moment when she gave him the news—she was pregnant! Never in his entire life had he thought that he would actually become a father. He couldn't respond when she told him. He was happy all right, but what kind of a father would he be? Like his father or his grandfather? At that moment, he could hear his mother's voice telling him he would turn out to be like his father. He couldn't let that happen. A flood of memories rushed back into his head.

As if Chunhua knew what was happening inside her husband's mind, she hugged him and whispered in his ear with her gentle voice. "You are going to be the best dad. We make our own destiny. We will start our own little family and our own traditions," she reassured him. They agreed and laughed with joy and danced the night away in celebration. He saw a bright future ahead and started making plans.

Nine months passed in the blink of an eye. They had made plans to renovate the house and paint the spare room, and Chunhua was busy organizing before the baby came. Elham was working double shifts so his wife could rest more. However, something was not quite right in her body. She suffered severe abdominal pains throughout the whole pregnancy. They had countless visits to the doctor that resulted in no diagnosis. Chunhua was very optimistic and brave despite the pain. She kept telling Elham that all would be well, and he believed her. He had no heart to think otherwise.

One day, he came home from work and found her half-conscious on their bathroom floor. She was bleeding. He picked her up and rushed to the hospital. No one could give him immediate answers. He was told to stay in the waiting room for what seemed like a hundred years. Sitting in the hospital waiting room, he let his mind take a negative turn, hearing voices that told him, "It's all over. You thought you could get away from your past?" He didn't want to listen to those voices in his head, so he jumped out of his chair, ran to the bathroom, and stuck his head under the cold water, shouting at himself, "Snap out of it, Elham, she needs you—don't you dare get weak." He went back outside and waited for the doctor or anybody who could tell him something.

Finally, a doctor emerged to talk to him. "Your baby is okay," he said, "but your wife was bleeding too severely. We tried everything, but we just couldn't save her."

Elham couldn't hear the rest of the doctor's words clearly. It couldn't be true. His whole world was crashing down in front of his eyes, and he was helpless, confused, and uncertain of what to do next.

Sitting on that cold waiting room bench, holding his head in his hands, Elham could barely comprehend the doctor saying, "Her heart couldn't take it anymore, so it just gave up. She was too weak. We did all we could. Your son is healthy, and you can see him when you are ready. I am very sorry for your loss." He walked away.

Elham was numb. It felt like an out-of-body experience. Everything that made sense to him was gone. Everything that gave him a reason to exist was gone. He wasn't sure if he was ready to see the baby. How could he look at his son? How would he explain it all to him? He couldn't sit there any longer, and he didn't have the heart to go look at his son without his wife, so all he did was just walk back home. He walked all the way home, not caring how far their home was from the hospital. He just wanted to get home and realize it had all been a bad dream. He opened the door, expecting to see her at any second—she would run toward him and give him a welcome kiss. But instead, the house was dark, and the silence was screaming at him. He felt the emptiness all throughout the house.

"It was true," he whispered to himself in the quiet house. "She is gone." Once again, everything had fallen apart, and he had no idea how to fix it. He had spent his whole life trying hard to stay above the dark water, but she had taught him how to swim, how to let go of all his fears, and how to let his body rise above his demons. Now she was gone, and once again, he was afraid of everything. Without her, he was homeless, hopeless, and all alone.

Darkness pulled him back in so fast. The voices grew stronger every second, and finally, he gave in to the screaming demon inside of him. The monster inside him took control. He lost himself in the darkness once again; he didn't deserve to be saved. His mother was right, he was going to be just like his father: good for nothing, worthless, and not deserving of love. He was back in the same dark place he had been years ago. He lost himself. This time, he didn't even want to be saved anymore. He had no reason. He neglected his baby boy and tried so hard to remove his son from his mind. Later on, he found out that when he'd walked away from the hospital and didn't return, someone took his son to an orphanage. He knew he couldn't be the father his son deserved to have. He wasn't worthy of having his son in his life.

Without Chunhua, he was helpless. The church was the best place for his son. If the boy wasn't a part of Elham's life, then he wouldn't turn out to be like his father. Elham was ashamed of his existence and full of rage toward everything and everyone, especially himself for being so weak.

The seasons changed, and he kept feeding his inner monster. He started smuggling drugs from city to city again. Truly, he was hoping to be arrested or wake up dead. He rejected himself and abused himself. No matter how much he abused his body, his mind wouldn't allow him to forget the pain of his past. Seeing Chunhua's face every night in his dreams wasn't a sweet reminder but was more like a nightmare. In those dreams, she was lying on the floor, her body covered in blood, her eyes open, and her hands reaching out to him as if she wanted to say something to him. He used to wake up in the middle of the night, drenched in a cold sweat, thinking to himself, "Why did I let her love me? Why did I destroy her life? She is dead because of me." He would get himself drunk, hoping to not dream again. Abusing his body pushed him to the point that one day, he woke up feeling sick, with the most horrid pain in his stomach. He didn't have enough money to go to the hospital. To be honest, he didn't even care. He could hardly walk but somehow dragged himself to the neighborhood temple and couldn't go any further. He felt himself wasting away. He was still wasted and eventually just passed out.

When he opened his eyes, he was not at the temple but in the hospital. A person sat beside his bed, holding his hand. Elham had no idea who the stranger was, but the way he talked made him feel strangely calm. He told Elham that he'd found him outside the temple. He told him that he was lucky to be alive. "Someone must have prayed for you and loved you. You must have good heart," the stranger said.

Elham told him, "There is no one, and my heart is dead." He turned his face away from the man.

"God has always been in your heart, and your heart is alive. You just need to listen carefully to hear him." The man spoke with the kindest voice. Elham didn't want to hear any more, but he also didn't want to break this old man's heart, so he just let him talk. Hour after hour, day after day, the man filled Elham's heart and mind with his hopeful words and prayers. Elham assumed the man was a priest or something, and he was around seventy or maybe eighty years old. He had a small figure, pale skin, and light colored eyes. He also had an accent. Elham knew for sure the man wasn't from around there, since he looked foreign; however, he never asked about it. It didn't matter to Elham who the man was. He wasn't interested in anyone's words or advice anyway.

But this man kept coming back and visiting Elham while he was in the hospital. Somehow, his kindness was getting to Elham. Every day, he would look out his hospital window to see if he could spot the man coming to visit him.

They kept him in the hospital for a while, though he didn't know why. They put him through some detoxifying cleansing program. The program was making him feel a bit better, but he hadn't heard the worst news yet. The doctor told him that he'd tested positive for HIV/AIDS, perhaps from sharing used needles. The flicker of hope he had received was dimming. They put him on a treatment program, and he was supposed to check in once a week. All he wanted was to get away from the hospital. This place had brought him nothing but bad news so far. He was determined to get back to his old ways. What was the point of anything else? He was going to die soon, and besides, he couldn't stay in the hospital forever. They soon released him, but he was told to come back once a week for his medication. He didn't have any money and, to be honest, just wanted it all to be over, his insignificant life and the whole ordeal.

The day that Elham was released from the hospital, the old man showed up, and as much as Elham resisted him and told him to leave him alone, the man pretty much demanded that Elham go home with him and that he had no choice but to accept. Elham was angry and annoyed by this man but still didn't want to hurt his feelings. He told him, "Look, mister, leave me alone. I just want to be left alone, okay?"

The man told Elham, "Okay, I will leave you alone, but believe me, I am here for a reason. I don't know what that reason is, but I think somehow it was meant to be."

Elham looked at him, and with a smirk on his face, he said, "It is just a coincidence that we saw each other, old man, so don't get too deep, okay?" Elham felt the man's hand on his shoulder.

The man shook his head, saying, "Son, everything happens for a reason. I wasn't supposed to be at the temple that day. I had an appointment to see my doctor in the opposite direction of where I found you. You see, Elham, there is no such thing as coincidence. Everything happens for a reason. That day I found you outside of that old temple, I knew God had a plan for me, and you were going to be part of it. You need a place to stay, and I need someone to help me out with our community herb garden. So, what do you say?"

Elham was tired and brokenhearted, with no money and no place to go except back to the streets, so he said, "Okay. But just let me be and give me my space. Don't lecture me, okay?"

The man smiled and said, "Okay, it's a deal."

He kept his promise. During the day, Elham would work on the community garden around the temple. He had always been good at fixing things and enjoyed it too, so pretty soon he became the neighborhood's handyman. He took care of roof repairs, plumbing, and mowing lawns, and he even worked as an electrician. He didn't know how or when he'd learned to do all those things, but he was doing well, and everyone at the temple called him the handyman. As long as he kept busy fixing stuff, he had a roof over his head and food to eat. It was enough for him. He was busy all day till late at night, and he was okay with that because it stopped him from thinking about his life.

He wasn't truly living. He was just breathing and letting life pass him by. There was no spark in him. He just did what he was supposed to do. However, day by day, things changed. It is true that time heals old wounds; time will repair the broken heart if you just let it happen. He had his privacy, and the priest never bothered him at all. All they did was greet each other in passing. Elham worked on assignments that were written on the kitchen blackboard. After breakfast, he would know what he had to do that day. His food was always ready for him in the mornings. While he was working, he would sometimes catch the priest watching him. The priest was a peaceful man, and sometimes Elham daydreamed about having a grandpa, imagining that he would be just like this old man. Elham had never met either of his own grandfathers, but whenever his mother had been in a good mood, she used to tell him stories about her father and how they had such a strong and loving relationship.

Not even once did the priest try to talk to Elham about religion or faith. Elham believed in God or a higher power but never followed any particular religion. After losing his wife, every belief and trust in a higher power was dead in him. However, without realizing it, he was looking for a way to heal and rest his wounded soul. He'd had a taste of love and faith in something before, and it had been amazing. That faith he once had was worth waking up to every morning. He was missing those elements in his life. He wanted to talk to this priest, but the priest was holding fast to his promise to let Elham have his space. One day, Elham decided to talk to him, and he responded. Elham told the priest that he could cook and that he wanted to cook something special from his hometown for the priest. He must have gotten that talent for cooking from his mother. The priest allowed him to cook, and they shared their first meal together after several months of living under the same roof. The priest was an avid chess player and would often practice by himself. Elham would watch him play, and one day he asked the priest to teach him, which he did. Chess became their nightly game.

One evening, Elham was standing by the river, smoking his cigarette and overlooking the temple, which he had been working on for the past few months, doing major repairs on the walls and the herb garden. He was so proud of himself because his work had made the old building look brand new.

Elham was still smoking and getting a fix from time to time, but because of his illness, he had to take some heavy medication, which would not mix well with alcohol. He was too weak to give up all of his old habits. It occurred to him that the priest didn't even care what he did. He'd never once told Elham to stop his bad habits.

This one particular evening, the priest came out with a cup of tea in hand. He asked if he could join Elham, so they both stood and looked over Elham's finished work on the temple. While they were overlooking the herb garden, Elham all of a sudden found the courage to ask, "Have you always been a priest?"

To Elham's surprise, the priest responded, "You can call me by my first name, Jay. And to answer your question, no, I wasn't a priest to begin with. Once upon a time, I was a father and a husband. I had a great life, but I never appreciated what I had. I was drunk and using opium every day. I lost everything I had. One night, I was driving home from a party. My daughter was asleep in the back, and my wife was sitting in the passenger seat. We were arguing about why I got so drunk at the party and embarrassed her. She told me that I was not only abusing myself, but I was also hurting those around me. She begged me to drive slowly. I was screaming at her to leave me alone. My loud voice woke up our daughter, who started crying. I screamed at her too, telling her to just shut up. I turned around to give her a smack, and before realizing what was happening, I lost control of the wheel and heard my wife yelling at me to watch out for the car in front of us. When I opened my eyes, I was in the hospital. I was told that I'd lost them both. I went to jail for years for killing my family and driving under the influence. That was a turning point. I had lost my life and, most importantly, my family. I was angry with everyone. I was angry with myself. I realized that I was a selfish, self-centered, ignorant, and arrogant man, and the only way for me to reach that realization was to lose everything that was precious to me. It was too late; I'd paid such a heavy price for that realization. Destiny had nothing to do with this. I took myself down that path. I had gotten drunk and sat behind the wheel. I chose to ignore my wife when she told me to stop drinking. It was all me, not God, not destiny, not anyone else—it was me and my stupidity. Not a day goes by that I don't think about that rainy night, my wife's scream, and the look of fear in my daughter's eyes. That night will haunt me for the rest of my life. There was no way to erase my mistake."

Jay paused, looking at Elham for a second or two, then he continued, "I'm telling you, son, it was an eye-opening moment for me, and I had to take a harsh look at myself. I fought suicidal urges. I became determined to change my path. A man needs something to hold on to when he loses everything, and I chose faith. We all have choices to make when we come to this road. Some choose to abuse their bodies further in every possible way, with drugs, sex, or alcohol. I had done all that to no avail. I had never tried faith, so now I chose God and faith. I chose faith because I discovered that I was worthy of a second chance. In life, we are bound to fail and make mistakes. The beauty of faith is that there are second chances."

Jay looked at Elham again and smiled, then turned his gaze toward the sky, saying, "I don't know about you, but it's getting cold, and I'm too old to stay outside for too long. Goodnight, son." He turned and went inside, leaving Elham outside with a glimmer of hope starting to kindle inside of him.

Elham looked back at the house and said to himself, "There is a road to redemption if I believe in myself again. I can do it! I can come out of the darkness if I start believing again." Jay's stories created a spark of hope in him that night, and he gave himself permission to feel something, to believe in faith and in himself. It was time to change his path. He looked up at the night sky and visualized his wife's face smiling at him with that beautiful smile. There were no stars in the sky that night; it was cold and cloudy, but he imagined in his heart the sight of millions of stars cheering for him.

That night was the beginning of a true relationship with Jay. The priest had helped him heal his wounds. Elham opened up about his past and his precious little boy whom he had left behind. He was ashamed of what he had done to his child. What kind of a father would be so cruel to a child?

He used to cry for hours in Jay's arms like a little boy, and Jay was always patient and sympathetic. Once again, Elham had been saved by a total stranger who became closer than his own family.

Even though Elham was on medication, he knew that sooner or later, this virus was going to kill him. He wasn't scared anymore. Everyone dies at some point, sooner or later. With his newfound hope and faith, Elham was determined to make the best out of his life.

Jay helped him restore his faith in humanity and taught him to trust and love himself, to be able to forgive himself. Elham wanted to find his son and take care of him before he died, even if just for a day. He'd done wrong by his son, which his son didn't deserve. His son needed to know about his beautiful mother, needed to know that he was the fruit of their love, not something shameful. Every day, Jay and Elham visited different orphanages in search of his son. After a year of searching, as Elham was working in their community garden one day, Jay approached him with such excitement in his eyes. He could scarcely breathe. Elham thought he was having a heart attack. After finally calming down, Jay took Elham's hand. "I found your little boy," he blurted out. "His name is Gabriel." Elham was speechless. He wanted to know everything and wanted to see him right away.

The day arrived for him to visit his son. Elham's heart was pounding inside his chest. He felt nervous and guilty and didn't know what he would say. He was in so much pain that Jay had to hold his hand as they walked into the orphanage. Jay had to fill in all the paperwork on Elham's behalf. Elham was filled with mixed emotions. They were led to a game room. A nurse pointed him toward a little boy next to the window. There he was, playing with a toy on the carpet— Elham's son. As soon as the two men walked in, the little boy turned around and looked at Elham. There was no mistaking him with those big, beautiful eyes, just like his mother's. Elham walked toward him and sat beside him on the floor. What a magical moment. This was a gift, a second chance.

Elham's eyes searched his son's face, wondering if he somehow knew who his father was. He was so tiny. Gently, Elham reached out and hugged his son's tiny body. "Hi, my sweet baby. I'm your dad." For the next two weeks, Elham was in the orphanage every single day. With the help of Jay, all the paperwork was completed. Jay became the guardian of the boy, and Elham had to sign a paper stating that he would live in the temple with Jay. The day they brought Gabriel home was the best day of Elham's life in such a long time. He took Gabriel to Chunhua's grave and told him how beautiful his mother was. Just like him. Every night, Elham held his son in his arms and read to him until he fell asleep. His world was peaceful; he'd never imagined that happiness was possible for him again. Gabriel changed everything. Elham wanted to be a better man and father for him.

Jay was a big part of their life too. He saved Elham and helped him heal his wounded soul. He gave him courage to overcome the shame and guilt he bore. However, Elham was sick and wasn't getting any better. Gabriel needed a brighter future. After a while, Jay helped Elham find out about his mother's whereabouts, and they found that she was a successful businesswoman and was married to a well-educated, kind man. Elham had never met this man, but apparently everyone in town knew him and had nothing but good words to say about him. He was apparently a man of honor and was always helping underdogs, so Elham thought that maybe marrying a man like that had softened his mother's heart. After all, she was still his mother, and he had never forgotten about her. Underneath the layers of pain and anger, he still loved her. He finally decided to take Gabriel and go see her. He wanted her to see her grandchild. He wasn't as excited about her seeing her own son, because he knew that in her eyes, he'd never be the man she wanted him to be. At least she could see the one thing in his life that was pure and beautiful.

Elham was nervous and worried about her potential reaction in front of Gabriel, but for his son's sake, he tried to be cool and calm. He told Gabriel that they were going to visit his grandma, and his son was very happy at the news. Jay helped them gather some fresh flowers and herbs from their garden so they wouldn't go emptyhanded to see her after all these years. It was a beautiful spring day, and her restaurant was packed. There were some tables and chairs outside where people were sitting, having a great time. Suddenly, there she was, in a white uniform with a beautiful orchid in her hair. She was smiling and talking to her customers as they complimented her food.

Elham just stopped and couldn't go further. He wasn't sure why, but maybe it was fear of rejection, of not being good enough for her, or maybe he was afraid of how she would react when she saw him with a small child. It would break Gabriel's heart if he saw how cold and cruel she could be. Elham couldn't do that to his son. He didn't want Gabriel to feel the disappointment and rejection that he himself had suffered so long ago. Instead, they just stood there and watched her. She was so beautiful, just like he remembered. Working hard, running around, doing everything just the way he'd expected, ambitious and full of zest for life. He and his son couldn't possibly have any room in her life. As Elham watched her from a distance and sank deeper into his recollections of the past, Gabriel's voice brought him back to the present. "Where is Grandma?"

Elham looked down at him and said, "You know, I don't think she is working here anymore. Let's go get some ice cream, and let's buy one for Jay. What do you say?" Elham distracted his son with such an exciting offer that the little boy was happy and forgot about the whole thing.

A few days later, Jay asked Elham to go try to talk to her again. This time, he was willing to go with him. He told Elham that time changes people, and he was certain she would be happy to see her son. She had to be concerned about his whereabouts. Elham didn't want to mess things up for her new family. Jay reassured Elham that the best place for Gabriel would be with his grandmother. Why was he so concerned? Why didn't Jay want Gabriel to stay with him when Elham was gone? Elham tried telling Jay that he didn't want his son to grow up the same way he did, but Jay reassured him that it wouldn't happen, because this time he was here to watch over Gabriel.

Jay said, "As long as I'm alive, I'll make sure he gets the love he deserves from all of us. But you know, Elham, I'm old, and God knows how much life I have left in me. Same for you. You have two younger sisters now, which would make a happy environment for Gabriel. A proper family." Elham guessed that Jay was right, reluctant as he was to admit it.

The sicker Elham became, the more worried Jay got. Elham could see in his eyes the concern for Gabriel. Jay was an old man, and he was doing too much at his age, taking care of Elham and Gabriel and other people in their community, and the work was stealing all of his energy. Elham knew that sooner or later, Jay would be gone, but he chose not to think about it. Elham always thought he would go first, so Jay had to stay alive for Gabriel's sake, but life never works out the way you plan. One morning, Elham went to Jay's room to wake him up for breakfast, and the priest lay perfectly still, resting peacefully. Elham just knew it was over; he was gone. For the second time in Elham's life, he'd lost a person who had tried so hard to save him.

Elham stood beside Jay's bed, looking down at the lifeless body and thinking to himself that once again, he'd lose hope. The past crawled back from the darkness to get him. He could hear it saying, "You worthless creature. Look at yourself. Anyone who gets close to you and wants to help you gets destroyed by you. Just like your father, you're good for nothing."

Elham slapped himself in the face. "Snap out of it, Elham, it is not about you anymore. Now you have to be a real father and be strong for your son." He knew that this time, he couldn't just bail. This time, he had to be a real man and face the reality of his situation for Gabriel's sake.

After Jay was gone, things got difficult. The looks and whispers in the neighborhood told Elham that he had to come up with a new plan. The old man had a lot of influence in the community, so because of him and his supervision, Elham had been allowed to stay at his place. To have HIV was so shameful in the community and culture, so he couldn't blame people for talking. After all, he was a former drug-using alcoholic with a deadly disease. His main concern was for Gabriel, and he knew that sooner or later, someone would take action and perhaps report him to the authorities. He had to do something to secure Gabriel's future.

With his background, all he could come up with was to do one more drug job and make enough money to be able to leave Gabriel with someone Jay had trusted, Mr. Wong. From time to time, Mr. Wong had welcomed Gabriel in his home to play with his kids. The Wong family would be able take care of Gabriel after Elham was gone. The only problem was that Mr. Wong had a few kids of his own to take care of, so Elham had to make enough money to provide some sort of financial security for Gabriel's future. Elham knew his way around the drug business, so it was all too easy get back in. It took him only a few days, and all he had to say was, "I'm in." Everything was set to make his move.

The night before the job, Elham took Gabriel to Mr. Wong's house. Gabriel always got excited when Elham told him they were going to the Wong's house, because the family had children around Gabriel's age, and they would play all night long. Mr. Wong was a decent family man with four children of his own, and Elham knew he was working so hard to support his family. It wouldn't be easy for them to take in one more mouth to feed. However, they never said anything to indicate they needed money. They were such a generous and giving family to begin with, but Elham knew how tough life was on them. He told Mr. Wong that from then on, Gabriel would need to stay with them. Elham would leave some money with them if they would take good care of his son and, when he was old enough, help him understand why his father had to leave and how much he loved him.

Mr. Wong took Elham's hand and said, "You don't have to worry about Gabriel's wellbeing. I consider him one of my kids, and you don't have to leave any money for me. Please, I don't expect anything from you, Elham. Father Jay did so much for all of us, and it was his last wish that I take care of both of you. You are safe with us. Don't worry about other people or what they say; it's just words, and you don't have to do anything dangerous. I know you are sick, and you are welcome to stay until the end and be with your son in my home. Please don't do anything foolish, I beg you."

Elham realized how decent a human Mr. Wong was, having barely enough to support his own family but still opening his home to Elham and his son, even begging him to stay in his home. Elham gave him a hug, thanked him for his kindness, and left.

There was no turning back from his plan now. He just had to go ahead and finish the job and not think about it anymore. Besides, how hard could it be? He'd done jobs like this many times before, but for some reason, he was afraid and on edge this time. Maybe it was because he was now a father, and he knew someone was counting on him. Or maybe he just wasn't the same person that he used to be. All he knew was that if it weren't about Gabriel's future, and if he himself weren't sick, he wouldn't have done this job in a million years. Regardless, he tried so hard to just put all those thoughts behind him and move forward.

The day before, he'd made breakfast for Gabriel and tried to explain to him that he must go away for a while, and that Gabriel was going to stay with Mr. Wong's family. With his innocent, childish voice, Gabriel had asked, "Daddy, are you going to work in the garden? Then we can go to the park to play?" Elham had taken his son in his arms, wanting to freeze that moment. His son said, "I love you, Daddy." He whispered as if he wanted it to be their little secret, and Elham whispered back with a big kiss on Gabriel's chubby cheeks.

He had told his son, "Promise me you'll be a good boy for Mr. and Mrs. Wong while I'm gone, okay?"

Gabriel sat up straight in his chair and looked at his father with those beautiful eyes. "I promise, Daddy," he said, and those were the words that Elham carried in his heart to the end.

The final hour came, and Elham was ready to make his move. He was still nervous; his gut was telling him something wasn't right, but he chose to ignore it.

He was responsible for driving a van to the location downtown. It was a location he wasn't familiar with, not the usual spot that he used to work. He'd been out of the game for quite some time but thought it would be okay. He just needed to stay cool, and everything would work out. His companion sitting next to him in the car was a young man he didn't know at all. The young man seemed extremely nervous and kept moving and fidgeting in his seat, making Elham more nervous too, so he told him, "Sit still, you're making me feel uneasy. What's wrong with you, man? Is it your first time?"

The young man looked at Elham and said nothing, but Elham knew something wasn't right. The plan was to meet, pick up the goods, and hand over the cash. It was so simple, and he'd done it a thousand times before, so that part wasn't the problem. The problem was the location and this guy sitting beside him in the van. Both gave Elham bad vibes, and as if to make his suspicions stronger, his passenger suddenly told him he had to pee and that he had a bladder infection and just couldn't wait any longer. Something was definitely going on.

Then again, the guy who had set up the deal was an old pal from the streets, so Elham knew he wouldn't betray him. However, Elham toyed with the idea of just starting the engine and disappearing with the bags full of cash. He and Gabriel could escape tonight. By the time anyone figured out what had really happened, they could be a hundred miles away from here, possibly even out of the country so no one could find them. They could start a new life and secure Gabriel's future for good. But then, Elham remembered that he didn't have much time to live, and no amount of money in the world could change that. The best thing for Gabriel was to be with a kind, loving family like the Wongs. That family could give his son the things that Elham couldn't provide: stability, security, and a proper family.

As Elham wait for his accomplice to return, he heard a loud voice telling him to raise his hands and get out of the car. He looked out the window—it was his accomplice. It was a setup. It was all over, and this time, he was going to jail for a long time.

All he could think about was Gabriel's face and how he was probably sitting in a kitchen chair, waiting for the phone to ring. He had let his son down for the second time in his short life.

The shame and guilt were worse than he could have ever imagined. Everything happened so quickly. Days turned into nights, and all the while, he imagined his son sitting on that chair, asking everyone about his father. Every time Elham asked to use a phone, he was ignored. Finally, he was found guilty, and as soon as the HIV came to light, the judge decided that his punishment should be death, a harsh but swift penalty. Elham was relieved that everything would be over. He didn't care about himself; he just wanted to make that phone call to Mr. Wong and let him know he wasn't coming and that the money he'd been hoping to provide for Gabriel's future was no longer an option.

Finally, he made that phone call and found out that Gabriel was taken away by child protective services. They didn't allow Mr. Wong to keep him. The Wongs hadn't known what had happened to Elham. A social worker simply stopped by and took Gabriel away. Elham's days were filled with horrifying thoughts about his son's whereabouts, as he imagined what could have become of him. After many phone calls to Mr. Wong, Elham found out that his son had been sent off to an orphanage. Mr. Wong promised to follow up on Gabriel's case and see if he could take him away from that place and bring him home to take care of him. The poor man was doing all that was in his power to do, but in reality, Elham knew that without money and connections, Mr. Wong wouldn't be able to do anything for Gabriel. Elham was powerless.

His case was finalized in a few days. As he was waiting, his pain came from the fact that his son would grow up thinking that his father had abandoned him. Elham wanted him to know that as stupid as the drug smuggling idea had ben, he'd done all of this for Gabriel and his future. If Elham died now, his son would never know the truth.

Gabriel would grow up and feel exactly the same way Elham had felt about his mother, thinking to himself that no one ever loved him, that he was worthless then and worthless now and not deserving of love. He was going to make the same mistakes that Elham had made with his life, all because of Elham's selfishness and ignorance in leaving his son in the first place. What was he supposed to do? What could he have done otherwise?

That was the end of Elham's story. There was a heavy silence on our prison floor. We had not realized that everyone was listening. My heart was heavy. I could hear sniffles in the darkness.

He took his pillow, hid his face, and cried. Our cells were not made for private conversations. Elham had just poured out his heart and life story in a whisper, but it touched everyone on the floor. I could not see everyone, but judging from the silence all around me, I could tell that lives had been touched that instant. I believe it was fate that brought us together in this room. It was meant to be that we started talking. You see, my dear Eldana, I wanted to tell him that he was my stepson, but I didn't know how he would take it. Would he be angry at me, or would he accept that he didn't just open his heart to his friend but to the husband of his mother? I could feel his pain, so I decided to tell him who I was. He wasn't angry at all, and I think that honesty brought us closer to each other. I told him we might be able to help him find Gabriel. We all got excited for him, and finding Gabriel's whereabouts became our mission. This was now bigger than Elham—now everyone in our prison wanted to help this young man!

That night, in our small cell, Elham wiped his tears from his face, looked at me with eyes filled with gratitude, and let it all sink in. To tell you the truth, I was letting it all sink in too. What are the odds? I saw a glimmer of hope in his eyes. Eldana, I want you to know that I felt so much love for your son. We talked nonstop till morning. I had no idea how I would find his son, but I had to fulfill that promise. I had made a promise to him that I would find both you and Gabriel, and that his son would be united with you and our daughters and that you all would have a brighter, happier future, far away from all this madness. I didn't know yet what had happened to our daughters. I begged him to forgive you, my dear Eldana, for all the pain that he went through, because the woman I married is full of compassion and generosity.

I told him to forgive you for his own sake as well so he could break the cycle of pain, anger, and revenge. I reminded him that he did not want to pass that curse on to Gabriel. My promise of finding Gabriel brought much joy to him. Elham was happy knowing that I would keep my promise and send Gabriel to you. I convinced him that you are such a good mother, and if he could just give you a second chance, I knew you would take care of his boy.

I told him, "No matter how much we try to escape from our destiny, in the end we have to let it go and trust the higher power. Surrender yourself to the hands of destiny. The life lesson lies in the answer of forgiveness and love." In that tiny cell room, I felt the presence of God. I hugged Elham, and we both cried. That night, I felt as though I was lifted high in a way that I had never felt before, and I decided that if we were to find his son, we should hurry. I knew people outside of the jail, and I used all my connections to find Gabriel. I wanted to find him before Elham passed away. He was getting weaker each day. He wasn't allowed to take any proper medication, and I had a promise to keep. To find Gabriel, I was willing to do anything in my power.

Finally, we received good news from one of our allies, a friendly prison guard, that Gabriel had been found after somebody had made contact with Mr. Wong. Gabriel had been sent to an orphanage that was only a few blocks from our prison! We were all so excited and wanted to share the news with Elham, but he'd been transferred to another level because of his worsening condition. We all knew that he had to see his son, no matter what, and I knew that only money could solve this problem. I arranged everything so that the guard who would be in charge of the night shift would get paid off. I also planned to make arrangements for Gabriel to leave the country immediately so that he could be with you.

Finally, after much bribing and begging the night shift guards, my plan was set in motion. Elham deserved this special moment after all he had gone through. He deserved to die in peace. I wanted Gabriel to know that his father never abandoned him. It was important that he knew his father loved him and had worked so hard to give him the best life. Closure was necessary for both of them.

The day Gabriel was set to arrive had become a big event among us. The truth was that all the inmates and even the prison guards were excited and happy for Elham. We could all feel his pain in our own ways, as most of us had families and missed our loved ones too. Seeing this moment come to pass was closure for all of us as well. Elham had become a symbol of love and humanity among us. I had longed so much for that. I saw officials and inmates carry out this special gesture for him. This type of unity has never happened before in this prison. Everyone stepped up to make it good for him. We even had a barber give him a fresh haircut. We found him a nice, clean outfit. The guard on duty even allowed him to take a shower. I was privileged to wash him and dress him, as he was too frail to do so himself. When he was done, he looked handsome. He looked so much younger and was finally ready for his son. We all encouraged him and tried to help him feel relaxed. Poor Elham was extremely nervous and couldn't even walk.

The moment that father and son were reunited, there was not a dry eye in the prison. Most other prisoners couldn't even see the reunion, but word spread like wildfire. What a beautiful sight. Gabriel was shy and scared at first, but when he recognized his dad—oh, the joy! Elham couldn't get off his mattress, but he was happy and free as a bird. Gabriel lay beside him. They were in each other's arms for two hours, catching up. I could hear him talking to his son.

Separating them after two hours was heartbreaking, and to see that Gabriel did not want to let go of his dad was the worst sight. We had no choice. When Gabriel was gone, Elham asked me to sit beside him for a minute. He said, "All my life, God always found a way to save me. This time around, I thought my luck was over, but God showed me that he never left my side. Even when I thought I had no one, he found a way to save me over and over again. Heng, you became my savior. It would be my honor to call you my father, if that's okay with you."

I held his fragile, tiny body in my arms and told him it was my honor to have a son like him. I told him I couldn't be more proud if he were my own flesh and blood. He is my son, and I love him dearly.

Tomorrow is our scheduled execution day, and none of us can sleep. As it is our last night, we were surprisingly permitted to sleep in the same room to pray. We talked, we prayed, we laughed, and we tried to make these final moments last as long as possible. We talked about our families, hopes, and dreams. Elham was quiet and just lay down beside me, and I rested my hand on his shoulder. As I was trying to rest my eyes, one of the guards requested to see me in private. I thought maybe it was about the arrangements for Gabriel, but it was about you and our girls and what happened to all of you.

Apparently, the guards had known the news for a long time, but the prison management had told them not to share the news with me. The guard told me they were afraid that I might use my influence among the prisoners to create a demonstration or something, but now, with all that had happened, the guard couldn't keep it a secret any longer. He asked me not to tell anyone about this because then he would lose his job, and he had a family to feed.

Just before the guard left, he said to me, "You have been so good to everyone here, and the least I could do for you was tell you the truth before you send Gabriel to your wife."

I wanted to shout, cry my eyes out, and break something, or even break myself into a million pieces for letting you go and letting all this happen to you, to us, to our beautiful girls, but I couldn't do anything. I returned to Elham, who was sleeping on the floor, curling his body to one side. He looked like a little child, so small and helpless. In that moment, I knew that my mission was to let Gabriel have a new life with you. I lay down beside Elham, put my arm around his body, and imagined that I was holding my girls and you, my whole family, in my arms. Now was the time for me to be the man that I always preached about and save at least one child from all this madness. Freedom starts with a single step in the right direction, and Gabriel's future is my last step. That's why I started writing this letter. As Elham slept, I recorded everything I could remember from his story and his past so that you may feel closer to your son and grandson.

I thought that I might end the letter there, but I fell asleep next to Elham before I could finish it. I woke up, now the next morning, and saw that Elham was still sleeping. When I tried to wake him up, I found out that he'd passed away peacefully during the night. I guess he was ready to go. We are not sad, because we know he went in peace and was happy. I also am glad that I don't have to watch him be executed; instead, he went in peace by himself. I am happy for him, and I am ready too. In a few hours, we will be in the prison yard waiting for our execution. We are all in such high spirits that, from the outside, no one could imagine that these are the last hours of our lives. I guess that listening to Elham's story, seeing him with Gabriel, and then having him die in such peace among us just made the road so clear for all of us. Life is all about love, compassion, and peace, and all this time, we were searching for something else; finally, this tiny, fragile young man gave us the answer that we had all been looking for. Elham showed us the kind of love that none of us had known before. He gave us hope for the future, even if it was just for a moment. We all felt something special in our hearts and are prepared for our journeys to end today.

So, my Eldana, if you are reading this letter, please meet your beautiful grandson, Gabriel. He is going to change your destiny and create love from hate. He is an angel who is going to heal you. Love him with all your heart. He carries the pieces of Elham, our precious girls, and me. He is your chance to be able to change your future and find happiness again. We all make mistakes in our life's journey, and sometimes, if we are lucky, we get a second chance. Love him and give him all you have in you. We can always find a road that takes us to redemption.

I am with you in spirit. I love you with everything in me. My love, my lover, my heart, and my beautiful lavender eyes, goodbye.

I looked up at Eldana as I finished the letter. Gabriel jumped into her arms, awake from his nap, and she gave him a kiss then smiled at me. She said to me, "Now you know my story, my pain, and my regrets. Not a day goes by that I don't wish I could turn back time and relive my life without any revenge, hate, or regrets. I know it is impossible, but now all I can do is give all my love to my grandchild and hope to someday be united with my loved ones and ask them for their forgiveness." She stood up with Gabriel in her arms and walked away.

That was the last time we spoke about her past. I was moved from the shelter two months later and sent to a different location, along with ten other families. Eldana and I decided to go to our usual bench in the park one last time to say proper goodbyes. I asked her when she was moving away from the women's shelter, and she smiled and said, "I'm not going anywhere. I requested to stay here and work in the kitchen, and they were more than happy to give me a job!" She laughed. "I guess they love my cooking."

I was so surprised, recalling that her dream was to open her own restaurant. She told me that after receiving her husband's letter and taking in her grandson, she had decided to give back to society by helping other women like her at the shelter. A lot of refugees lost everything in their escape to freedom.

"Gabriel is also happy here," she said, smiling at him. "He has lots of friends, and we are both happy. All I want now is peace, and I found it here in this place, giving back." We hugged and kissed each other goodbye. I told her I would keep in touch with her, and she shook her head and told me, "Don't. Start your new life, new friends, and new beginnings. Just keep me in your memory box and in your heart."

I told her she would always stay in the special jewelry box of my soul forever. That was the last time I saw her, the woman with the most beautiful lavender eyes.

The End

ANOUK'S CAFÉ

Her name was Anouk. She was blessed with age-defying genetics and a jaw-dropping body, even in her early fifties. Looking at her, you could never guess that she was the mother of two grown-up children. She had such a young innocence about her. It was her infectious, happy laughter that captured my attention. I met her while I was living and working in Sydney, Australia. She was the owner of Anouk's Café, where I worked many hours as a waitress. I often pondered what her history was. Step by step, we grew to be great companions. She was an astonishing cook and a skilled businesswoman. She was a lady loaded with such empathy and benevolence, handling everything she did with composure and ease. It was in my nature to learn people's life stories—in some way, it just fed my soul. I had always been curious about how each person's life journey molded them into the person I knew. I remember my mother often giving me an evil eye when I asked someone too many questions about their childhood or asked why they were doing this or that.

My mother used to tell me, "Stop asking people private questions, Roxana, it's not polite. Why are you so curious, child?"

Now that I was a grown woman, I still had that urgency in me to get to know people in a closer and more personal way.

Very quickly, Anouk became my personal interest. Generally, she was quiet and extremely organized, inside and out. Once in a while, however, a glimpse of her grieving soul would escape from within. Something inside her seemed to hold her captive, refusing to let her go. The more time that I spent near her, the easier it was to identify the anguish in her eyes.

As time passed, we became closer than just average companions. She had a thirty-three-year-old daughter and an eighteen-year-old son. They both lived in different nations, so she didn't see them often. She used to talk about her children constantly and how she missed them a great deal.

The café was by the lakeside. There was a spot outside the café where a little round table with just a single seat offered an idyllic view of the lake. Most evenings, I would see Anouk sitting alone, a cigarette in hand and a half-empty cappuccino cup nearby, with her head resting on her palm as she gazed out toward the lake. Even from a distance, you could sense that she was crying; I never dared disturb that private moment. It was an unspoken rule that once she sat in that seat, there was an invisible "Do Not Disturb" sign to which the rest of us must adhere.

One day, before Anouk and I had really become close friends, she was perched on her seat outside, and I chose to disregard the imaginary "Do Not Disturb" sign and stroll straight up to her exclusive corner.

Once I was close, I whispered, "What's wrong? You can talk to me, Anouk. I can be a decent audience, on the off chance that you'll let me."

She pivoted to face me, and my speculations were confirmed—her entire face was streaked with tears. The shadows in those wonderful hazel eyes resembled a dark, stormy evening.

She grasped my hand and held it against her wet cheek. "What do you need me to say? We all have a past, and not every one of us is so fortunate to have a flawless life. Please keep your focus on your job, my dear," she said, with a bitter smile on her lips.

She wiped her face and strolled into the café. I remained by the table for a moment, slightly lamenting what I had done. That was it then, no more discussion. We submerged ourselves back into the bustling afternoon business, and there were no more opportunities to talk. That episode troubled me so much, and I determined that I would not ask her anything personal again.

One evening, not long after the incident with Anouk, I went home after work and had a major fight with my husband. He began to yell and shout at me. He took his beer bottle and threw it toward me, shouting that I should get out of his home. He offered one last angry warning, yelling, "I'm letting you know that if I finish my cigarette and you're still around, you are dead!"

I knew that he was not kidding this time. He had manhandled and abused me before, but I had never seen the heartless expression that I saw that night. I took my two-year-old daughter and ran outside. It was eleven at night. Unfortunately, I had no place to go on this cool, stormy night. I had a key to the café, in light of the fact that I was in charge of unlocking the café doors each morning. I had no cash to take a taxi, so my daughter and I walked the distance to the café. When we arrived at the café, it was nearly midnight. My little girl, Samira, was sleeping over my shoulder. Poor youngster couldn't walk any further. I was exhausted. I set my daughter down and was searching through my bag when I realized I didn't have the key with me. I must have misplaced it. I smacked myself on the head so hard and began to cry aloud. My crying was more like shouting from the top of my lungs. I finally just sat down outside the café, unsure of where else to go. My little girl had woken up, startled by her mother's frenzy, and she began to cry too. I recalled the table and seat out back, behind the café. Perhaps I could find some food remaining in the trashcan so I could sustain little Samira and myself. I held her in my arms and attempted to quiet her while I strolled toward the back of the café. The smell of cigarette smoke surprised me, then I saw Anouk.

"Who is it?" she asked, puffing out the cigarette smoke. Despite my alarm, I had no way out and no place to go, so I swallowed my pride and stepped toward her. I mumbled something so she could know who was approaching. She turned toward me and, with wide eyes, looked me up and down. She stood, took my crying daughter from my arms, and ushered us inside. That simple, considerate invitation unlocked a hoard of compressed feelings, and I burst into tears, overwhelmed by her benevolence and aid in offering a sheltered place to rest.

Anouk warmed some milk for Samira and gave me hot tea and something to cover my shoulders. She inspected my wounded face and seemed to come to a conclusion about the situation just from her own observations. She brought an ice pack wrapped in a kitchen towel and started to nurture my injuries, with one hand pushing aside my hair. She glanced at me, clearly probing for answers. What overcame her next was startling, given my present circumstances—she burst out giggling, and before I could significantly ponder the wellspring of that chuckling, I joined in on her infectious laughter. There was some solace in that giggling during a less-than-ideal situation.

Leaning forward, she rested her temple against mine, and she whispered, "This too shall pass away; let it roll. Cry as much as you need. It's all right, you are protected here."

I felt so sheltered, as though my mom was here with me, encouraging me. I was drained, and all I needed was a pillow. Anouk could likely sense my uncertainty, and she immediately locked up the café behind us and offered me a place to rest in her loft, which was above the café. I could feel that tea working its enchantment on me, as I became so sluggish and just couldn't think straight. She took my resting infant in her arms and walked upstairs. I recall falling onto a bed and nothing else thereafter.

When I woke up, I had no clue where I was or what time it was. It took me a few moments to recollect that I was in Anouk's flat. I glanced around, not seeing my daughter. I sat on the bed, calling for my little girl, but there was no reply. As I attempted to stand, I heard a door creak open, and Anouk entered the room. I was so humiliated as recollections of last night flooded back. Disgrace filled every fiber of my being. In that moment, I was speechless, trying to find the right words to apologize for the previous night.

As I was attempting to make my lips move, Anouk set her finger against my mouth. "You would prefer not to wake up Samira now; she just had her lunch and is resting in the next room. I need you to go wash up and get comfortable," she said. I was shocked that it was already after lunch. Had I really dozed that long?

Anouk was extremely kind to me. With such graciousness in her voice, she instructed me to feel at home. "Roxana," she said. "Look, I live independent from anyone else, and this place is enormous. To be straightforward, I could use a little companionship." She grinned. "Stay here until you decide what you need to do with your life, all right? I'm not going to address the situation or give you an exhortation. I simply need you to realize that you are not the only one. That is all." As she was leaving, she turned back and said, "There is sustenance in the refrigerator for you to eat. Take as much time as necessary, and you don't need to return to work for two days. Shelley assumed control over your work shift, so unwind, my sweetheart." Then she walked out.

Her warmth and care provided a sense of security, and a surge of satisfaction and relief overcame me, along with a feeling that all was well with the world. I knew I had discovered somebody who comprehended me and felt my torment. At that idea, I shut my eyes and let my mind wander back to the day I met him—my husband.

It was love at first sight. When I met my husband, I was fresh out of high school and he was a new college alumni. We met at our neighborhood café, where I was working as a server. He and his companions had been hanging out, drinking espresso, and after I gave them the check, he requested that I put my name and telephone number on the bill.

"Why?" I had inquired.

"So I can know the identity of my future wife!"

We both laughed, and I wrote my number and handed it to him with a cheeky smile on my face. "Roxana is my name."

I exited, feeling imprudent for having given him my telephone number, but I reckoned that he would not call. I was sure of that, actually. The liberal tip that he left allowed me to feel prosperous for just one night.

What a surprise it was that he stayed faithful to his commitment. "My name is Bruce," said the voice on the opposite side of the telephone. He let me know that his dad was a major Bruce Lee enthusiast. He told me about how his dad had been disillusioned when he discovered that his son had no enthusiasm for karate. Bruce was enchanting and brought a comical inclination to the conversation. I cherished that about him. I spent so much time laughing during that first telephone call, feeling like we had known each other for a considerable length of time. We actually talked until dawn. That was the nature of our telephone conversations moving forward, as our evenings transformed to nights and then to mornings. He called me each and every day without fail. My mistake came when he let me know that he had enrolled in the Army Reserve. He was bound for Afghaniastanas a mechanical engineer. I couldn't envision my existence without hearing his voice during those daily calls.

Before he was deployed to Afghanistan, we chose to get engaged and get married quickly. It was a delightful function. Everything was extraordinary. He loved me so much; I could see it in his eyes. I was insanely in love with him. We chose to move in together. We found an excellent two-bedroom apartment in a pleasant neighborhood. I was delighted about this place. Dressing that little loft gave us so much joy and excitement. However, shrouded under a cloud of happiness, I could start to see glimpses of his terrible temper and awful judgment. Nonetheless, I excused his jealous tendencies as demonstrations of his love for me. His possessiveness caused a rift between my friends and me. Whenever I was with my friends, Bruce would call and let me know he was missing me and needed to be with me. It was so sweet to hear that, so I would make excuses to leave my friends.

At last, the dreaded deployment day came. Nothing on the planet could have prepared me for such bittersweetness. We couldn't stop crying, and he wouldn't relinquish my hand until the very last minute. Watching the plane take off felt like my entire life was taking off before my eyes. Would he return alive? I couldn't bear to think about that. I missed him as soon as we said goodbye.

Each night after his deployment, I returned home after work and impatiently anticipated a call from him. On the third day, he called. I was so energized and excited, but the conversation was horrendous. I had anticipated that I would hear my clever, caring husband let me know that he missed me. Rather, he was shouting, hollering, and blaming me for not calling him.

"Where have you been? Answer me now. I'm isolated here, thinking about you and going insane, yet you don't answer the telephone when I call?" he shouted.

Crying uncontrollably, I let him know that I was sad, so I had gone to my mom's home when I got frightened and lonely in the apartment. I told him that I missed him so much and needed him. I continued crying until he calmed down and said, "Roxana, my love, I cherish you so much. I was very worried that something horrible may have happened to you. It never dawned on me to call your mom's home. I love you so much and it pains me when I can't contact you or converse with you."

He had to go then, since phone privileges were limited. After that, I realized that I must be home by seven thirty each night without fail, on the off chance that he would call. I just couldn't go out anymore, dreading that he would call while I was gone.

My family reprimanded me for my seclusion, which I despised even though I sort of knew they were right. I pulled back from them and my friends. My mom was extremely stressed about me, but I just berated my family and instructed them to allow me to live unbothered. I insisted that they didn't comprehend our love. I regarded my husband's upheavals and outbursts as affection or his way of showing that he missed me. I told my family that they didn't realize what it was like for him to lose his folks at a young age, and that was why he needed me so much. I rationalized everything. In all honesty, I was the only good thing he had in his life.

My family quit troubling me after that. I felt desolate and needed to be with them, yet I did not have any desire to be judged. I kept running from every one of my friends and grew used to being separated from everyone else. I would sit in the house, waiting for his phone calls. That way, I didn't need to explain or disclose anything to anybody.

In life, it is not always difficult to make certain choices, but the hardest part is remaining committed to your decisions and accepting the outcomes. Living with the choices I had made for the following ten months was difficult. Every day, I would rush home after work. I would do most of my shopping and errands midday, and any meetings must be finished before my daily telephone call. Bruce didn't want anybody to be around me while we were talking. He simply didn't want anybody in the house during that time frame.

Some way or another, I persuaded myself that I was a fortunate young lady. I was nursing my desolate heart, and, without realizing, I surrendered to depression. I told myself that it was because I missed him. My family could see the changes in me, but who had a heart to tell me anything? Deep down, I knew that the relationship was poisonous, but I was so wrapped up in his web that finding a way out was out of question. I was in love with him, or at least I thought I was.

Finally, one day, I received news that our soldiers were returning home. I went to the airplane terminal without anyone else to welcome him. I knew he would only want me there, and I wouldn't want to surprise him with unnecessary company. I also needed to be separated from everyone else and just be with him for those first few days. I was so excited and anxious. Sitting alone among all those people who were waiting for their loved ones to come home made me feel so lonely and sad, realizing that I couldn't even share those important moments with my family and friends. As I was looking around and watching all those joyful faces, he walked in, clutching his knapsack and searching for me in the crowd. He had lost so much weight and was walking with a slight limp. I didn't show myself for a few seconds. I simply needed to watch him search for me. I finally raced to his side, and his expression made me feel as though I had given him the world.

He dropped his knapsack and held me in his arms, whirling me off the ground and kissing me. "I missed you like crazy, Roxana," he cried. I had missed him excessively too. Suddenly, everything and everyone else that I had been consumed by were disappearing from my mind. I was simply happy that he was back and we could start our life together once and for all.

That night, we couldn't sleep. We couldn't even move in the opposite direction of each other, so we stayed side by side all night. We had never experienced such enthusiastic, passionate love. I had never felt that way before. He was delicate, tender, and passionate. We talked throughout the night and made magical and passionate love over and over. For three days in a row, such was our happiness. I cooked him all his most loved meals. We took our showers together, and I washed his body while he washed my long hair, kissing me everywhere on my body. Life resembled a garden of white lilies, swarming with a million brilliant butterflies. For the first time in our relationship, there was nothing but gentleness. Looking back, I remembered everything about those three magical days, but the rest of our life together was so blurry to me.

The lilies passed on and the butterflies took off too rapidly. I was soon pregnant. Bruce didn't want any children, but my heart just couldn't bear to have the fetus removed. I misled him and told him that specialists said it was past the point to choose an abortion. Much to my alleviation, he didn't contend with me after that.

He had been injured in battle. Due to his injury, he was released from service. That was simultaneously excruciating and relieving. His release orders included instructions to not carry heavy objects, to not walk long distances, and to avoid overwhelming situations. I felt that his release was why he resented having any children, since he couldn't do much after the injury. This truly hurt his self-confidence and, to him, was a major disappointment. Before he had joined the armed forces, he had been at the gym each and every day and was always eating healthy. He never smoked, and liquor was not his drink, ever. Well, this time the change was distinct; he was an entirely different person. He got an office job, where his status as a veteran earned him a considerable amount of regard, and his workmates adored him. Really, the whole neighborhood adored him and respected that he was a veteran, and that even though he was injured, he was still willing to work for his family. At work, he could pick any shift he was comfortable with. They also accommodated his doctor's very specific orders. He was a man of principle, and that was honorable.

Everybody respected him for his dauntlessness and valor. He was the town's legend. At home, when it was just the two of us, he was a completely different person. He was no legend in his own mind, as he fought feelings of dread and fear. Bad dreams visited him every night. He would wake up either with a shout or by taking a gander at me as though I was a total stranger.

A few times, I approached him with a suggestion that he go to counseling, but he generally made excuses. Even after my assurance that I would go along with him, he berated me, saying, "Goodness now, you can't wait to dispose of me, Roxana." His accusations made me so irate, and I eventually chose not to mention it again.

We were blessed with a beautiful baby, Samira. That was Bruce's great grandmother's name; it was a beautiful name, and I loved it. I was happy when the pregnancy was over. I worked throughout my whole pregnancy. I cherished my employment, since it kept me far from home. That was the one thing I didn't give Bruce a chance to steal from me. Regardless of the number of fights and contentions we had, I never surrendered my employment. I cherished serving people.

My supervisor was incredible as well. He picked up on what was going on in my life and guaranteed that my job was secure. He once said to me, "Roxana, you are my best worker, and customers like you. Don't worry about anything, okay? Worse comes to worst, you always have your job." That place was my getaway, far from home.

Pregnant as I was, I worked my heart out as much as the pregnancy would let me. Soon, my beautiful Samira arrived, and she made the end of each day a bit more cheerful. Much to my surprise, Bruce changed as well. Parenthood was benefiting him. He was loving and kind at the end of the day. Those first couple weeks, I would wake up to feed the baby, and Bruce would also wake up, making me hot cocoa and a nibble every now and then. He would help me with the infant. He would change diapers and solace the baby and urge me to rest while he dealt with the baby for some time. I contemplated that perhaps Samira could transform him—possibly, now that Bruce was a father, our life might improve.

Then, the end of those first couple of weeks arrived, and this life that we had built slowly deteriorated. I was compelled to quit my place of employment. My kind manager had resigned and left his son in control, but Bruce didn't want me to work for his son in light of his own insecurities. Bruce was not concentrating on his job either. Drinking overtook him. I needed to land another job, and it was then that I discovered Anouk's Café.

It was by coincidence that I discovered Anouk's Café! I first met Anouk at a strip mall. Indeed, I overheard her telling another woman that she needed help at her café. As frantic as it may have seemed, I inserted myself in the middle of their conversation and presented myself as her solution. That day, it didn't matter that I was shy and couldn't always communicate effectively with strangers—I was desperate for a job. I informed Anouk that I had years of restaurant experience and would be happy to be considered for that position. Imagine, right there in the middle of the strip mall.

I needed to work again, not only to provide for my family but also for my mental health. I needed to get away from Bruce and the house. Samira could stay with my mom while I was working. Bruce did not have any desire to try and watch our daughter, and I was happy with that arrangement. He was often intoxicated and remained in his room with the door closed. The few nights that Bruce did have responsibility for our daughter, I would get back home and see Samira sitting alone in her filthy diaper, crying, with clear indications that she hadn't eaten in quite a long time.

Approaching my family for help was difficult for me. My mother was like an angel, and she had a good idea of what was going on, but she never meddled. One time, just a single time, my dad let me know, "Roxana, we love you, and we are here for you whenever you need us, all right?" I knew the implications that were hidden under that simple statement. It was his way of discreetly acknowledging my situation.

I had embraced him and said, "I know, Dad. Be that as it may, I'm not going to give up on my marriage." He appeared to understand that. That was my last discussion with my family regarding my marriage.

I opened my eyes and realized that I had been wandering down memory lane for quite some time. I had seen my life playing before my eyes, much like a motion picture, bringing me to where I was in life presently. I needed to consider Samira's wellbeing and my own. No more abuse; no more rationalizing every wound and bruise on my body. I was sinking in an ocean of shame, anger, and frustration, and I just wanted to get away from everything. No more being a victim.

I got up and stopped briefly by the next room, where Samira was sleeping like an angel. Poor kid. For the past couple of weeks, she hadn't been able get any sleep because of Bruce's screaming, shouting, and breaking dishes. She was constantly woken up by the commotion. At least now she was resting peacefully. I felt remorseful for putting her through all that abuse.

I cleaned up. I made myself tea and sat in the lounge, checking out this delightful place. I felt safe. Anouk had such a delightful taste in furniture and decor. Everything looked extremely costly and had an exemplary European style. I knew she was half French and half Moroccan, which contributed to her stunning look.

Beyond that, there was so much that I didn't know about her. I knew something wasn't right, however, after our last discussion that we'd had behind her café. We usually didn't talk much throughout the day, with the exception of the customary discussions about work. Be that as it may, perhaps now it would be different, as she had taken me in and offered me shelter. I had already heard of her kindness, since she used to do numerous benevolent deeds around the town, but this time, she was taking a personal interest in my situation.

By the time I finished my tea, it was very nearly six in the evening. I went to wake up Samira since I wanted her to be able to sleep through the night. She already seemed to be liking this new place, and I was cheerful as well, considering that we had a place to rest for at least a couple days or until I made sense of what to do.

I heard Anouk's voice calling Samira, who ran toward her and gave her a major embrace. Samira was grinning, which I hadn't seen for some time. My poor baby had overcome all the absurdity of our life. She had been frightened and afraid for several months, which I could see every time I glanced at her face. I blamed myself for her hardships.

In this moment of happiness, I settled on my choice, telling myself, "Roxana, you are leaving Bruce and beginning another life." I could do it. Now that I had Anouk in my corner, I was feeling more grounded than ever before.

I looked at Anouk, and I didn't even need to tell her anything, because without a single word exchanged between us, she hugged me and said, "You can count on me all the way. Think of me as your mom. Stay here as long as you want. I love to wake up every morning and see this beautiful face every day." She was pointing to Samira, who again ran to Anouk's arms and said with her innocent, childish voice, "Thank you." We both laughed at her attempt to say it correctly.

That night, when I placed Samira in her bed, I knew I needed to talk to Anouk about my contemplations and what I needed to do. We were sitting on her lovely overhang that faced her beloved lake. It was a quiet night. I felt calm. She gave me a glass of red wine. It was her favorite drink, which was known by most of us who worked for her. We all realized that Anouk drank great quality red wine. To be straightforward, liquor and wine were never my top picks. Notwithstanding, I contemplated the situation internally—what was just one drink with her?

Her balcony was much like a little modernized rainforest. There were green plants all around us, along with candles, little water fountains, and a Middle Eastern carpet on the floor. White ribbon drapes surrounded us. It was otherworldly. A delicate breeze made the drapes flutter around us. I felt as though I was in paradise.

I glanced at Anouk and said, "I had no clue that this perfect place even existed, just sitting over the café."

She grinned at me and answered, "This is where I hide from the entire world." We both stayed silent and let the quiet night bathe our minds and souls with delicacy. I opened my eyes after a while and glanced at Anouk. Her eyes were shut, and she was not present but rather far away. I did not wish to trouble her.

Without opening her eyes, though, Anouk began to talk. "You asked me a while back what wasn't right with my life. I know you folks in the restaurant believe I'm inaccessible, distant, and icy. It's all right. I wouldn't fret. People make their own particular assumptions about others just by taking a mere glance at them. Tonight, I will give you a little access into my life, my identity, and where I originate from, on the grounds that despite what you are experiencing at this moment, you have to realize that life goes on. Life has its high points and its low points. Whatever you feel at this moment, simply know you are not the only one. The lady that you see sitting beside you isn't the same lady who lived in different circumstances fifty years ago."

I was tuned in, listening to her narrate her story, and had no intentions of letting her stop, even though I knew it could be a long, taxing night. This was a rare opportunity to open the door to Anouk's heart.

Little by little, she proceeded. "I was five when my folks separated. My father was mentally ill. He was expected to take medications for his sickness. However, for reasons unknown, his own parents never wanted to concede that their child was debilitated. Rather, they believed that if they found him a spouse and he got married and had children, everything would work out. He was engaged and married in under a couple of months. They found him a young lady from an extremely poor family. Tragically, my father's family had ulterior motives, intending to control my mother and ensure that she would not question his mental illness. Apparently, his behavior and actions did not improve; instead, he became more violent and abusive.

"When his family saw that he was truly crazy and their little arrangement hadn't worked, they all chose to overlook the entire thing. He was rough toward my mother and me. When I was mature enough to realize what was going on, my mom packed her things and left, to everyone's astonishment. I returned home from school that day, and my father was perched on the patio. He was smoking and pulling his hair tenderly, which was never a good sign. As I walked toward the house, fear grasped me. Looking down at the ground, I very gently asked him where Mother was. He took a glance at me with those unnervingly menacing eyes and let me know in words that still echo in my mind to this day, 'The bitch left us.'

"I realized that was it, and I was stuck in an unfortunate situation for the foreseeable future. I had to live with him, but from that minute, I knew I needed to take care of myself. As a child, I made up colors in my psyche and separated my life into hues. When my father had a decent disposition, everything was green, which was my most beloved color. Green represented those days when my father was caring and loving, those moments when he used to dance for me in his pajamas and sing a song while he prepared a traditional French dish in our kitchen. Green was the color of hope that one day my father would be cured and then every day would become a green day. When Father had a terrible temperament, those days were a bright, violent red. Just like the color of a dragon in my nightmares. Red was the color of dread, perplexity, agony, bad dreams, and dejection. Red represented giving in to my father's madness. I hated red.

"My father used to be an engineer, and he worked for a major organization. He was an exceptionally savvy man and handsome to a great degree. I recall that whenever we would walk down the road together, ladies used to stop to give him their telephone numbers. When it came to the ladies, he was a remarkable charmer. I wanted him to be with somebody and maybe even get married so that he might leave me alone. From the outside, he was an attractive, well-educated man from an exceptionally affluent family. Away from public scrutiny, my dad was an irrational, debilitated individual with numerous intricate layers. My frustration grew with each one of the ladies he attracted, since they had no clue what they were getting into. They had no idea about his mood swings, and they didn't know about the colors of his emotions that he could turn to at any second.

"I knew he was not well, and it broke my heart at quite a young age. At nine years of age, I turned into an analyst, learning how to read him, to know when to talk or when to simply not, to not look directly into his eyes, to be imperceptible. I used to give him guidance about his lady friends, and sometimes, I even approached women on the road and acted so charming and blameless, then I gave them my desolate father's telephone number when he asked me to. I turned out to be extremely manipulative and subtle. That was the main way I learned how to survive. Everything about me was like a mechanical robot, programmed in a certain way to protect myself from physical punishment or the repercussions of his violent temper.

"As a child, I learned to put up a front. I couldn't stand to show other people who I truly was. I felt safe that way. I hushed up about my home life and learned not to talk about my issues to anybody. I couldn't converse with my dad either. If I ever tried, I invited his torment on me just for sharing my perspective. To teach me a lesson, he would smolder my fingers under hot, boiling rice for not cooking the rice the way he loved it. On the off chance that I broke a glass or a plate while washing dishes, he would force me to expose myself and stand on the other side of the room. He would look me up and down and let me know how wonderful I was and how much a well-off man would pay to take me from him. He would tell me that he planned to make a profit by offering me to the most noteworthy bidder. Those moments and those words are still with me. I was never permitted to have friends or go to anybody's home, since he believed that all other people were shrewd and were attempting to send him to a mental health center.

"The main way out for me was to create an imaginary identity—my own fanciful companion. She was an alternate Anouk. This Anouk was happy and had a lovely family. She had numerous brothers and sisters. She lived in a large house, and whenever I needed her, she would join me. She was my warrior. Each time I was locked up in the storage room or was up to my neck in the snow because I behaved poorly or didn't do my chores, she was the one who fought the battle for me, talking with me and letting me know not to surrender. She would even take me away to an imaginary life, far away from that one. It was so lovely and serene.

"Father used to have a bad disposition at work, and they eventually sent him to a mental health facility to get some treatment. When that happened, I was sent over to one of our relatives. I felt like a bag that nobody needed, yet somebody had to take me. While I was staying with my close relatives, one of their children played with me inappropriately. When it first happened, I went straight to the adults and told them what had just happened. My aunt's reaction was to slap me across the face and shout at me, 'You are only a little prostitute like your mother!' Then she chased me out of her home. After that episode, Grandma assumed liability for me, which was more awful than living with my insane father or my debilitated cousins. Grandma was barbarous, and she despised my mother and all young girls especially. To her, having a granddaughter was more regrettable than having a debilitated child.

"I can still recall the day that my aunt chased me out of her home. There was no one else to take care of me. I was old enough to fend for myself, so they just threw me out on street. I knew that these feelings of rejection wouldn't help me fix my situation. I was still a child, so I allowed a tiny light of hope that maybe my grandmother would like me. My uncle agreed to take me to her. With that ray of hope in my heart, I was eager to see Grandma. I needed to make a decent impression. I thought that if I smiled and gave her a major embrace, she would be kind to me. I knew that if anybody were to want an undesirable young girl, the girl must be cheerful and kind. I knew how to shroud my actual sentiments, how to wear a veil. However, every one of my hope and dreams that I would have a close relationship with my grandma broke when she opened the door and saw me. Her eyes showed just how much she loathed me. My uncle informed her that my father was extremely sick and not fit for dealing with me. My uncle also explained that he and my aunt didn't want me interacting with their children. None of the relatives wanted to assume any liability over me, but since Grandma lived alone, my uncle explained that she could be a great help and companion for me. I was hidden behind my uncle, listening to each word that he said to her. I was ten years of age, yet a great deal more developed for my age. Inside, I was praying that she would take me, hoping God realized what might transpire if not.

"Grandma was living in an isolated area on a little ranch outside of the city. She was a small, thin old lady, but she held her own with an independent personality. I learned from my eavesdropping on my close relatives that after Grandpa passed on, Grandma assumed responsibility for everything and didn't want any of the youngsters to disturb her. To the extent of my knowledge, she brought forth ten children, and just four survived. There were bits of gossip that Grandpa had a stroke and was incapacitated for a long time, then one morning he was just discovered dead in his bed. Nobody ever discovered how he kicked the bucket. Be that as it may, my cousins used to claim that Grandma executed him, but none of them had the guts to tell anybody outside of the family. So, as should be obvious, Roxana, my dread was genuine, yet she was my only hope.

"Grandma pulled me by my hand and told me to sit in the corner. She stepped aside to talk to my uncle and ask him what they were supposed to do. I overheard her say, 'Even that whore, her mother, did not want her.' She told my uncle that she would take me because she had no other choice. She walked toward me, looked me straight in the eyes, and asked me, 'Do you know what they would have done in the old days with an unwanted child, especially a worthless girl like you? They would have thrown her into the river to drown. I am a very kind person, so I will not do that to you. You will become my little servant.'

"Even as a child, I knew that she was outright mean and cruel. Those words were planted in my head and heart for a long time. Grandma was right, because from that day I became her slave. No matter how hard I tried to make her love me, she never did. All I was to her was an unwanted granddaughter from an unwanted daughter-in-law.

"Every time there was a family gathering at her house, she made sure that I felt less worthy than her other grandchildren. I was never allowed to sit at the same table with my cousins or play with them in the yard. If she caught me playing with them, she would scream at me in front of everyone, 'Anouk, get in the house and clean up the kitchen! You are not allowed to play with my grandkids. You are just here to serve them!' I would run into the house, wishing that the ground would open up and swallow me. The humiliation was brutal and soul-crushing.

"After a while, I knew how to avoid humiliation in front of everyone. I would just act invisible. I would do everything she expected me to do without being asked. I would stay in my corner of the kitchen—I practically lived there. Sometimes I would disappear to the basement until everyone was gone. Only then was I allowed to eat the leftovers, not from the pot but off their plates as I cleaned. She used to feed me rotten food and moldy bread because she believed it would build my character, and she used to tell me it was good for my digestive system and would make my body strong for work. I used to eat those rotten foods and pretend that I enjoyed every bite, but deep down I knew it wasn't right. After a while, I stopped caring as long as I wasn't hungry.

"Grandma had thousands of rules in her house. I followed every single one of them, because failure meant severe punishment. I never had a room of my own; like a dog, I used to sleep on a small mattress on the floor beside her big, king-size bed, and the minute the light was off, I had to close my eyes, lay in the darkness, and just go to sleep. She used to say, 'No matter what you hear, never open your eyes or get up from your mattress. Don't you dare get up or get curious, because if I see you out of your spot, I will put a snake under your blanket in the middle of the night while you are in a deep sleep.' I was terrified even thinking about it, so I never once disobeyed her rules.

"She had a lot of different snakes slithering around her farm. That never seemed to bother her at all. I remember everyone used to tell her to do something about that, as it posed a risk to customers who came to buy her farm produce. She never cared about her customers, only about herself. She didn't like people anyway, and to be honest, I think she was happy that I was terrified of snakes. She used it as a tactic to scare me so she could punish me or control me, I guess. She had a small house at the back of the farm, but she would never let me go to that house or anywhere close to it.

"I stayed with her as the years passed painfully. Then I turned thirteen, and my body started to change as puberty took its course. Even boys seemed to notice it too, and I liked the attention. I started to look at myself in the mirror more often. Everyone started to tell me that I looked more Moroccan than French. My father was French and my mother was Moroccan, which is why I think Grandma used to call her a 'gipsy whore.' Grandma had agreed to my parents' marriage because the whole family thought they could control my mother, but I guess her gipsy heart ran wild and she finally left us. Grandma hated her, and the idea of me growing up to look just like my mother was unbearable to her. In her mind, I was going to become just like my gipsy mother. I was looking more like her every day. Grandma hated the fact that my breasts were growing, and she used to tell me that my womanly body was so disgusting that she couldn't even look at me anymore.

"I was confused and felt ashamed of my body. I used to wrap my breasts with a long shawl so they would not grow any bigger. I was shy, and my self-confidence was as low as it could be. I wanted to have my own bed and sleep in a separate room, but she enjoyed treating me like a dog. I slept on that dirty, thin, small mattress beside her bed so that if she wanted something in the middle of the night, I could help her. But as I was growing, the mattress became smaller and smaller for me, and I also developed a huge appetite. I started to eat more, which she hated the most.

"After a while, things started to change around me. Suddenly, Grandma became much nicer to me, and I noticed that she would watch me while I was walking around the house or doing my daily chores in the backyard. She'd ask me to turn around and walk straight toward her. I had no idea why, but I liked the attention from her. I thought that she was finally growing to love me and be proud of me.

"One day, when I got home from school, I headed to the kitchen as usual to start making her supper, but she was waiting for me. She told me to sit beside her, then she gave me an old suitcase. She had a tiny smile on her face, which was very strange because the look I usually got from her was an evil eye or a look of disgust—but now, all of a sudden, she was smiling at me and telling me to open this suitcase. I opened the suitcase; it was full of beautiful clothes and a small bag with lipsticks. I looked at her in shock and confusion, and she told me, 'Go on, try one dress. I want to see how it looks on you.'

"Quickly, I went to the other room and put on the dress. It was exactly my size. I returned to Grandma, and she studied me. She told me to turn around and put lipstick on, then go brush my hair and come back. She wanted to see the whole thing. She had such excitement in her voice. I was still shocked and didn't know what was happening, but I liked the new Grandma, and I loved the attention that she was giving me.

"I felt like a whole new girl. I came out with my hair down on my shoulders. I had very long hair, almost down to my hips. I was wearing a pink dress that had puff sleeves and dozens of beautiful white flowers all over. I was wearing red lipstick. I smiled nervously at her and tried my best to act just the way she wanted me to. She was very quiet and observed every move I made as I paraded the dress around for her. She asked me, 'Do you like yourself like this? Pretty, like a little princess?'

"I smiled at her and replied, 'Yes, Grandma.' She walked toward me and told me to take the clothes off and hide them. She did not want anyone to know or see that she had given me those clothes. I was confused when she told me to hide them, but she just smiled at me and told me that it was our little secret. I promised her I wouldn't tell anyone, then I quickly put everything back in the suitcase and hid it in the back room.

"At school, I had no friends at all, and to be honest, no one wanted anything to do with me because of Grandma. She was like an evil witch, and everyone used to be afraid of her and feel sorry for me, but I didn't care about being a loner at school. I was so wrapped up in my own miserable life that I never wanted to get to know anyone; I knew it would only bring me more humiliation and embarrassment, but now life was getting better since Grandma had begun to notice me and like me.

"Sharing a secret with Grandma made me feel special. I had no idea what was happening, but I liked it. From that day on, she was different, and her calmness toward me surprised me. Nightly, as I curled up on my floor mattress, she started telling me stories about her childhood. She told me that the betrayal of her family, friends, and even her own husband taught her to learn to rely on herself only. She told me that her own kids had used betrayal as a weapon against her.

"Our new bond inspired trust and love inside of me. She emphasized how important money was, that it was the most powerful element of any woman's life. She'd say, 'Make it and hide it and never tell anyone how much money you have or how you made your money. This is the most important rule—never tell a soul where you keep it.' Grandma told me that when I started making my own money, she should be the only person who knew about it, no one else. Before that, I'd never thought about money that way, but as she taught me, money would keep me safe and give me confidence, and that was her only advice to me. I guess in some way she was right.

"She told me that she came from a very poor family, but she had used her good looks and her charm to make money. Basically, she wanted me to follow in her footsteps. She felt that she was obligated to take care of me, and her advice was her gift to me. She wanted me to be her little protégé, which she said would be my gift to her for her kindness.

"Every night, I would listen to her and soak in every single word, but I still had no idea what exactly she was talking about. Finally, after almost two months of talking and giving me advice, she decided to let me in on her secret. That hot summer night, I was in a deep sleep, when suddenly I heard a whisper so close to my ear. 'Anouk, Anouk, wake up.' I opened my eyes; it was Grandma. I looked at her, fearfully expecting a punishment of some sort. Instead, she smiled and just motioned for me to follow her. Remembering her rule for me, I told her it was after ten and I could not move from my mattress or leave the room.

"She pulled my arm, yanking me up out of the bed, and raised her voice a little higher with authority and harshness. 'I am telling you to get up and get ready because it is time for you to see something, okay? Get ready now!' she yelled at me. 'Also, wear your pink dress that I got you. Use your makeup kit too, and make sure you look nice, okay?' Then she pushed me toward the other room and walked away from me. Those words were the beginning of the next chapter of a life that I wasn't ready for, and I had no choice but to obey without asking any questions. I knew I had to hurry; otherwise, she would get mad at me for taking too long.

"I was half asleep still, and I had never been woken up at such an hour. I had no idea whether to be afraid or curious. Everything in me resisted what she was saying, and I had no clue why. I wanted to go back and sleep, but this was Grandma. I did as I was told. My personal opinion never mattered. After a few minutes, she walked in the room and told me to hurry, so she helped me finish dressing and put on some makeup, then together we walked outside.

"I could hear the night creatures making noise. Grandma took my hand and reminded me to be cautious, lest I wake up those snakes. I was scared to death and held on to her hand as if my life depended on her. She told me to close my eyes, hold on to her tight, and just walk with her. I closed my eyes hard so I could not see anything, just in case something scary was in my path.

"Finally, she asked me to open my eyes. We were at the back of the farm, near Grandma's small house. That was the forbidden part of the farm, from which she always told me to stay away. It was surrounded with trees and tall bushes. It was hidden from the rest of the farm. Had it not been for the moonlight, I would not have been able to see at all. The smell was different from the rest of the farm too. Grandma had a key, so she unlocked the door to the small house and we entered. What was this place? It was so beautiful. Everything was adorned in gold and red velvet. The furniture looked very expensive, at least to my young eye. There was a beautiful candelabra and a table with fresh flowers and a silver bowl with lots of fruits in it. She told me to go sit in a chair, then she reminded me to be polite. She went to another room, and I could hear her talking to someone very quietly.

"I had a strange feeling and wanted to run back to the main house, but I had no idea how to get there in the dark. Everything was happening too fast for me. My thoughts were interrupted when Grandma came out of the other room with a man walking behind her. The man was dressed very nice. He wore a suit and had a single white rose in his hand. Grandma told me to say hello and shake his hand. He gave me the flower and asked me for my name. No one had ever given me a flower before. I looked at Grandma, uncertain of what to say. I needed permission to talk or keep quiet. I was never allowed to talk to anyone in her house or her presence without her permission. Tonight alone, she was making me break rules for which I was certain I would be punished. Talking to a stranger with a flower was certainly a death sentence. Her reassurance was more eerie than anything else.

"She held my shoulder and looked straight into my eyes, trying to calm me down. She said, 'Anouk, listen to me. You have to be very nice to my friend, okay? He wants to get to know you, and he wants to be your friend. Be polite, and don't embarrass me, okay?' She lowered her head slightly so that her gaze met mine with a threatening look, accompanied by a tone I had never heard before. This was not the woman I knew. This was a whole new side I was seeing, and whatever it was, it confused and terrified me.

"She told me to sit on his lap, and I froze. The sharp look on Grandma's face urged me to sit on this man's lap as she walked to the other side of the room. Pouring a drink for herself and the man in the suit, she said, 'Just be the nice little girl you are.' The man told me to talk to him about my school, asking about my classes and what I liked the most. He even asked me if I had a boyfriend. I could not respond, and I felt my body shaking on his lap. I was scared and shy, so I looked down at my fingernails.

"He pulled my chin up and looked into my eyes, saying to me, 'You are a beautiful girl, Anouk. I will teach you everything you need to know about boys, okay?' He offered me his drink and told me to sip from his glass. I tasted it, and it was horrible, but he forced me to drink little bit more, and then a little more again. He was laughing and talking at the same time. My heart was pounding as much as my head was pounding. The more he talked, the more everything sounded like incessant buzzing, and I was feeling dizzy. I'd had enough of this game and wanted to go back to my little mattress. I told him I wanted to go back, and he lifted me up and held me tight. I tried to turn my head and look at my grandma, but I just couldn't move my head. He took me to the other room and put me on this big bed.

"Until this day, I have no recollection of that night and what he did. The next morning, I felt pain throughout my body and head as soon as I woke up. I looked around. It was morning, and I was on my little mattress. I had no idea how I got back home. I was still wearing the pink dress, so it hadn't been a dream. The previous night had really happened. My relationship with Grandma changed from then on. I was old enough to understand what she had done to me. There wasn't a single soul for me to tell. There was no point in telling anyone, anyway. Who would believe that behind that façade of a hardworking old woman was a cruel person who had just sold her own granddaughter for money? Who would believe that she had a secret life hidden from her family all this time? All I could do was go along with her plan and try to turn this against her when the timing was right.

"I think I grew far beyond my age once I found out the truth about good old Grandma. She ran a brothel that was hidden well, even to visitors at the house. Her husband had known, though. She told me that my grandfather knew of this secret, but he was a weak man and didn't have a good job to support his family. She told me that she was a strong and powerful woman and had him under her control. Money was good, and he had failed to simply look the other way and enjoy the financial benefit.

"Now I was her fresh new bait—her own flesh and blood—and God knows how much she sold me for to that old pig. Whatever happened to me, I promised myself that I would survive. After all, she thought well of me now. I kept all my fear and anger inside of me, and I let her believe I was still that fragile, innocent girl in need of her advice and guidance so that she wouldn't get suspicious.

"Since we had grown closer, we used to talk every night about the business and her past, and I once asked her about my grandfather. 'Grandma, did you ever love Grandpa?' That question was answered with the painful yanking of my hand. With clenched teeth, she uttered something I could not hear. All I wanted to know was that if she did love him, how could she treat him like she did?

"I knew I had touched a raw nerve when she responded, 'Don't you dare talk to me about love. You have no idea what love is. It is just an empty word that turns to hate, disgust, pain, and anger. It is just lust that disappears from your heart.' She pushed me away. I knew then that she must have been hurt so much to become that bitter and mean. Maybe her soul had been damaged permanently.

"I never again spoke to her about love. That night was also the last time I called her Grandma. She preferred from then on to be called Madam Aniss, but she was still Grandma in my mind. Every Friday and Saturday night, I was her little china doll. I belonged to her. She dressed me up, did my makeup, and brushed my hair so I looked proper. She would take me to the fun house. That was no fun house for me. Those were the times that I had to disconnect myself from truth and reality. I allowed my soul to fly to unknown dimensions so that I could feel nothing and remove myself from the act. This became a routine for me. No one from the outside ever got suspicious or asked any questions. At school, I was doing surprisingly okay. We still maintained the monthly family gathering at Grandma's house.

"I had graduated to my own room but was rarely allowed to close or lock the door. The only time I was allowed to lock the door was when my sick, perverted cousin was around. With all the evil Grandma was doing to me, the hypocrisy of trying to keep my cousins or anyone from raping me was absurd.

"I remember the last time family came over. My cousin pushed me in the corner and tried to kiss me. My grandma walked into the kitchen and stood behind him as I was struggling to get away from him. Grandma just tapped him on his shoulder, and when he let go of me and turned, I was shocked to see my grandmother slap him and grab him by his manhood. He passed out. When his mom heard his screams, she stormed into the kitchen and demanded an explanation. As if she did not hear a thing Grandma said, my aunt grabbed my hair and pulled me out of the kitchen, slapping me. She was furious with me for what her son had done. She blamed me for her unconscious son and called me a liar. To my surprise again, Grandma pulled my aunt's arm and pushed her outside, saying, 'Take your demented son away, and don't you dare bring your wacko son into my house again, because next time, I will cut his balls off if he gets near her.'

"They all left immediately, and after that day, I never heard about my aunt or her pervert son again, and honestly, I don't think my grandma cared at all. As she told me later that day, all her children cared about was the money she would leave behind when she died. She told me, 'They showed me their true faces a long time ago. I carried each of them in my womb for nine months, but there has never been any connection between my children and me. I never felt motherly love toward them and they never grew to love me, so none of us feel guilt or anything toward each other. It's just an obligation to them to come and visit me from time to time, but I prefer that they don't. As I made certain, from today on, those two won't bother us again, so let's not talk about my children, and instead we'll focus on the business.'

"I watched her walk away as I thought to myself, 'What a woman.' I didn't know whether to admire her strength or just simply hate her, but regardless, that incident made me feel closer to her. Somebody had actually fought on my behalf to protect me. I had never seen her speak like that and stand her ground in front of her family that way. I mean, I knew she had no love or caring feelings for them, but still, she fought for me, a girl nobody even wanted to look at, much less let stay in their house. I don't think the family knew the true reason behind Grandma's defiance, and even if they did, none of them would have cared.

"It was a screwed-up family, and I was caught in the middle of it. Every time I wanted to let myself feel something for my grandmother, I reminded myself that she was only protecting her asset, not her grandchild. That reminder kept me focused and sharp. It was so strange to me that she was changing me to be like her, and I somewhat despised her for it. I think that what I felt for that woman was something between love, hate, and admiration.

"As time passed, fewer and fewer family members came over to Grandma's house. She was becoming easily agitated and weaker in health. Not her business, though—it was booming with silky suits spending money in the fun house. I found out that I wasn't the only china doll at Grandma's farm. One day, she told me how proud she was of her china girls. I asked how many, and she responded, 'Oh, there are about six who come on the nights when you are not working. They are all unwanted girls who need money for their families, and I provide that for them. You see, I do them a favor.' She spoke with such pride in her voice, but to me, it was so sickening that my grandmother took advantage of those poor families who needed the money and got them to surrender their girls for 'service.'

"Upon my visibly horrified look, her justification was, 'Well, bills are paid, food is put on the table, clothes and school fees are provided, so everyone is happy. Besides, this is a platform for the girls to get a rich husband. I don't care what you or anyone might think about me and what I'm doing here, because to be honest, I am the god here. You know why? Because God don't pay their bills—I pay. God doesn't take their sick kids to the hospital or warm up their house during the cold winter nights, I do. So don't give me that look, because if not for me, you would be living on the street right now, okay?' I think that in some sick way, she was right—or maybe I was being brainwashed by her sick logic. She couldn't fool me entirely, though. I knew it was a bunch of lies to make her feel good about herself. I hated the whole situation, but I was at her mercy and could do nothing about it.

"Turning sixteen is a big moment for any girl, and I was no exception. I had no idea what to expect. Well, Grandma organized a small gathering in the fun house, and she told me what to wear and said that I should get ready for a surprise. I wasn't looking forward to a surprise. It was the usual Friday night, which entailed working at the fun house. I entered the room; there were candles, flowers, music, and Champagne bottles for me. Grandma had also dressed nice for the occasion. For the first time, I got to meet the other girls too. We didn't talk much, as Grandma was watching us closely. We all seemed to abide by the same rule to not talk unless instructed to.

"In the room was a young man I had never met before. Grandma introduced me to him. He was not very tall and appeared extremely shy, much to my advantage because I could control the situation, which made me feel safer. It was his first time being in a 'place like this,' as he said to me. He asked to spend more time with me. I asked if he wanted to get to know the other girls too, and he quickly responded, 'No, it's just you that I'm interested in.' I laughed at him because he was extremely nervous and had a strange accent. His French wasn't that good. I told the poor guy that he could speak English, thinking that perhaps it would calm him down. One advantage of living with Grandma was that I learned to speak several languages because most of her clients were very wealthy men, and my ability to speak their language was considered very classy and a big advantage for Grandma's business. This man seemed surprised that his French was not perfect, and he was also surprised that I could speak English. He asked, 'Is it that obvious that I am not from here?' He was so funny to me, and I just laughed and told him that it was way too obvious.

"That night, for the first time after all those years of abuse, I actually had a good time. For once, rather than just 'working,' I actually sat down with a guy and had a meaningful, normal conversation for hours, laughing constantly. As we sat in the corner, Grandma kept shooting me sharp looks that said, 'He is a client, child—go to the private room and give him a drink.' The nod of her head toward the bedroom was a clear enough signal. All she was thinking of was making money, but it was my birthday, and there was no way in hell I was going to let her control the night. I made a decision that it was going to be my way, and it was going to be my night.

"His name was Kevin. He was handsome and had an interesting look for an English man who lived in the south of France. He told me that he was a single man, thirty-two years old, and had never married before. We talked till early morning. He was the perfect gentleman. He did not ask for anything except my company to talk and laugh. Grandma's anger with me became more obvious as the night went on because I refused all her instructions and the advances of other men, all to just sit with Kevin. She charged him for the whole night, but he never complained. This had never happened before in her business. I had spent many nights with several men at her request. She had never allowed a guy to spend the whole night with me, but *I* did, and boy, was that hard for her to swallow.

"The night was over, and we said our goodbyes. Kevin asked me if we could see each other like normal people do, outside of the fun house. I told him the timing wasn't right. I wasn't sure how Grandma would react if I told her that I liked him. I was not allowed to have a boyfriend or any relationship with anyone outside the fun house. Even though I used to get requested a lot on repeat, she warned me to never be emotionally involved, as it was just a job. She told me that these were not real men but 'clients' or 'men in silky suits.' She would say, 'Men are a bunch of evil creatures, and sooner or later, they will crush your spirit and your soul. The only way you can ever deal with men is to charge them by the hour. Never give them your heart, or you'll end up carrying it in your own hands, broken into thousands of pieces. Your job is to take control of the situation and their pockets. Don't ever forget that.'

"God knows that old witch was full of wisdom, but I wanted to do things my own way. I wanted her to know that I was grown up and could make my own decisions. I had just turned sixteen and was old enough to stand up for myself. I liked this guy. I wanted to get to know him better. Who knew? Maybe he was my way out of this wretched place and the life that I hated so much.

"The next morning, as I was sitting on the couch in the living room, I pretended to read a book but was really watching her every move as she hid money in her special cabinet. I had known for a while where she was hiding the money, but I never let her know that. Now that I'd met this new guy, I started to plan for my future. All of the sudden, she caught my eye and quickly closed her bedroom door. When she came out, she looked at me and said, 'Don't you dare get any funny ideas. I will chop off your finger if I catch you doing anything.'

"I gave her a dirty look and a cynical laugh, then said, 'In all these years, I have never asked you for anything. I want you to know that the day I decide to leave this place, I will get every penny that you profited and solicited from me. Listen, old woman, do not hide your money, because I know every hiding place in this house.' I was surprised at my own confidence in speaking to her.

"She pounced at me like a wolf. I dodged her. She wanted to pinch my cheeks like she did every time she was upset with me. It was extremely painful and always made me cry. I intercepted her hand and grabbed her wrist and twisted hard, which forced her to bend to her knees in front of me. With her other hand, she swayed to slap me, but I grabbed her hand before it could land on me.

"I told her, with such strength and disgust that I'd never known I had in me, 'Look at you, nothing but a miserable, greedy, old woman. Your own flesh and blood despise you and your neighbors hate you. You're just a lonely, miserable old woman who has nobody else but me. And even I plan on leaving you soon.'

"She hurled insults my way, screaming, 'You're an ungrateful little whore just like your mother! Who gave you shelter? Who fed you when no one wanted you, including your own mother? Wake up, sweetheart, and see the reality of your own life too—nobody wanted you! I was the only one who put a roof over your head, and this is the way you pay back my kindness now? You are a cold slut, just like your mother!'

"I had never heard her say all of that before. I pushed her back and she fell on the floor. Oh, she must not have heard me right, so I stood over her and yelled back, from the deepest part of my hurting heart, 'Oh, you clothed me? You fed me? You turned me into a child prostitute who sleeps with strange men old enough to be my father or grandfather. Let me remind you, I became your bread and butter. You turned me into your money-making machine so you could stack money under your mattress. That's right, I know all the places you hide it.' I never could comprehend why she hid the money. I was so angry, and as I screamed at her, I knew I had to tell her that I did not care about her either. 'You are going to die soon, and I'm going to dance on your grave. I am the only one here who is going to close your eyes for you when you take your last breath. Look around, Madam, no one is here. No one wants you. No one can stand you. They all know who you are, what you are doing, and that's why no one is coming around anymore. Stop acting like you are in control of everything, because you are not. I will take every penny you made off of me. As a matter of fact, this is goodbye. I am leaving.'

"Strange things do happen. As I was taking my first step to walk away, I took one last look at her, and suddenly, she looked more pathetic to me than ever before. She cradled her head between her hands and remained on her knees, just rocking her body back and forth. I couldn't believe it, but I felt so sorry for her at that point. Gosh, I wanted to leave, I wanted to hate her and walk away. But there she was, crying like a baby. I looked at her and all I could see was a fragile, tiny old woman who was basically just a sack of skin and bones.

"I sat beside her. I seemed to have already made my decision in that moment. Without lowering my voice, I continued in the same stern manner. 'Listen to me and listen good, Madam. From now on, you are going to work for me. I will decide which clients I want to see or be with, not you. I am in charge of my money, not you. One more thing—I want you to remember that from now on, not one word about my mother. She is dead to me like the rest of you.'

"With that, I stood up to walk away from her, but she had the nerve to respond, 'I taught you everything you know. You are who you are today because of me. You want to take over the business?' She hesitated as she looked at me, then conceded, 'Okay, you want it? Take it.' She could have ended there, and I would still have been surprised at the turn of events, but she continued.

'Yes, you are right, no one likes me, and I am the most hated person in this town. You are right; you are all I have now. Stay, and I promise to teach you everything that I know. You might think you are so knowledgeable now, but believe me, you still need me to teach you everything about this business. But if you are waiting for an apology from me, you are wasting your time, because what I did to you was the only way for you to get out of your useless life and become like me, a strong and independent woman. I saw that you had a beauty, and I knew this would be your ticket to a better life, while in the meantime, I could also profit from you. So we both used each other,' she said, with a bitter smile on her face.

"She raised her arm for me to help her up. As I pulled her up, I looked her in the eye and told her, 'I'm not here for your apology. Those are just words that will not undo the past or buy me anything for my future.'

"She smiled and said, 'You see, you are already thinking like me. I made you a good businesswoman.' Deep down, I despised her and everything about her, but she was right. I needed her as much as she needed me. She went to her bedroom and lay down on her bed. I just sat there, thinking about what had just happened. I was proud of myself for standing up for myself and letting her know who I was. I was satisfied. I was only sixteen, making all those decisions to leave, but as if in an agreement to the universe and not to Grandma, I had decided to stay until my eighteenth birthday. I knew life outside Grandma required money, so I set my mind to save up as much as I could to start a new life. I was back to work every weekend and during the week as well, under my own terms. No, I was not embracing the business, but it was the only way I knew how to meet my financial goal for quitting. Every weekend that I worked, Grandma was the hostess, but now I chose which clients I did business with. I felt as though I was in control.

"Each night, we counted the money together. We did all the accounting to pay the other girls too. I made sure she gave me my commission. She showed me the hiding places for her money and our relationship changed to a mutual partnership. I learned many things from her about business and how to never trust anyone with money except myself. She told me that business always comes first. She taught me to always be alert in this business, to keep my head up and have pride in my work.

"One day, she told me, 'Listen, child, you were born a nobody, and if you ever want to become somebody meaningful, follow my instructions carefully. Remember, be inconspicuous, because when no one notices you, you can see everything and hear everything, and that makes you powerful. The loudest person in the room is always the idiot and the most ignorant. Be quiet, be observant, and listen. Information creates opportunity, and opportunity will bring money, power, independence, and freedom.'

"Interestingly, those words helped me. I found a purpose to live and to breathe, knowing things would eventually change because I had a goal. I did not want to be a victim. I learned to embrace each moment, but I reminded myself that this was all temporary. I had bigger and greater goals. I was just learning to survive for the moment.

"I would see Kevin at least once or twice a week. It started off with just enjoying each other's company. The feelings grew stronger, and I could not complete a day without seeing Kevin. Grandma noticed what was happening and cautioned me to be careful. She told me not to fall too deep for him, but I wanted to do this my own way and have something just for me, without her interference or her words in the back of my head telling me, 'Be careful, don't be foolish,' and all those negative directions. I was proud and young and stupid. I was in love. There was no logic left in me when Kevin was involved. Grandma kept bugging me about it, and I told her that I was totally in control. She shook her head and said, 'Well, Anouk, time will tell, and you will see.' Every time she talked to me about Kevin that way and then walked away, fear crept into my heart. What if she was right? What if I was a fool, and it all was a lie, a deception that I had bought into? But then one look into Kevin's eyes would melt away those cold, bitter thoughts.

"Well, time did reveal that I was pregnant! There was no question about it; I was sure it was Kevin's child. I had no idea how to deal with it or how to tell him, and for the first time, I felt so vulnerable and so exposed in front of this man. Unable to control the situation, I decided to just come out and tell him and see how he would react. It was a beautiful night with a full moon and a gentle summer breeze cooling the air. We were sitting outside in the luscious garden, enjoying each other's company.

"He was kissing me softly and passionately, when I whispered into his ear, 'I am pregnant.' He paused for a second, and my heart missed several beats. I didn't know whether to pull back or stay wrapped up in his arms. It was only a second or two, but it was the most excruciating silence I'd ever experienced. He just looked directly at me, and I saw tears of joy in his eyes.

"He hugged me so tight and, much like a little boy, was overly excited and kept telling me, 'Wow! I'm going to be a father! It's so amazing; I'm going to be a father!' I was trying so hard to cover his mouth and stop him from yelling, because I didn't want anyone else to know, but at the same time, I was overjoyed too and a thousand times more in love with him when I saw how happy he was about the news.

"I silently told myself, 'You see, Grandma was wrong after all, he does love me. It's real.' He began kissing my belly and then all over my body. That night, we made love under the moonlight and it felt like an out-of-body experience. So much passion and love, I just felt so lucky to be alive.

"That night, we talked about our future together. It was almost dawn when, all of a sudden, Kevin looked at me and said, 'Marry me.' I was shocked. I had never expected a marriage proposal, and it made me feel scared, nervous, and excited. For a second, I wasn't sure if what I felt for him was pure love or a desperation to get away from Grandma and the life that I was trapped in. I hated to feel that way. Here I was with a guy in front of me, wanting to marry me, and I was dwelling on the legitimacy of my feelings toward him. What I was thinking? I reassured myself, 'You love him. You love him desperately, and what you're feeling right now is just you being overwhelmed. By tomorrow, you'll know what to do.'

"But still, I told him to give me time. He responded, 'No, don't overthink this, Anouk, let's just do it. You are almost seventeen, and you saved enough money, right? Let's book a train and go to London and start our new life together!' I knew he was rich— otherwise he couldn't afford to come to the fun house—but still, the way he reminded me that I had saved enough money sparked worry in me.

"He must have seen the doubt in my eyes, as he quickly reassured me, 'Look, you know I don't need your money since my family is well-off and I'm the only son, so we won't ever have any issues with that. It's just that I know how proud you are, and I don't want you to think that I am going to control you financially or that you will be powerless. You can keep your savings for your own security and peace of mind. Besides, you worked hard all these years, and it would be a shame to leave the profits for that cruel old woman when you can have them for yourself.' When I thought about it, I realized he was right—why shouldn't I keep my money? Besides, I never wanted to have to rely on anyone, even the man I loved. I wanted to have my independence, and who knew, maybe even start my own little café, which had been my dream since I was a young child.

"We both got so excited about the whole idea of running away and getting married. Kevin knew my past and what I did for a living, yet he still wanted to be with me? I was projecting myself as a very proud, secure, and strong-minded young girl, but underneath it all, I knew that what I did for a living was dirty and humiliating. I mean, I was selling my body to men for money, and that was nothing to be proud of. I knew that the only way I could cope with that lifestyle was to create the façade of a strong, proud young woman, but really, I was ashamed of myself and everything about my life—that was the true me, without any mask. And now this man—rich, educated, and from a good family—wanted to marry me?

"I looked at him and said, 'Yes, I'll marry you.' We kissed, then he was in such a hurry to go let his family know about the whole thing and to start the preparation for our trip. As for me, I just couldn't wait to see Grandma's face when I gave her the big news that I was getting married to a wealthy, educated young man, and guess what, Grandma? I was pregnant, and he still wanted to marry me! To my astonishment, Grandma was not surprised at all. Perhaps she had seen it coming. All she told me was, 'The path that you have chosen has been walked by thousands of girls just like you, and they all ended up on another path, homeless and penniless. Just remember that.' Then she walked away.

"I was angry with her for not having any faith in me, for not even believing that after all those years of living under her roof, listening to all the advice that she had given me, I was wise enough, strong enough, and smart enough to know what was real and what wasn't. At least she could be happy that I was carrying her great grandchild, but no, she had to ruin it for me. However, I didn't want to give her the satisfaction of knowing that her words had hurt me, so I pretended that I didn't care, even though I did. My mind was made up, and for the next couple of days, I was packing, collecting, and organizing for my new life. During that time, Grandma and I hardly spoke to each other. While I was packing my suitcase, I could see her watching me, but neither of us wanted to talk. I think she'd noticed that I was not the same person anymore, and there was nothing she could say that would change my mind. I was in charge of my own money, and for the past few years, I had managed to save a lot. Also, most of my customers would give me expensive jewelry—gold necklaces, diamond rings, and earrings—and with all those gifts and the money I'd saved, I knew I could start my own business without any problems or even asking Kevin for help.

"The night I had chosen to finally leave couldn't come any faster. I had been living in that house for almost seven years, and although I hated the place, there was still some attachment, a feeling of belonging to the place and even to that old woman. Miserable as she was, I still loved her deep down. She'd given me shelter when nobody else would, and she'd made me who I was. Although I finally had my chance to break away from her, it wasn't as easy as I thought it would be. For the past seven years, she'd instilled in my heart so much fear of the outside world, the people, and the evil that existed outside of those walls. I was still terrified of everything, but I knew I had to break that spell of fear if I wanted to move on with my life. Otherwise, her life would become my future: an old, angry, bitter woman with no love in her heart. I hated that image.

"I decided to knock on her bedroom door to say goodbye before I left, but she chose not to come out of her room. I spoke through the closed door, 'Goodbye, Madam.' As I was walking toward my new life, I looked back at the house and remembered the first day that I had arrived at that place with my uncle. I'd been a child then, so innocent, insecure, and desperate for someone to love me. Now, after all that pain, I was a young woman who had finally found my place in the world, was crazy in love, and was hopeful for the brighter future.

"Kevin came to pick me up, and as we were getting ready to leave, I heard my grandmother's voice. She was standing beside her window, watching us. I looked at her and said, 'Goodbye.'

"She looked at me with her devilish smile and replied, 'No matter what happens to you, don't you dare crawl back here again. From now on, you are on your own. Goodbye, Anouk.' She closed her window and disappeared. That was our last conversation.

"I looked at Kevin. He pulled me toward him and said, 'Who needs her? Forget about that miserable old woman. We have our own new life to think about.' Then he started kissing me. It made me so happy, and my excitement resurfaced all over again. We were traveling first class to London. We arrived at midnight. At this point, I was nearly five months pregnant and I was tired, so all I wanted was a place to rest.

"I asked Kevin if someone was coming to the station to greet us. He said, 'My darling, I didn't tell my family we were arriving tonight. I talked about you a lot, and I know they are all excited to meet you, but I wanted us to have some time to adjust, so tonight we'll stay in a motel. First thing tomorrow morning, after we freshen up, we are going to have breakfast with my family—or, should I say, *our* family.' He was right; it was already past midnight, and I didn't want them to see me like this. I wanted to be in my best clothes with my hair done and impress them with their son's choice in his future wife.

"We arrived at a not-very-classy motel, and I very slowly asked Kevin if this place was nice. He replied with a whisper in my ear, 'Of course. I'm sorry, Anouk, but it is midnight, and I didn't have time to make a reservation in a better location. But don't worry, it's only for a few hours. First thing in the morning, we are out of here.' I'd never been anywhere but Grandma's farm in years, and traveling to a new place was so exciting to me. Besides, I had nothing to worry about. Kevin was by my side, and this was his country, so I ignored my inclination to be scared and suspicious of this new place. As I was waiting in the lobby, Kevin went to the front desk and came back with the key to our room. It was an old building and it smelled funny, so I asked Kevin about it and he said with smile, 'Welcome to London, sweetheart.'

"The room was on the top floor. It was a small room, with only a twin bed and a side table. Everything in this room seemed to be a hundred years old. I looked around with disgust, and Kevin caught my eye and threw me on the bed, tickling and kissing me. We laughed loudly, and he told me, 'You spoiled little princess, I told you it's just for one night, okay?'

"I looked into his eyes and said, 'I don't care as long as we have each other. I'm happy, and if you decided not to work with your father, we could start our own business. You know that I saved up some money, which would be more than enough to live a comfortable life together.' Kevin took my hand and reassured me that he didn't want to touch my money and that I should keep it for myself or anything I wanted to do with it. He told me to never mention that again, because he was the man and he was supposed to support his family, so it hurt his ego when I talked about my life savings with him.

"I kissed him and apologized; I was so proud of him for wanting to build our family all by himself, never intending to take my money. I trusted him more than ever. Suddenly, that old room wasn't that bad, and it felt like I was in a five-star hotel. We had a bottle of Champagne in our suitcase that Kevin opened, and we celebrated our first night in London together.

"That night, Kevin was so kind, gentle, and understanding toward my feelings. We had a simple dinner, and he gave me a glass of Champagne to celebrate our life together, even though I shouldn't have taken it because I was pregnant. But, after all, it was a big night for us, and a small glass of Champagne wouldn't harm the baby. We talked about our beautiful future that we were going to build. He was going to work for his dad's company for a while, and he told me of his dreams to work hard so his father would entrust him with the business when he retired. That whole night in that motel, all we did was daydream. I kept thinking about how many wonderful things were happening in my favor. I wished my grandmother could see me and realize that not everyone in the world was just evil, ready to get me or destroy my life. But I said to myself, 'Let go of the past, Anouk. This is the new chapter of your life. Never look back.' I closed my eyes and rested my head on Kevin's shoulder, thinking to myself, 'This is what I dreamed of.' Finally, I could see my deliverance and success on the horizon; all I'd wished for was a normal life and a normal family. Kevin held me in his arms and told me to sleep, because the next morning was going to be full of excitement. First, we'd have to stop by a boutique to choose a dress suitable for meeting his family for the first time, then we would get beautiful flowers for his mother so we wouldn't be empty-handed. I went to sleep with all those beautiful thoughts, knowing that tomorrow would be the start to an amazing new life.

"Loud noises from outside woke me up. I felt a massive headache and thought I might get sick at any moment. I couldn't even open my eyes without feeling pain coursing through my body. What was that noise? It seemed like construction workers were shouting and screaming. The constant whir of a drill on the asphalt combined with the sound of passing cars was just making me so dizzy. I looked around and didn't see Kevin. Perhaps he'd stepped out to get some coffee or breakfast. I went to the bathroom and took a shower, not wanting him to see me all messed up. After all, we had a big day in front of us. I went to get my personal things from my suitcase. It was laying fully opened, and all my clothes, shoes, and personal belongings were strewn everywhere. What a sight. Quickly, I reached to the bottom of my suitcase where I had hidden the money and my jewelry. The bottom was ripped off, and there was nothing in sight. I just couldn't believe what I was looking at. Were we robbed? Did they take Kevin—perhaps even kill him? Or perhaps he went after them. What was happening? I was confused, in pain, and scared of what might have happened to Kevin.

"I was certain that the receptionist downstairs would help. I dressed quickly and headed downstairs. There was an old woman arguing with an older man about something. I didn't recognize them from last night, so they had probably taken over for the morning shift. As I walked toward them, they noticed me approaching their desk, so they abruptly stopped arguing and just stared at me. Very politely, I said hello, told them my room number, and asked about my husband, which was what Kevin had told me to say if anyone asked about us. I told them that we had been robbed and I could not find my husband. Expecting sympathy and help, I was shocked when they instead looked at each other and busted out laughing. I couldn't understand how being robbed was so funny. 'Call the police, please! This happened at your stupid motel, and all you can do is laugh? Call the police now!' I demanded.

"The old woman walked out from behind her desk, stepped close up to my face, and said, 'No, your highness, you are the stupid one who just got robbed. The guy who you claim was your husband just paid for the room till tomorrow morning and left. He told us that you are a prostitute and he paid for your service, but he asked us to let you stay a little bit longer since you are from out of town. But since you gave me attitude, pack your crap and leave immediately before I call the police, because we don't let hookers stay in this establishment. Get the hell out, right now!' she screamed and pushed me toward the door.

"My world was crashing to pieces right in front of my eyes. Today was supposed to be my brand-new start. I was so confused. Was it true? Was anything that Kevin had told me true? My head was spinning from the rage, anger, disbelief, and confusion inside my head. Every kind of emotion was racing through me at once. All

I could hear was the receptionist yelling at me, saying something that I just couldn't understand. As she continued to yell, I could hear my heart beating faster and louder. I felt the shattering of my own heart as it broke into a million pieces, and I was sure all the construction workers could hear it too amidst the noise of the drill. I was bleeding, but no one could see the blood. I was screaming, but no one could hear me. I was dying, but no one was crying for me. I don't remember how or when I left the motel, but next thing I knew, I was walking away with a bundle of clothes under my arm. I had no idea where I was going.

"I don't know how long I walked, hoping that I would wake up from this horrible dream. I was sure that at any moment, I would wake up to Kevin sitting beside me with two cups of hot coffee and a sandwich that we could share like old times I was looking around, trying to find his face in the middle of all the strange faces crowding the street. Every face looked colder, stranger, and more distant. I was tired, so I sat on a stone bench on the corner of a street. It seemed that I'd been walking around London for the past twelve hours. My feet were killing me, I didn't have money, and I was so hungry and thirsty that I couldn't walk anymore. Fear of police arresting me any second or me dying on the street made me try harder to figure out what to do next. At that time, I remembered my grandmother's last words to me: 'Don't you dare crawl back here again. From now on, you are on your own.'

"I must have dozed off, but I was startled awake by a voice saying, 'You can't sit here, child. You have to go.' I opened my eyes and looked up, seeing a dark-skinned elderly woman extending her arm to me. She had a strong accent, and as I stood up to go, she stopped me, asking, 'Do you have any place to go?' I shook my head, tears streaming down my cheeks. She reached her hand out again to take my bundle from my arms, and I pulled back in fear and distrust. She looked at me and said, 'Don't worry, I'm not after your belongings, child. You just have to move on from here or the police will come and take you away, you know?' Then she started to walk away, pointing toward a building nearby. She said, 'This is my shop. If you'd like, come in and eat something, then do what you got to do, okay? I'm not holding you here or anything; I just want to help you.'

"She walked away, and I followed quietly. What else could possibly go wrong? I'd already lost everything. My mind was numb, and I didn't know what to do except surrender to destiny. We entered a shop that had writing in pink and gold that said, 'Abrianna's Beauty.' Inside the shop were a few other ladies helping customers, and upon seeing me, they stopped working and looked at me as though I were a ghost. My clothes were dirty, my hair was messy, and I'd lost one of my shoes at some point while I was walking. My face was dirty and puffy from crying for several hours, and I was shivering from hunger and cold.

"My cheeks burned with embarrassment. The old lady yelled at them, 'What's wrong with you? Haven't you seen a crazy girl before? Get back to work.' I figured she was the boss. She turned back to me and told me that her name was Abrianna and she owned the shop. She offered, 'If you'd like, you can stay here until you get your feet on the ground, okay? You are safe here. Let's go to the back room.' She took me to the back of the shop. There was a small room with a single bed. It had most likely been a storage room originally, but whatever it was, it was heavenly to me.

"I must have been lost in thought when Abrianna shook my shoulder, asking, 'Have you eaten anything today?' I shook my head quietly. She pointed to the bed and told me to sit, then she left the room. I lay on the bed, looking around. I tried hard to keep my eyes open, but it seemed like my body was shutting down. The exhaustion overpowered me. I woke up to a peaceful quietness. I panicked, imaging what else could have gone wrong while I was sleeping. The last time I slept, I woke up to Kevin's absence. I was certain that I could not handle any more bad news.

"In the midst of my confusion, Abrianna walked in with a tray of food in her hands. 'Eat, girl. You sleep like a cow.' She laughed at me. 'Come on, I am just teasing you.' I was starving and started to eat. I stated very clearly that I was not a beggar, but she looked at me, appearing somewhat disappointed at my statement. She said, 'I know you are not, but you are something, aren't you? Listen to me, I'm not asking you anything until you are ready to tell. However, I ask that you tell me nothing but the truth. Don't steal from me, don't bring boys, no drugs, no funny business. If you follow those simple rules, we will be just fine with you here. How far along are you?' I looked at her with such undisguised shock and asked her how she knew. My bump was small, and I'd concealed it with loose clothing. She shook her head and replied, 'Child, you are not the first girl to sit outside my shop, and I am certain you will not be the last. Besides, this hair is not gray for no reason.'

"I responded, 'Almost five months.' Despite all my distress and my shattered heart, I could not believe how tasty this food was. It was so delicious, and for a minute, I forgot I was in so much trouble. The food was that enjoyable. I could barely talk with my mouth full, as I told her, 'I have never tasted food this good. What is it?'

"She laughed loudly. 'I know it's tasty; I cooked it. It's from my country, Jamaica. You people don't know food. Everything is tasteless. No wonder you are all so pale and skinny.' Abrianna was a short and fairly stout woman. From her head to her toes, you could not find any distinct curves, but she was more like a balloon. She exuded a lot of charm and charisma. Her larger-than-life personality was very attractive. She was strong and had a loud voice. Overall, she was a very happy person. I liked and appreciated this woman who had just saved me.

"A few days passed, but to me it seemed as though it was a whole month. All I did was sleep and eat. Abrianna would force me to eat because of my baby. Daily, before Abrianna began her work, she would leave a tray of food for me. Her simple instructions were to lock the door at all times. She would lock the door from the outside just to be safe and leave me inside. I had to stay in the back room. Despite the few magazines she brought for me, I was not ready to be distracted from my misery. All I did was lay on the bed and cry, thinking about my life and how I could have let this happen to me. Why did I never ask Kevin where he was staying while he was visiting the farm? Why did I simply believe whatever he told me and never once ask him a question or dig deeper into his life? Grandma didn't care; as long as he paid for my services, she was okay with him visiting. But now, when I looked back on the whole situation, I remembered that she used to tell me to watch out for this guy. But I was too ignorant and stupid to accept her warnings, and I had just wanted to spurn her and do the exact opposite of what she advised. Kevin always carried cash around, wore flashy clothes, and was the only young client amid all those creepy old suits, so of course I fell for him. Why didn't I listen to Grandma instead of assuming I could trust Kevin? How could he be so heartless and treat me like he did? All those thoughts consumed my every minute and every hour. The hurt of being used, abused, and abandoned did not leave me, and above all that, I'd lost all the money that I'd worked so hard for, selling my body day after day, month after month, in hope of a better future. Now look at me—pregnant, poor, and heart-broken. I just didn't know how to move on from that stage, how to start all over again. Abrianna used to watch me and tell me to snap out of it, to start my life again, no matter what happened, to just get on with my life. But I just couldn't. I didn't know how.

"Well, Abrianna was not going to let me off that easy. One day, after she had closed the shop, she came to me and said, 'Anouk, how long are you going to sit in the back of the shop and let life pass you by? You are going to be a mother very soon. You can't just sit and stare at the wall and cry all day long. Sooner or later, you will have to let go of whatever is holding you back and move on with your life. Think about it, and let me know by tomorrow, because I have a job for you.' She did not wait for my response as she walked out.

"Left alone, it was reality time for me. I realized that I knew nothing that would help me get by in the real world. The only thing I knew how to do was talk to men and seduce them. I knew how to be the best in bed. Well, this was where those skills had landed me. Underneath all the hurt and doubt, though, I remem-bered my dream that I would one day own a café. The thought of my dream lit a small flame in me. As soon as the excitement came, however, so did the despair of realizing that I had lost all my money. That was all of my life savings. The man I'd trusted had become my biggest downfall. Those thoughts kept me busy until dawn. I couldn't sleep. I heard the shop door open as the girls trickled in, laughing and talking with each other. Another day had begun, and I was still stuck on yesterday.

"I had only seen the other girls once. They were not allowed to come to the back room, in order to give me much-needed privacy and time to gather myself. I looked at myself in the mirror, and what I saw could not have been Anouk. I used to keep my hair in a bun, used makeup daily, and always wore a beautiful dress. My life with Grandma had trained me to be ready just in case a customer stopped by. Abrianna had given me a few dresses. They were a bit big, but they were clean. I washed up and decided to dress up, then I took a deep breath and went downstairs.

"It was still too early for any customers to walk in. Abrianna was behind the cashier's desk, doing some work and drinking what I assumed to be her morning coffee. Two other girls were walking around and getting the salon ready for the day. Abrianna saw me, and a big smile crossed her face. 'Good morning, Anouk,' she said with her loud voice. 'Come over here and let me introduce you to the girls. This is Alice.'

"Alice was a beautiful English girl. She had long, curly blonde hair. She looked so excited to see me and came forward to shake my hand. Alice had such a baby voice that was very funny to me. She said, 'Hey, you can call me Ally,' then she giggled like a little girl.

"Abrianna continued, 'And this is Imani.' Imani had thick, short black hair and uniquely large almond-shaped eyes. Later, I found out that she was from Nigeria. Her mother was from India and her father was from Nigeria, so she was tall with a beautiful figure. The third lady Abrianna introduced was Najima. Her father was from Pakistan, and he had married an English woman, so Najima was mixed too. To me, she looked more Middle Eastern than English, but she had beautiful green eyes that made her whole face so unique and mesmerizing.

"Abrianna said, with such a loud laugh, 'As you can see, this is my own United Nations. I have girls from all over the world working for me. As long as we all respect each other and appreciate our differences, we won't have any issues. Right, girls?' In unison, all the girls responded, 'Yes, boss,' then laughed together.

"Abrianna pulled me aside and said, 'This is a single mothers' club too, Anouk. We all have kids. Don't feel ashamed or uncomfortable about your situation, okay? We have all been there, but we learned from it.' She spoke a little louder so all could hear now. 'We don't judge each other, and we certainly don't use our pasts as excuses for the decisions that we make today. Right, girls?' Again, everyone agreed. 'Anouk, you have a home and a family if you choose to stay.' I looked around at all their faces, and soon, tears were rolling down my cheeks. Alice came to me and gave me a big hug. All the girls were now surrounding me. In the midst of tears and hugs, I could hear Abrianna's voice telling everyone, 'Okay, okay, that's enough. Give her room to breathe and go make me a cup of English tea, Ally.'

"Ally responded, 'Yes, Ms. Abrianna,' as she skipped her way to the kitchen. Abrianna told Najima to put me in one of her chairs and tie the apron around my neck. She told her to wash my hair first, then she herself came over and gave me a new haircut. By the time I looked at myself in the mirror, I felt like a new person. I couldn't believe how a wash and a cut could change my whole mood, but it did. Ally was so happy for me and kept telling me that I looked beautiful. Yes, I looked beautiful on the outside, but I still did not feel beautiful inside.

"Abrianna asked, 'Anouk, what are your skills? What can you do for a job to support yourself?' That was not a question I wanted to be asked. I was not ready to talk about my past, so I told her about my dream café and that I loved to cook. She eagerly told me that she could teach me how to cook her own recipes and that she knew someone who would hire me. I thought to myself, first things first. I should be taking care of myself until the baby was born. Abrianna told me that I was welcome to stay at the shop until the baby was born. After that, she made it clear that I had to find a place suitable for a baby. When she saw the obvious disappointment cross my face, she quickly said, 'Look, I live all by myself. My children are all grown and moved out, and my husband, God bless his soul, passed away. If you can't afford to find a place yet, I am sick of eating by myself, so come stay with me for a while. We will sort things out later. First, have your baby, then we'll get you a job. Once you get a job and make enough money to pay for food and bills, then you can get your own place. Until then, you'll be in my home like a daughter. You'll keep my place clean and learn how to cook.' She was more than generous, and I was trying to take all of that in. I wasn't used to that sort of kindness. She was a total stranger to me, yet she was willing to call me her daughter and take me in.

"I soon moved to Abrianna's place, which was very close to her salon. Her house was colorful and decorated with so many memories from her country. She decorated her house in such a way that she would not get so homesick. It was like a little Jamaica, and it was beautiful. My first lesson was in spices. She taught me spice by spice, dish by dish, and ingredient by ingredient. By the time the baby was born, I was making delicious, flavorful dishes. Abrianna was very pleased and called me her 'Little Chef.'

"The first week of spring, my little angel was born. I gazed upon the most beautiful little girl I had ever seen. She already had lots of dark hair, big hazel eyes, and milky white skin. Her fingers were so long, which reminded me of my father. She was my little angel sent from heaven, and everything else in my life seemed to blur into the background, irrelevant. I named her L'ange, which means angel in French, but everyone just called her Angel. My life finally had some meaning. I was only eighteen years old, but I felt so old after what I had been through. I think that giving birth made me wiser and more aware of how fragile life can be and how everything can change in the blink of an eye. After having a new baby, I faced a season of depression while I was nursing Angel, but thank God that I had Abrianna in my life. She took care of both of us. She helped me cope with the emotional roller coaster and, like a true mother, took care of me, something that I had never experienced before.

"She taught me how to be a mother and how to be kind to myself as well. She told me that her husband had died a long time ago, and her son had also died in war. Her life was all about the shop, and all of us were like her family. She never asked me about my past, and I never told her about it. I chose not to share and did all I could to erase my past from my memory; however, from time to time, I used to have nightmares about the farm, Grandma, and especially Kevin.

"A few months passed, and Angel was growing beautifully, while I was getting stronger physically and emotionally. I told Abrianna that I was fit enough to get back on my feet and start working. She took me to her friend's restaurant and secured me a job as an aid in the kitchen. Every day that I was working in the restaurant, Angel was in the salon with the girls or at home with Abrianna. I watched Angel when I got home from work so that Abrianna could get some rest. Angel was growing up so fast. She called Abrianna 'Aba.' Abrianna had a soft spot for Angel. She loved that little girl like her own child. She would honestly drop everything for Angel, and her expression would change instantly from a frown to sheer delight at the sight of Angel. I loved that bond between them. I eventually enrolled myself in college classes with the intentions of getting properly trained as a chef. Time continued to fly by so fast, and after three years, I had my first graduation and big life achievement. I was now a certified chef, and I owed Abrianna for everything.

"I got a job at one of the top restaurants in London. Every night, I brought home a different cuisine from around the world for my small family to taste. Angel and Abrianna loved that. I was making enough money to find my own place, but Abrianna would not hear of it. She'd ask, 'Why are you rushing? Save your money. There is plenty of time to live on your own.' I knew that she had grown used to having us around. However, as much as I enjoyed living with her, Angel was growing up, and I wanted to prove to myself that I was capable of taking care of her on my own. It was hard for me to say those words to Abrianna because I loved her to death, and never in a million years did I want to break her heart, but I had to let her know how I felt. Finally, as we sat around the kitchen table one afternoon, I told her about my plans of moving out. She understood how I felt, so she gave me a hug and said to me, 'You are like my little sparrow. Now that you have your wings, it's time to fly away, but remember your nest and come back whenever you like. This is your home now and forever.' How could I not love that woman? If only words could describe the gratitude I felt.

"I hugged her and kissed her soft, chubby cheeks and told her, 'How I wish I was born from your belly, Aba.' We both laughed and cried a little too. Moving day was a sad day for all of us, but I made sure to move only a block away, so we could still visit each other anytime. Angel was already in school when we finally moved into our own nice apartment. For the first time, we each had our own bedroom. I worked during the day and Angel would go to school, then in the evenings I would pick her up from Aba's place. Usually we all had dinner together, then Angel and I would go home. We kept the same routine month after month. Life was peaceful and happy; our life had an order and routine, which was wonderful. Ten years passed by so fast. Working and raising Angel kept me busy, and I never once went back to France. I never heard about anyone from my past, and I was just so happy and content with my new life. With help from Abrianna, I legally changed my last name. I just didn't want to be connected to my past.

"I had no problem staying in England. Every time Angel asked me about her father, I found it hard to tell her the truth. I just didn't think that hurting her feelings was a good idea, so I just told her that he was gone. I left it at that, with the possibility that maybe someday she would meet him. I wanted her to know that she had me. She was happy with my explanation and never asked me anything more. Maybe in her young heart, she understood but never mentioned anything out of respect.

"Her life was full of happiness, joy, and love that was showered on her by everyone around her. She never missed much. I never thought about another relationship and didn't want to get involved with anyone. Deep inside, I still felt hurt, betrayed, and unsure about myself. As much as I had shut the door on my past and ignored it, once in a while it haunted me. A dream here and there would cause that pain to resurface. Having a relationship was not on my plate. I was not capable of doing that again. At least, I thought so, but I guess you can never be sure about anything in life.

"I hired a girl named Michelle as a waitress at the restaurant where I worked. She talked too much, but she became my good friend. She used to talk about a guy she knew and how his girlfriend of seven years had just left him and all that. Mondays were usually my day off, and after dropping Angel off at school, my favorite place to go was Abrianna's salon. After becoming friends with Michelle, some Mondays we would go watch a movie or go sit at a café on sunny days. One particular Monday, she asked me if it was okay for that guy who'd been dumped by his girlfriend to come with us to the movie. She said his name was Joe and that she was just trying to help him out as a friend. He was depressed, and they were all worried about him. I agreed, and I also invited my other recently divorced girlfriend to come, hoping those two might become friends. Maybe they could comfort one another.

"The first time I saw Joe, he wasn't much to look at. He was a very sad, average-looking guy. He had such a weak handshake for a man, and I hated that. He was also kind of creepy in some ways. I thought that maybe he had some social issue, because he didn't make eye contact while he was talking to me. Regardless, I introduced him to my girlfriend in the hopes that they might hit it off. After the movie, I asked my friend if she liked him, and she almost screamed at me, 'Not at all! He's not normal. Something is wrong.' She was so insulted that I'd wanted her to meet him, and I just told her to give him a break since he'd just been dumped. I asked if she would give him another chance, but my friend was so mad at me that she didn't want to talk about it. We ended the conversation there and she left.

"After the movie, Michelle also said goodnight and left. Then it was only the two of us, so I started to talk to Joe and show some interest out of pity. I mean, I knew heartbreak, and no one deserved to go through that alone. After a while, we became friends, and that eventually evolved into a deep friendship. I used to go see movies with the girls from the salon, but pretty soon it was just the two of us. He would frequently come to the restaurant just to see me, and he started helping my Angel with homework. Slowly, gradually, he found a place in my heart. He was a gentle, quiet guy, but something still wasn't right about him. We dated on and off. I asked him about his family, but he didn't want to talk about them. I could understand that because I too had a past I was not going to discuss with anyone.

"As interesting as he was, something was still out of sorts with him. This time around, I did a little background check. I knew where he lived and that he ran a clothing manufacturing company. I knew where he worked and who his workmates were. He had a house in the city, a nice house that had no furniture except a bed and a chair. After some time, I asked him why it was so empty. He used to tell me that he was waiting for me to decorate and furnish the house to my liking. It was odd, but I chose to ignore the signs.

"We had dated for only a couple of months when he asked me to marry him. I said no immediately. I wasn't ready yet, but he began begging me, over and over. There was something about him that I still couldn't figure out, and, as always, my intuition was telling me something was wrong. I asked him why he was so socially removed, and his response was that he had an abusive childhood. He blamed his terrible and painful childhood for most of his odd behavior.

"My heart just wasn't in the right place. He was very pushy when he wanted something to happen his way. I finally met his family, and it was obvious that it was a very dysfunctional family. When I met his grandmother, I had a déjà vu moment. She had a kind of eerie effect that made my skin crawl. Her aura was dark, and she did not like Angel from the beginning, which I could quickly sense. She reminded me of my own grandmother. I didn't like her at all. She was in charge of his whole family. Joe loved his grandmother, but I could see that she knew how to manipulate him. When I look back now, I can see that all the signs were there, but I just didn't want to recognize a bad situation, or maybe I chose not to see the warning signs. Finally, I gave in, and we set a date for the wedding.

"By that time, my Angel was fourteen years old. She was happy for me, and she liked Joe a lot. Angel was so excited for me and used to tell me, 'Don't worry too much about his family, Mom. Joe loves us, and that's all that matters.' Angel just wanted a father figure in her life, and the thought of that propelled me to go on with the wedding plans.

"Two days before our wedding ceremony, I received an anonymous letter asking me not to marry Joe. The letter explained what kind of a person he really was. He'd had an affair with his best friend's wife, and that wasn't his first time. He was a cheater, and if I married him, I would regret it for the rest of my life. I also found out that he was going to be a father with the woman he'd had an affair with.

"I felt betrayed and angry. He wasn't the person I thought he was. I gave him back the engagement ring and told him that the wedding was off. However, he didn't give up, and for the next two days, he sat outside my apartment door, crying like a child and begging me to forgive him. He kept saying it was a big mistake, and he kept talking about his mother and how she screwed him up mentally, so it wasn't his fault. He claimed that the other woman had seduced him. He pleaded, and he kept telling me that I was his second chance to live and love. In all that, I somehow understood the part about second chances. I mean, after all, I had a dark past too, one which no one knew about.

"I could feel his pain, and maybe because I had survived a similar childhood, I forgave him. In spite of the protests of my inner voice, we got married. The moment we became husband and wife, his grandmother stepped into the picture and started interfering with our life. She told me that my daughter could not live with us. She went on and on about Joe and I being newlyweds who needed to grow together and pay attention to each other. I heard her telling Joe, 'Send her daughter to stay with her relatives for a while.' Those words got to me, and for the sake of keeping peace in my marriage, I sent Angel to stay with Abrianna. When I look back now, I hate myself for allowing other people to make a decision about my child. They forced me to send her away, to let my Angel go, and that was a big mistake. She felt abandoned and rejected.

"I was devastated, and my husband told me not to worry so much, as it was only temporary until we got a bigger place. Then she could come back and live with us. But Angel was mad; she felt betrayed by me and refused to see me. I had let my daughter down, but Abrianna told me to just give her some time and she would be okay. She was too young to understand the situation, but in time she would come back to me. I could tell that even Abrianna was disappointed with me. She never tried to lecture me or tell me how wrong I was, but I could see in her eyes that she wasn't the same Abrianna. She had to manage her own business and handle an angry teenager. This was too much for her. Abrianna was also getting older, but she was doing her best with my Angel. Every night, I used to call her and ask if Angel wanted to talk to me, and every time, Abrianna would say, 'Not yet, my dear.'

"I was living in my own hell, and the flames of guilt and regret were burning me bit by bit. This was supposed to be the happiest time of my life, but instead I was miserable and cried every day. The biggest shock was the change in Joe; he was so obsessive, controlling, and jealous. I was not allowed to go anywhere by myself. I wasn't allowed to see my daughter any time I wanted to. Abrianna hated him from the start. She'd warned me about him, but I had chosen to ignore her. I had a great job, but he asked me to quit my job and stay home to take care of him. I was slowly being suffocated, but in my mind this was my second chance, and I couldn't let myself believe I had made the same mistake again.

"I kept telling myself that he would get better when he felt secure enough. I made excuses for him. I thought that if I gave myself to him completely, with all I had in me, he would trust me and let me be free from all the rules and control that he smothered me with. As I was trying to be a perfect wife, my daughter was getting angrier and more distant from me. She started to hang out with the wrong people. She hated me so much that she refused to see me. She started giving Abrianna a hard time as well. Finally, she ran away from home. Abrianna was devastated and didn't know what to do, so every afternoon, she and Ally would drive around the rough neighborhoods, looking for Angel. At the time, they didn't tell me about it, and later on Ally told me that Abrianna had forbidden anyone from telling me about it because she knew what I was going through with Joe and she didn't want to add more trouble to my life. Poor Abrianna—how she coped with that entire situation, I'll never know.

"My life was tanking, and I was worse off than the woman I used to be a long time ago. I was so depressed and isolated from everyone. I missed my baby so much and hated myself. I was not strong enough to fight for my Angel. I didn't want to see Abrianna anymore, because seeing her reminded me of what a horrible mother I was. Seeing her reminded me of the time she'd helped me and I'd worked so hard to rise up, and now I was destroying everything. Once again, I lost everything that I'd worked so hard for.

"Abrianna became very sick, and I wanted to go and see her. Joe kept refusing, which caused a lot of drama between us every time I brought it up. One afternoon, Ally called me. Abrianna had passed away the previous night. She wanted me to go over and help prepare for the funeral and all the other arrangements. Before all this happened, before Joe existed in my life, Abrianna had made me the guardian of her shop and her belongings. I had become like her daughter, and I had to be there, so I didn't wait around to ask Joe. I just drove to her place. They had taken her body to the hospital, and she had died in her sleep. They said it was a heart attack. Her big, beautiful heart that had saved us all finally gave up on living. I took care of the funeral and her shop. Najima was going to supervise the shop while I sorted out my mess. This salon was more like a family business, and those girls had been working in that shop for more than a decade. That shop was life to Alice, Imani, and Najima.

"As time passed, I learned to deal with my loneliness. I became pregnant soon after Abrianna's passing, and I gave birth to a beautiful son, Jacob. He became everything to me, and when he was born, I promised myself I would be a better mother for him than I had been for Angel.

"As hard as I tried to be a good mom and a good wife, Joe could always find something to criticize. He was not very affectionate toward Jacob. He viewed their relationship as a set of fatherly obligations, but he demonstrated no affection to our son. He was a smart man when it came to his business, and he busied himself with his work. He ran a clothing manufacturing business, and he asked me to help him build the company and expand the business. I was also a full-time mother and his personal chef. He was very fussy about his diet. Cooking three meals a day for him was quite a task, and I had to be careful not to add or subtract anything from what he was used to. The titles he gave me slowly added up, and I realized that I was becoming just a nanny, a chef, and a housekeeper. Most of the time, he was in his office or spending time with his friends instead of spending time with his family. This realization only deepened my loneliness. Every time I tried to share my feelings with him, he didn't want to listen. He did not care. He found a reason to fight with me all the time. After a while, I just gave up and tried to create my own little universe. I looked for a job as a chef, which he was not happy about, but I had to do something to avoid going crazy. I was getting fed up with him, and I didn't care anymore what he thought or what he might say.

"As we became more financially successful, he grew colder and distanced himself even more. Whenever he was home, we simply tried to avoid each other. He had high expectations for Jacob and me, even for the smallest issues. I thought this was just a reason for him create arguments. I think Jacob also felt the weight of the situation around the house, especially since he didn't have a close bond in his relationship with his father. Eventually, our house was a ghost house every evening; each of us kept to ourselves in our own rooms, except for me, as I sat in the kitchen all by myself, reading a book or cooking something.

"The next few years passed painfully and slowly, and I noticed that Joe had a tendency to watch and stare at other women. I had a hunch about his faithfulness to the marriage, and low and behold, my suspicions came to light. He had cheated again with another married woman. When I found out, he denied the whole thing, which just hurt me more because he told me that I was emotionally unstable and it was all in my mind. But I knew the truth, and I chose to forgive him again, and we didn't talk about it anymore. Unfortunately, the wound didn't heal in my heart; I just chose to ignore it for Jacob's sake. I promised myself that I would not take him away from the stability of having a home and family, even though we weren't a happy family by any means. Still, I couldn't leave purely out of selfish reasons just because I wasn't happy. To me, it was all about my son.

"I had a brief period of happiness, because after years of separation, my beautiful Angel forgave me and came back into my life. Unfortunately, while she was away, she had been involved with drugs, alcohol, and the wrong crowds. She was so angry and aggressive toward Jacob, and I also knew she blamed me for Abrianna's death, for letting her go, for not protecting her, and for choosing Joe over her. I knew she had every right to be mad at me. She was my child; I was supposed to protect her, and I had failed. I knew the pain she was feeling, and it was all because of me. I probably drove her to drugs too because of the rejection she felt. It was so painful to see my child in such pain and know there was nothing I could do to help her. Each time I tried to get close to her, she became more hateful toward me. I tried to write a letter to her and apologize for everything, but the pain and anger inside her couldn't let her see anything else. During the time that she lived with us, she had a good relationship with Joe. He even offered her a part-time job so she could make some extra money. I was happy for her because it would change her focus. I was also happy that I finally had both my kids under the same roof, but that changed very quickly. She moved out without saying goodbye. When I asked Joe if something had happened at work, he told me that she was unpredictable, and he blamed it on the drugs. He assured me that she would come back home again.

"I could not just accept that defeat. I called her again and again to no avail. It took me six months to locate her and talk to her. I found out she was staying with Imani's family. I was happy because at least I knew she was safe. I found out she was working at Abrianna's beauty salon and was apparently clean from drugs and trying to get her life together. I was grateful to Imani for taking care of my daughter. I wanted to give her some space and then eventually go see her from time to time so that we might grow closer again.

"One day, I took Jacob and went to see my Angel as well as all the girls at the salon. I just wanted to see if everything was okay, especially with my daughter. I had no idea how she would react, but I just missed her like crazy and I had to go. When I walked in, she was working on a client's hair. My beautiful Angel seemed happy. She saw me and came to me with open arms, gave me a hug, and announced to the customers at the shop, 'Hey everyone, this is my mother!' She was laughing, and I was overjoyed to see her like that.

"Imani settled my fears by telling me that Angel was doing all right. Apparently, she was studying at night and working with Imani during the day. She promised me that she would take care of my baby. She told me that Angel would be okay, and I should focus on Jacob and myself. My family at the salon was there to help me. I had missed this place. Imani reminded me, 'Remember what Abrianna used to say? No judging. We have all been through so much and are still going through it. You have us, sister, and we will always be your family.' It was good to hear that.

"I tried to persuade Imani to encourage Angel to come home and stay with us, but Imani shook her head and instead encouraged me to sit down with my daughter. Just to talk. Just a mother-daughter talk, which had been long overdue. She told me that talking to my daughter would heal a lot of wounds, both hers and mine. She told me that Angel was dying to talk to me. I looked at Angel, my mind racing, wondering about the conversation to come.

"I waited until she was finished with her customer. I suggested that we go to my house, and she opted for her place instead. I was happy, though, because it was the first time I would get to see her place. My Angel was all grown up at eighteen years old; she was more mature than her age. She gave me her address, but she wanted to see her brother, so I drove home to pick him up. I was overjoyed and excited. I got home in a rush and quickly packed a small bag for Jacob. I didn't want Joe to know or ask questions. That would only end in disaster, so I did not tell him. It was best to just get in the car, drive off, and park somewhere, waiting for her to call me and tell me to come over.

"We eventually got to her place. Her one-bedroom apartment was small but cute, and it seemed perfect for my daughter. I especially loved her kitchen, because cooking was a huge part of who she was. I was so proud of her. I could see how happy and proud she was of her own achievements. I made sure I hugged her so she could also know how extremely proud of her I was. She was unusually calm and peaceful, which was new for me. She had changed since I had last seen her, which I told her. I loved the new change. She told me that she had found a nice boyfriend who was helping her emotionally after what she went through with Joe. 'What do you mean?' I asked her.

"She shook her head, clearly struggling with words. 'Mom, I don't know how to tell you this, so I'm just going to give it to you on a platter.' My heart started beating fast. 'Joe tried to make me his mistress,' Angel told me. I could have died right there. Not my child. She continued explaining, 'Mom, when he gave me a job at his company, he started treating me differently.' She just let the words pour out now. 'He confronted me about how miserable he is with you and how you are so incompetent, weak, and emotionally unstable all the time. He said the only reason he is still committed to the marriage is Jacob. He really believes that if he leaves you, then you won't be able to take care of yourself, and that could hurt Jacob. Why do you put up with him, Mom? He is a loser, a bastard, a cheater, and he doesn't love you. I hated him then and I hate him now. I am sorry, I didn't know how to tell you. I also hated you at that point for turning into a weak and pathetic woman with him. You used to be a strong, independent, and admired businesswoman, remember? You raised me to have pride and dignity. I remember that you used to study, work, and still have time to be happy and spend time with me. You used to have a life, Mom.'

"The whole time she was speaking, my mouth hung open from shock. My soul cried out in such pain. I didn't want to interrupt her; I just wanted to know everything. How did I lose who I was? One thing about my daughter was that she had such a strong personality and never held anything back in speech or deed. Her words were like a knife, cutting every little vein that sent blood to my heart and mind. Ironically, I wanted to feel the sharp pain of that knife in my soul. I desperately wanted to feel something, because for so long, I had not felt anything. For the longest time, I would wake up each day, hoping it was all just a bad dream.

"Angel continued, 'Mom, Joe sent me letters and made phones calls in the middle of the night. He had flowers delivered to me often. He bought me expensive gifts and kept vowing his attention to me. I am telling you, Mom, I hated you at that time, and in my mind, I took my revenge on you by not telling you. I could not get over the fact that you abandoned me for this crappy man. Mom, you abandoned me for this douchebag. Look at him—he wants me, not you. Is that not sick? He tells me he misses me every day, saying he wants his lips on every inch of my body. Those words make me sick to my stomach.'

"I covered my ears and told her to stop. She protested, 'No, Mom, you need to hear this. You need to wake up, because I know that somewhere down in your soul, my mother is hiding and begging to come out. I know the only reason you are still with him is because he's rich. Is that it? But you never were into materialism. I know you. You can survive without him. I will help you. Imani, Alice, and Najima will help you too. I told them everything, and they are just waiting for you to make your move. We are all going to be behind you, like they were before.'

"Shame overwhelmed me. I felt so ashamed that those three women knew what was happening in my life, when even I didn't. Angel told me about my last birthday, when he came home with a basket of eighteen red roses and one white rose in the middle. 'Did you guys make love that night in the guest room that used to be my room?' I was shocked by the details and asked how she could possibly know that.

"She smiled sadly and told me, 'Mom, what do you think? He told me exactly what happened that night. He went out on the balcony and called me and told me everything. He insisted on using my room because my scent was still in that room, and he said he thought of me the whole time.'

"I felt sick to my stomach. My airways were closing on me. I was about to pass out, and Angel handed me a glass of water. 'Mom, you have to be strong to hear all this. I know it's a hard pill to swallow coming from your daughter, but you have to hear it all.' I looked toward where Jacob was playing, thankful that he wasn't hearing a thing. No words of encouragement could fill up the empty space in my heart at that moment.

"I asked her to show me proof of the letters that she said Joe had sent. Not because I didn't believe her, but because I wanted to see his handwriting. Indeed, it was his. The most piercing part was that the words he used to say to me were the very words he used on my daughter. I asked if I could keep them, and she just said, 'All yours, Mom.' After that heart-wrenching conversation, I was in no hurry to rush back home. I was glad when she said, 'Mom, it is getting dark. A storm is coming. You are very upset, and it's a long way home. Please stay the night. I want to have my mom for at least one night.' I was so happy to hear her say that.

"As a conclusion to the conversation, I gave her a hug and muttered, 'Baby, I am so sorry for everything. You are my Angel, and I didn't protect you. Forgive me if you can, please.' Then I started to cry.

"She responded, 'Do you believe me, Mom? Do you blame me?'

"I quickly shook my head. 'Angel,' I said 'I do not blame you for anything. You are his stepdaughter. You are a sister to his son, Jacob, and you both shared the same womb. I failed to protect you. He is to blame. He is the evil one, not you. I can understand why you were angry at me and everything else that you felt, my darling, but never, not in a million years do I think that it was your fault.'

"I gave her a hug and decided to stay with her. How could I even go home that night and look that monster in the face? I was not ready to go back; I wanted to stay with my daughter and comfort her. Angel made dinner, and we talked a lot in the kitchen about anything and everything. Watching Angel play with Jacob brought me some peace, even though I was hurting so much. I had not felt that kind of warmth in a long time.

"As I drove home the next morning, I accepted the fact that I was afraid of Joe. My mind was filled with potential ways to approach him, what to say to him, and how to react when he lashed out. I was scared of being alone again, of starting all over again. I was reminded of how difficult it was the last time I had to start over. I never thought I would tread those waters again. I thought I had finally found someone to lean on. I thought that with Joe, I could put down my shield and do life with someone who cared. The man who had sat at my doorstep, begging me to be with him, was supposed to be different. I'd known he had his own issues, but he had me convinced otherwise.

"I walked in the house as bravely as I could. As usual, he was sitting in the living room doing his office work. He lifted up his head when he heard us, then he ran toward me and yanked Jacob's hand, leading him to his room. I braced myself as he came back. He yelled, 'Don't you ever leave this house without my permission and especially don't take my son anywhere without telling me first! You betrayed me last night. You broke your wedding vows.' He must have been delusional to think that I was in the wrong.

"A hot rush came over me. I lost it. For the first time in our marriage, I raised my voice and yelled back at him, 'What did you just say to me? *I* betrayed you? *I* broke my wedding vows?' At that point, I took out all of the love letters he'd written to my daughter and threw them in his face. He was stunned when he recognized his own handwriting, and his whole demeanor turned around instantly. He sat on the floor like a child, crying and hugging my legs, begging me to forgive him. In between his sobs, he told me that he was a sick man. He blamed his mother and his upbringing, basically divorcing himself from any fault or blame.

"His sobs and begging reminded me of the time he sat on my stairs and begged me to marry him. Watching a grown, abusive man cry like that could not change my mind this time. The sight of him made me sick to my stomach. I freed my legs from his arms. 'It is too little, too late,' I told him as I turned my back to him.

"I took my car keys and headed out the door. I could hear him begging me to stay, but I needed to go for a drive to think about how I felt about the events of these past two days. I was afraid of the unknown future, no matter the decision I made. I had walked this road before. One thing was certain; I was done with the desire to be cared for. There was no such thing as a perfect man, and I was done looking for one. I made the decision that I was going to walk this path by myself. I knew it was not going to be easy, but I was sure that I was ready.

"The transition period was not instant, even though the decision was. It took me two years to walk out. I walked out with my full share, custody of my son Jacob. Let me tell you something, the day I signed those divorce papers was the most beautiful day of my life. The sun was bright, the sky was blue, and there was not a single cloud. It was as though even the universe was cheering for me. I think even God was looking at me from above and telling me, 'You did it. I'm so proud of you.' Freedom is the best gift one can give oneself. I was blessed to have my daughter and my good friends, Imani, Alice, and Najima, on my side. If only my beautiful Abrianna could be with us to see this moment.

"The minute I walked out that door, Joe was as good as dead to me. With time, I stopped hearing from him except for the occasional call to check on Jacob. After a while, that stopped too. When I look back now, I realize that throughout those horrible years, it wasn't Joe stopping me from leaving him; it was my own fear of myself. Not believing in myself was the real enemy and real obstacle, but I'd blamed Joe because that was easier than facing the truth.

"I learned that being brave meant following my dreams and my heart's desires. Being brave doesn't mean you don't get to be afraid. It means you have to take one step at a time. One has to be hopeful while taking the next step in bravery.

"I'd always wanted to go to Australia. It was a childhood dream. The big, open space and the vast blue ocean called me. At least, that was the vision of Australia I had in my mind. I wanted to get away; I needed to open my wings and fly as far as I could. Imani had a brother in Sydney, and when I decided to go, everything fell into place. Jacob was excited too. We arrived in Sydney safely.

My old habits of saving all my money, combined with my years of culinary experience, helped me find a place to start my own business."

Anouk stopped her story abruptly and went to her room, returning with a little box in her hands. She sat down adjacent to me. She clutched that box as though she were holding on to something valuable.

She took a glance at me and said, "I think it is time that I pass this on to you. This is a box that Abrianna gave me many years back, and it has a letter from her inside. It transformed me. It changed my life. I now have the opportunity to pass it on to you, trusting that at some time or another, you will have the capacity to help another person." She reminded me that my past was behind me, and it was now time to push ahead. I was still attempting to wrap myself around her extraordinary biography, what she had experienced, and how she had conquered all the valleys of her life. I was astounded.

Anouk said, "You are the only person to whom I have recounted my biography of the last fifty years. I told you all of this today so you could know that this is not the end of the world for you. Bad things happen in our lives, and that is as it should be. Grow from it, and proceed onward. In the event that you listened closely to my story, then I don't have anything more to tell you. In any case, open Abrianna's letter and read the contents. The choice is yours. Your decision, your life."

She gave me an embrace and a kiss on my temple then retreated to her room. The last words I heard from her that night were, "Tomorrow will be a lovely, sunny day." I lay back in my seat and opened the envelope, starting to peruse through and read.

Open your heart, open your eyes, and read this repeatedly, first thing when you wake up and before you go to bed. At whatever time you feel double-crossed by the entire world or by somebody you trusted with your entire existence, read this and begin to have faith in every single word, since you are a piece of these words. Try not to give anybody a chance to make you lose yourself. Adore yourself, and recall that we are here only for a short time. Like a bloom in a botanical garden, we will blur into our surroundings. Live life to the fullest, without limitations, before the season changes.

"The Power in Me"

I am grateful for my health.

I am counting my blessings every day.

I am so happy with who I am and who I have become.

I am who I am today due to what I have been through in life.

For every teardrop on my cheek,

For every heartache that I felt,

For every sleepless night that I went through,

I gained wisdom.

I polished my soul and I became closer to my God.

I became closer to myself.

I discovered my courage and the inner power within me.

I have no fear, no doubt, and I know I can do anything, I can be anything, I can achieve anything,

As long as I believe in myself.

There is a beautiful sunny day after every storm.

There is a dawn beyond every sunset.

I know this too shall pass.

I know a day will come when I will wipe away every tear, bandage my wounded heart, and stand tall.

I will take a deep breath and take the first step toward my bright and glorious future.

I know I will make it.

This beautiful face is meant to have a smile on it.

This generous heart is meant to love and create joyful moments.

This brilliant mind of mine was born to be a creator of many magnificent stories.

We are all part of the greater power, and we all have that power in us.

The only way to reach that power is to believe in myself.

My greatest discovery in my life is that I don't need anyone else to be happy or to be complete.

I am powerful, I am beautiful, and I am everything that I want to be.

The moment I discover that I am the one holding my universe,

The moment that I realize the kingdom of God is in me,

Nothing can break me down, nothing can stop me from my dreams and goals.

The moment I discover the truth about my inner power, nothing else is relevant.

I will love myself unconditionally, with all that I am.

The End

THE DARK SIDE
OF THE SUN

"As you get closer to God, evil gets two steps closer to you until you turn around and look him in the eyes, and only then will you see the dark side of the sun."

These words were my first introduction to Ray.

"We all have a demon inside us. Either you accept it or you don't. That dark corner in your mind that is so scary, we don't even want to think about it."

He turned around and looked at me.

"Don't tell me you don't know what I'm talking about," he said.

Those piercing green eyes made me feel like he could see the deepest parts of my soul and dig out my darkest secrets. I looked away because it just made me feel uneasy.

I'd gathered all my information on Ray from a statement that he himself had written, which indicated that he was born in Turkey. When he was just a few days old, he was found in a dark alley behind a restaurant. He grew up in various orphanages until he ran away when he was around fourteen years old. He never knew his real parents. His first two murders took place in Turkey, and the third victim had been living in Australia. After he killed the third victim, Ray had been arrested. He had never been married nor had any children or other family, but he had made a name for himself as the best mechanic in his town. Although he could speak both Turkish and English, he hadn't been highly educated. Ever since he'd been in jail, however, he had been educating himself and eventually received his degree in creative arts. His cell was full of his paintings. They were all black and white. Charcoal. They were a mix of darkness, sadness, innocence, violence, and peace, and you could feel his pain through his paintings. You could see him and his whole soul right in front of you if you only looked deep into his paintings. His soul was dark, complicated, and full of mystery. It was rather chilling to look at those drawings, but I wanted to get to know him on a more personal level before I started to write about him. I'd heard that everyone respected him, even the guards. He was the quiet type, never causing any trouble for anyone, but there was also something about him that exuded an unapproachable vibe. "Don't mess with Ray," I heard from the guards. "Ray is a ray of sunshine, but you never want to mess with him when he gets stormy and wild."

I measured him up when he was not looking. He looked to be about in his mid-forties, and he was tall, with dark olive skin and curly brown hair. He was well built, with broad shoulders, and you could say he was a handsome man, but there was something about his look and in his eyes that made you feel guilty, made you question everything about him. I couldn't pin down why, but that guilt made me feel as though I had to help him, as though I was the last rope he could hang on to, like the last boat on the shore that could save him from the storm on the horizon.

There was an unusual energy about him too. As I entered the visiting room, I felt warm, sad, and scared at the same time. My first big break—it was exciting and nerve-racking to be here and to have this assignment. After all, Ray was a killer who was going to spend the rest of his life behind bars. For some reason, the media was particularly interested in his life, and our local newspaper decided that there should be a big article featuring him. It was a great opportunity for a criminal law student like me, right?

I knew all my classmates would kill to be sitting in this chair right now, so I told myself I couldn't screw this up.

I sat across from him. Only a small table separated us. I put my notebook and tape recorder on the table, turned to the first page of my notebook, took my pen out of my pocket, and started to write the date and Ray's name on the top of the page.

I knew I had to be direct and straightforward with him if I was going to find out everything. I had his written statement in front of me, but I hadn't had a chance to talk to his doctor or anyone else before coming to see him. My boss had told me to interview Ray first and hear everything from his mouth. Maybe there were some unanswered questions that no one except him could answer, or perhaps it was about me getting to know him first before I jumped to conclusions. Whatever it was, I had to be very strong and show no fear.

I looked straight into his eyes and asked my first question. "What made you kill those people?"

"You mean you want to know what started the fire of hatred inside of me?" He smiled. "Maybe I had the evil inside of me for a long time, but I never opened the cage to let it out until then. Humans are complicated creatures. We are capable of magnificent acts of kindness, and at the same time, we can be such ugly monsters that even God looks down in disappointment. There is a fine line between love and hate. It's a bridge that, once crossed, has no way back. Do you believe in that?"

He didn't wait for my answer, continuing almost immediately, "I crossed that bridge a long time ago, and all I wanted was to punish them. I guess I took justice into my own hands."

I watched him closely as he talked so calmly, with no apparent chip on his shoulder, no sound of remorse or regret that I could sense. There was no sign of guilt or shame in his voice. It seemed to me that he was happy with himself and what he had done.

He continued, "All my life, no one stood up for me. No one defended me. I was unwanted for as long as I can remember. Well, one day, as I was on my knees, waiting for a social worker to put his monster in my mouth, I promised myself, 'No more!' So I closed my eyes and bit the monster's head as hard as I could. The social worker screamed and hit my head so hard that I was hospitalized for a month. But it was worth it! When I woke up, they sent me back to the orphanage, but this time was different. I gained some respect among the boys. I could walk around with my head held high."

He had a smile on his face, and his eyes were suddenly full of life. He turned around, looked at me, and abruptly changed the subject. "Are you married?"

I answered him without hesitation. "I was."

"Do you have any kids?"

"A boy. He's two. His name is Alex."

"What is your name?" he asked.

"I am so sorry. My name is Lilli. I figured they told you about me and who I was before I got here." I looked down at my notebook, unsure of what to say next. The nerves were getting to me. I think he could sense that, as he tried to change the subject again.

He continued with his questions. "Who's taking care of Alex while you are here?"

"My mother. She takes care of him every day. Actually, she lives with us. My father passed away a few years ago, and I didn't want her to be alone. Also, I can rely on her to take care of Alex."

"So do you love your mother, or do you put up with her for the sake of having a free babysitter?" he asked, a little sarcasm in his voice.

"A bit of both, I guess." I smiled, then continued, "She blamed me for my marriage falling apart, and I blamed her for never taking my side."

"Why did your marriage fall apart?" he asked, and he seemed so genuinely interested that I couldn't just let it go. I actually wanted to tell this stranger what happened in my personal life.

"One day he just said he didn't love me and that he couldn't stand being with me any longer, so I filed for divorce. I got nothing from my ex in return except for my self-respect, dignity, and my son." I played distractedly with the pen in my hand, still staring at the blank paper in front of me.

"Good for you! Never sell your soul to anyone," Ray said.

Suddenly, the realization hit that I had just opened up to a complete stranger without any hesitation. This was the first time I had talked about my private life so openly to anybody. It was embarrassing and unprofessional of me.

Very quickly, I pulled myself back together and told him, "I am so sorry, that wasn't very professional."

He appeared to be a very sharp and perceptive man, and I think he noticed that I was uneasy with everything I had told him. He responded, "Look, I am glad that you told me a little bit about your life, because it means you are a human, not just a hungry reporter who's only after a story."

"But it wasn't professional. I crossed the line," I said.

"Screw the line and screw being professional." He started to raise his voice. "I asked you a question and you answered me, so don't give me crap about ethics and rules, okay?"

His feet were chained to the table and he had handcuffs on both wrists, but the way he lost his temper was still quite frightening. He yelled for a guard, then told me, "Get the hell out of here. I'm not going to talk to you."

The guard opened the door and said, "Hey Ray, watch your manners, man. What's wrong?"

Ray said nothing and waited for the guard to unlock him from the table. Just before leaving the room, he turned around, looked me in the eye, and told me in an angry whisper, "Get lost. I've got nothing to tell you." Then he left the room.

My first big interview was over just like that. I was truly shaken, but I tried to hide it from the guard, and especially from Ray.

On the drive back home, I was so angry with myself that I kept punching the wheel and screaming at myself, "You're stupid! You're stupid! You blew it."

For the next few days, I just focused on my paperwork at the office, distracting myself so I wouldn't think about Ray and our first meeting.

My boss kept asking me what happened and what Ray told me. I didn't want to tell him that I blew up the whole interview with my own insecurity and unprofessionalism, so I told him that Ray wasn't ready to talk, so I might go back next week.

My boss accepted my answer, and he told me, "Don't take too long. We need the story by the end of the month, okay?"

I nodded, wondering how on earth I was going to pull that off. I had to find a way. Maybe I could just simply wait a few more days and call the prison to see if I could go back or not.

I was studying law and working at the local newspaper office in Adelaide, a city in southern Australia. I wanted to become a criminal lawyer, and in order to get more experience and knowledge, I also worked part time as an interpreter at a refugee center. I was born in Australia, but my family had come from various parts of the world. My father left his homeland, Pakistan, when he was a young man. In our house, my father never let us speak English. He was very patriotic about his culture and always forced my twin brother and me to learn about our history and where we came from.

He used to say to us, "Remember, my children, we are all citizens of Mother Earth. Cherish the planet and all the creatures that God created for us. Be kind to everyone, respect everybody's beliefs and faith, but never forget your roots and where your ancestors came from. Cherish the place you were born, and honor your mother tongue, as it is the first language your parents taught you."

My mother was from Turkey, so naturally I had to learn to speak Turkish, Urdu, and English. In our house, from the age of one, we had to learn to speak three languages. Believe me, it wasn't fun. As my brother and I grew up, we began to enjoy it more because we could sit in our school cafeteria and speak Urdu or Turkish, and no one else could understand us. Besides, our English teacher used to brag about us to other students, saying, "Look at Lilli and Firouz! They can speak three languages."

Then she would look at the rest of the students in the classroom and say, "You are from Australia, and English is supposed to be your only language, but you still fail to speak it properly. Except for those two, most of you get horrible grades in English." We used to be so happy every time our teachers praised us like that, because by then, we knew that the hard times our parents had put us through were worth it.

Still, we sometimes had teachers who never wanted us to speak anything but English to each other, even in the cafeteria. One teacher in particular, if she caught my brother and I talking to each other in a different language, would yell at us in class, saying, "You are in our country, so speak bloody English, for God's sake!" Kids would laugh at us, then give us a hard time out on the schoolyard, pushing us, punching us, or making fun of our dark skin. That became a frequent punishment for us, so from an early age, we started to feel the racism and prejudice against us. They used to call us "FOB," which meant "fresh off the boat." I guess it was a sign of disrespect.

Our parents taught us to ignore the disrespect. They'd tell us, "That's just how some people are. Be sure to always see the good in people, and every time someone shows prejudice or says a racist comment, look toward the wonderful people who opened their hearts and shared their country with us. Those people are the true Australians and the best of humanity. A word has no power unless you give it a reason to be powerful, so if you don't give them reasons, they just are empty words. They don't mean anything."

I loved the way my father used to break down any obstacle into a million pieces, like every problem was just a huge Lego set. You think that it's impossible to put all the pieces together and see the finished result, but one by one you set them up, then all of the sudden, you have your masterpiece. That was how my brother and I used to see our dad when he dealt with our school problems. He'd break the problem down, and by the time he finished his explanation and assessment, we'd begin to feel sorry for those kids and learn to brush their comments off like dust.

Our family came from an educated background; my father had been a university lecturer back in his country, and my mother had been a schoolteacher. Once they came to Australia as refugees, though, they lost everything, including their titles. Dad became a taxi driver, and Mom worked at a nursery, helping elderly people. I could see the pain in my father's eyes from time to time. His education meant something special to him, and some nights, we could hear his conversations with our mother in the kitchen, talking about how some people in his cab insulted him or treated him with no respect. He wished he could go back to teaching again.

Our mother would comfort him with a cup of hot tea and tell him, "It's all for our kids, and who knows? Maybe when we pay off our mortgage, you can get another job or apply for a job at a college."

Every now and then, I used to catch my mother crying in the kitchen while she was cooking. As soon as I asked her what was wrong, she would laugh and say, "It's just the silly onions," but we all knew the truth. She missed her family back home.

My parents loved each other dearly, and we could see and feel that every day through their body language and the way they talked to each other. My father used to tell us, whenever he was in a jolly mood, that our mother was his first and only love. Mom would immediately act shy and blush, and Dad would give her a kiss on her cheek and tell us, "Look, this is my beautiful angel. She is still that young girl who used to get all red-faced whenever I looked at her." We loved that about our parents—their sacrifices for us were the reason that my brother and I did our best to make them proud of our achievements. My brother and I both received incredible education. He became a young doctor with a dream of becoming a heart specialist, and just a few months after his graduation, he was engaged to a beautiful young girl from the hospital where he worked.

Life couldn't get sweeter than that for my parents and us. As the years passed, my father forgot about his dream of teaching again. To pay for our home and education, he saved up and purchased one more taxi so he could rent it out and make more money for our family to live a better life. I guess you could say he measured his success by our bright futures.

My brother's wedding day was drawing closer, and even though his fiancée was from an Australian family, my parents still wanted to give them a magnificent, traditional Turkish and Pakistani wedding ceremony so the other family could know my brother was from a good family, with parents who loved and cared for their future daughter-in-law.

Firouz and his future wife, Christina, set the date for May 28. The day they announced it was an exciting day for all of us, especially my mother. She was over the moon with the news. It was a Friday night, and we were having a special family dinner in our home, as was tradition. After Firouz and Christina's announcement, my mother got up, kissed them both, and told my father to open the bottle of red wine that he had been saving for many years to only be opened on a very special occasion.

My mother shouted with such joy in her voice, "Karim, darling, please go to the basement and open your special bottle of wine! Our son is getting married next month!"

I remembered that moment like it was just yesterday. We were all screaming with excitement and hugging each other, and my father had tears in his eyes. He took my brother into his arms and told him, "I only wish our own parents could be here and see you all. They would be so proud of you, son." Then he looked at me. "Both of you."

There were no dry eyes in that room, but it was all tears of joy and happiness.

May was approaching fast, and every day, my parents were making purchases or renovating the house. Our parents had requested that the wedding ceremony be out in our big backyard. I was so involved too that I often complained to my mother about the whole thing, and she used to tell me, "Don't worry, Lilli, we will do the same for your big day, and then Firouz and Christina will do all this work." Then she would laugh.

The wedding was five days away, and everything was almost done. We were supposed to have a big rehearsal dinner at our place for close family and friends, and we were all waiting for the future bride and groom to arrive, when my father got a call from the hospital saying that there had been an accident. Firouz and Christina had been driving to our home when a drunken truck driver wrecked into their car, killing them instantly.

In that moment, all eyes were on my dad, as we were curious to know who the caller was that could make my dad's face turn so lifeless. I rushed toward him, took the phone out of his hand, and demanded to know everything. After he told me, my first instinct was to go to my mother, but how on earth were we supposed to give her the news?

We eventually had to tell her, along with everybody else at the rehearsal dinner. We were all shocked, and an eerie silence fell over the whole house. It is so painful to see your own parents go through so much heartbreak and not be able to do a damn thing to ease their pain.

After that, my father changed. I saw him grow old in just one night. Our happy home, which had been the house full of laughter, joy, and traditional Turkish and Hindi music, all of the sudden became the house of painful silence.

My brother's death broke my parents' hearts, and they never recovered from that tragedy. I guess Dad couldn't take it any longer, because we lost him the next spring. It was May 28 when we laid his lifeless body in the ground.

I was involved with a guy from my office, and I guess we fell in love. He knew about my family tragedy as I was going through the pain of losing my brother and then my father. He understood and helped me process all those emotions. He asked me to marry him, but with the loss of both my brother and my father, along with what was happening to my mother, I didn't think it would be a good idea to make a big fuss out of the whole thing. I didn't feel like the same person I had been before, so I told him that if he was okay with it, we could get married in a courthouse and just have a small gathering in a restaurant.

That was what we did. We got married at the courthouse then had a celebration at a restaurant with only his family and a few friends from work. My mother didn't come. She was like a zombie walking around the house, and I knew there was no point in even asking her to come.

Soon after, I became pregnant, and eight months after delivering the baby, my husband just packed his things and left. His reasoning was that my family was so depressing and he hated everything about our life. He couldn't take it anymore. After losing my father and my brother, I didn't think anything else could shake me that hard. At some level, I had noticed the change in him and had seen this coming. I would be okay. Besides, now I had a beautiful baby boy, Alex, to think of. We moved back to my parents' home and I let my mother's caretaker go because I could take care of my own mother. I was on maternity leave anyway.

My mother had been through all the stages of sadness, anger, and denial, but I think she finally just gave up and became like a lifeless piece of meat, standing by the window and staring outside, or she would go to her room and sit on the edge of the bed for hours until I would help her lie down and close her eyes. She would hardly eat, and I could see that if I didn't do anything, I'd lose her too. I wasn't ready to let her go, not like this and not now.

She loved Alex, which I could see in her eyes whenever he was around her, but she just didn't know how to be like she was before. It was as though she felt too guilty to let her heart feel some joy.

One day, I just couldn't stand to see her like that anymore. I went to her room, shook her shoulders, and told her, "Ma, look at me. They are gone, okay? You will see them, and we all will be together someday. All together, just like we used to be. You have faith; you believe in the next life, don't you? For years, you taught me about life after death and how beautiful it is, so snap out of this. While we are here on this earth, let's live and be happy and believe that one day we are all going to be together, okay, Ma? Please, let's be happy. I need you. Alex needs his grandma to be happy. Life is happening, Ma. Let's go to the kitchen and cook Dad and Firouz's favorite food and celebrate their memories and lives. Let's live again, Ma. Enough is enough. I can't take it anymore, and if you continue to be like this, I'll have to leave you and find my own place, for Alex's sake. Please, Ma, come back to me. Feel my heartbeat; I'm still alive. I'm here, and I need you."

All of the sudden, she looked at me and hugged me like she was seeing me for the first time after a long time apart. She started to cry so loud in a way I had never seen her cry before. Then she started laughing like crazy woman—actually, we both did. After that, my mother came back to us. She started to live again.

Perhaps that was why I started working as a translator for the refugee center, because somehow I needed to help people like my parents who left their homeland to create a better life for their kids. At the refugee center, we gave people opportunities in life that they could have never had in their own countries. Working as a translator was rewarding for me as well. I found joy in connecting people and helping them achieve their goals, which was why it was so hard for me to accept that I had ruined my first interview with Ray. I wasn't sure why, but in some strange way I thought that by telling his story to the public, I could help myself. As strange as it was, that was exactly how I felt. This was the first time I'd been handed such a big case, and I wanted to prove myself. My boss thought that since I could speak Turkish, Ray might open up to me easily. However, from the moment I had entered the visiting room, we had only spoken English, and he had no accent to even indicate that English was his second language. After many years speaking English, he must have felt more confident speaking in English rather than Turkish.

One week passed with no news from Ray. I was ready to go home on Friday afternoon, when my boss asked me to meet him in his office. Apparently, our newspaper had received a call from the prison, and all they said was that Ray was ready for his interview.

My boss told me, "I have no idea what happened in there last time, but try not to screw up this time. Get the damn story ready in the next three weeks or say goodbye to your job."

He wasn't laughing this time, so I promised that he would have his story by the end of the month.

I went to my desk and called the prison to set up a time for my next meeting with Ray.

This time, I decided to be more open and honest with him. I would just talk to him, not as a reporter but as someone who was interested in his story and what happened to him.

I went without my tape recorder, just a notebook and pencil tucked into my bag in case I needed it. I had to earn his trust first and then get the story out of him. I gathered that Ray was highly intelligent, and at just the hint of my pretending to be something else, he would pinpoint it very quickly. That would mean the end of my interview. With that in mind, I promised myself that no matter what, I was going to be anything but a reporter.

As soon as Ray walked in, I said hello and stepped forward to shake his hand, but the guard told me to sit back and not get too close. I noticed some bruises on Ray's face. I'd learned before the interview that he'd been injured during a fight with another prisoner.

He seemed happy, and as soon as he saw me, he gave me a smile. "Hey, how is my favorite reporter doing today?" he asked.

I was shocked to see how warm and friendly he was toward me this time, so I smiled back at him and, with excitement in my voice, told him, "I'm doing just fine, Ray! Thank you for asking."

The guard interrupted, "You guys only get two hours. And you behave yourself, Ray. You hear me?"

"Yes, sir," Ray replied, with a big smile on his face and a salute to the prison guard.

They had told me before the interview that it was my lucky day because he was in such a good mood. I planned to take advantage of the mood and get him to open up to me as much as possible.

Even though I already knew from the guards, I asked him, "What happened to your face, Ray? Have you been in a fight or something?"

He nodded. "Yes, I just had to defend my cellmate. I couldn't stand what was happening to him. He's young, and you know that jail can be a real eye-opening place. Someone had to prevent him from getting raped, and I think no one will mess with him from now on, so long as he has me in his corner. I hate when people prey on the weak. It just makes me sick." He spoke with such evident disgust on his face.

This man was a murderer, but he was still getting beat up for protecting a fellow cellmate. That just didn't make any sense to me.

Ray sat up to light a cigarette, which was a challenge with both wrists in handcuffs, then he looked straight into my eyes and said, "No bullshit today, deal? If you promise to just be honest and open with me, then I agree to give you what you want. Only as long as you keep your part of the deal. I want to ask you about your life, and you have to be open with me too. Two people sharing their life stories—that is the only way I will talk to you. Deal?"

I leaned forward and told him he had a deal. I sat back and let him take control of our conversation. I wanted him to be in charge and speak whenever he was ready, and even though we only had two hours, I wanted him to know I was there on his terms.

He leaned back and started to talk. "I want to tell you about me, about my life. I don't need anyone's pity or sympathy, and I definitely don't want you to feel sorry for me. Also, I'm not doing this interview to get a shorter sentence or get out of here. I just want to be heard, and maybe by letting people know about my life, someone else's life can be saved. Maybe I can help another poor bastard like me not end up here but instead make the right choice. I don't have any regrets for what I have done, because I believe I made the best decisions I could at that time. I don't blame anyone anymore. I'm just the result of bad circumstances."

Ray paused to exhale some cigarette smoke, and I took this opportunity to explain my actions in the previous meeting. "I'm so sorry about our first meeting. I was nervous, and, to be honest, that was my first interview inside the prison. Besides, I'm usually a very private person. I don't have many friends, so I was shocked at how easily I opened up to you. That's all. So please accept my apology, and I just want you to know, I'm here for you, Ray."

He looked me in the eye and took a deep breath in. After he exhaled, he said to me, "Maybe you feel safe because I'm not in a position to judge you. Or maybe I'm just easy to talk to, and maybe you need a friend desperately." We both laughed.

"I think you're right, Ray. I think I'm just a nerd who works too hard. All I do is bury myself in my work. I guess I need to be more open, and I want to start with you, if that's okay."

He sat back and said, "Okay, how about I start from the beginning? My earliest memory goes back to when I was four or five years old. I had been in an orphanage ever since I was just a few days old. As one of the sisters used to tell me, they found me in a big trashcan out behind a restaurant one winter night. I was wrapped in a woolen blanket, almost dead from the cold weather and starvation. That night, the sisters took me to the hospital first and then to the orphanage downtown. The sisters used to say that I was the sweetest child and everyone just loved me straight away. Well, that didn't last very long. Pretty soon, I was being passed from one place to the next, until one finally stuck for a short time."

While Ray was talking, I started to size him up. We were both created by the same creator, but, as an innocent child who hadn't even had a chance to commit any sins or do anything wrong, how come he had to go through all this pain in his life, while I had a perfect childhood and wonderful parents? If we believed in God or any higher power and we kept saying that God loved us, how could our God give him such a painful childhood?

Suddenly, I heard Ray's voice calling my name, asking, "Where are you, Lilli?"

"Me? Nowhere. I'm here, I just drifted off for a second," I replied.

"What were you thinking about?"

"I was thinking that you didn't deserve to have that kind of a childhood. That's all," I said.

He shook his head at me. "I told you from the beginning, I don't need your pity. Just hear me out." He continued his story, "I never knew my parents. For a while, the sisters tried to figure out what had happened to them, but then they just gave up. I became another case of a child without a face or name. I was just a case number to the world, another lost boy. From the earliest time I can remember, I was abused physically, and the routine of waking up in the middle of the night to be raped was part of my daily life. Sometimes I wished I were dead so they would leave me alone. Every time a new face came to the orphanage, I felt sorry for the poor soul. Very soon, they would lose the spark of innocence in their eyes, and that hopefulness on their faces would disappear in a flash. You could see the transformation as their eyes grew fearful and those dark circles around their eyes showed that their nightmares had begun.

"I tried to run away from the orphanage a few times, but each time the police found me, and the punishment was harsher every time. After a while, thoughts of freedom and living a normal life became just fantasies, and as time passed, all of us knew that no family would ever come for us. There was an old woman, Sister Rose, who used to work in the orphanage. She was the only person who treated us with kindness. Unfortunately, she always worked the morning shift. She was our so-called music teacher. By music, I mean one old piano. She was the only person who could play some songs on it, and we loved the chance to spend two days a week with her just to get away from our miserable lives and routines. She used to gather us and teach us how to sing. After all, every now and then, some rich people would come look around the orphanage to see that their donations were being put to good use and us kids were being fed properly. Ironically, every time we did get visitors, we were in our music class, singing and dancing around like clowns. The sisters dressed us up in nice, clean clothes, and we all gathered in the small performance hall and sang songs to our guests, so they got to go home and feel good about themselves, believing their money had been spent in a holy way. On such days, we were fed, showered, and treated as normal human beings, but we knew it was just a show. It wouldn't last, but if you were really lucky, someone might want to take you home. Usually it was the youngest and most beautiful children who got so lucky. I always secretly prayed for that moment, even if it was highly unlikely for me. The happiest moments were when we saw a car pulling away from the orphanage with a woman holding a child in her arms—I was happy to see any child saved from this hellhole.

"Sister Rose used to tell us that the moment we were born, we were like angels with two beautiful wings. If we were good and honest people, we would never lose our wings; one day, we would fly to God's kingdom to be an angel in heaven. She would say, 'So always remember to be kind and honest, and help those who cannot help themselves. That way, you'll get your reward by keeping your wings.' After she told us that, we began to call ourselves 'lost angels.'

"At night, when everyone was asleep, even the demons, I used to sneak to the roof of our orphanage. On one ledge sat a statue of an angel with one broken wing and half a face, looking down at everyone. I used to sit beside her, put my head on her rusty shoulder, and look toward the sky. I was searching for my star, the one that was my planet, where I originally came from. Ever since I was five years old, I believed that this wasn't my life, this wasn't my planet, and I had somehow fallen from my mother's arms on another planet to here. Someday, she would find me. If I looked up at the stars every night, the night would come when she would see me. But as I grew older, there were fewer and fewer stars in sky, and my faith was clouded. I realized that no one was looking for me, and this really was my planet. My mother didn't lose me; she just lost her faith in loving me."

Ray stopped talking for a minute or so. His eyes were filled with tears, and as he lit up another cigarette, he noticed me watching him and quickly wiped his tears away.

"Why can't our memories ever leave us alone?" He spoke with such frustration but continued his story, looking off toward the small window in the room. "Maybe my childhood did shape my present and nourish the demon inside me. If I had lived under different circumstances, perhaps my heart and soul could have more compassion, more humanity."

"But the choice is always yours to be made, Ray," I told him.

He looked at me with such surprise in his eyes. "Easy for you to say those words, but you'll never know what it is like for people like me. Don't you dare lecture me about choices, okay?" he demanded, slowly raising his voice.

I realized that he was right; I had no idea what had happened to him or what it might be like. "I'm sorry. You are right, Ray," I said. "Please continue."

He turned his gaze back to the small window, which was partially obscured by metal grilles, then continued, "I lived in that orphanage until I turned fourteen. Finally, on one snowy winter night, I escaped. This time, I was going to make sure no one would find me. It didn't matter how cold it was, I wasn't going to get caught, so I just ran and ran until I couldn't run anymore. I found a dark alley and chose a spot behind a big trashcan to curl up so I could warm myself. I didn't want to be noticed, so I covered my body with a bunch of empty boxes. I warmed up just a bit and went to sleep. I wasn't too afraid. I mean, what was the worst thing that could happen to me that I hadn't already been through?

"When I woke up, it was early morning. Across the street, I noticed a shed, or more like a garage, with lots of tools inside. It appeared to be a mechanic shop or something. I looked around the alley. It was too early for many people to be out, so I thought that I could walk into the shop, grab a few of those tools, and run away. Maybe later on, I could sell those tools and buy something to eat. As I was growing weak from hunger, I started to walk toward the shop, looking left and right to see if anybody was nearby. Suddenly, I noticed a man staring straight at me. I tensed up, ready to run like a scared street cat, then I heard him saying to me, 'It's okay, calm down. No one is after you.' He chuckled, tightly clutching the cup in his hands. He continued, 'This is my shop, and I am a mechanic who works from dusk to dawn, so I saw you sleeping in that corner beside the trashcan. I wanted to go over and wake you up to let you know that if you were looking for a place to crash, you could come over here, but I didn't want to frighten you, you see?'

"I was quiet and didn't know how to respond. My eyes darted back and forth between the empty street and this man. I was most interested in the cup he held, wanting to see what he was drinking.

God, I was so hungry, and I think the man noticed, because then he said, 'I'm going to bring you some food and leave it here, but if you like, you can come in and sit beside the fireplace while you eat your hot soup. Only if you want to. No pressure.' He turned and walked inside. I wasn't used to kindness with no demands for anything in return, so I wasn't going to jump at his offer, but there was a genuine honesty in his voice that made me believe him.

"He came back with fresh warm bread and a bowl full of hot soup. It felt so good to be able to eat something decent and delicious after such a long time. He sat in the corner of his shop and got busy with his work, as if I wasn't even there. That made me feel safe and comfortable. But still, just like a wild animal, I watched his every move, just in case he decided to attack me or come after me. I have no idea how, but in just a few minutes, I finished all the food he had given me. As I was licking the bowl, he asked me, 'Hey, there's still plenty of soup in the pot. Do you want some more?'

"I nodded my head and said, 'Yes, please,' so he took the bowl from me and came back with more food. By the time I finished the second bowl, I realized that he wasn't after me at all, not if he was going through all this effort to take care of me.

"He was working on a car, and I tried to see what he was doing. Cars interested me, and working on them sounded exciting. As I was looking around at the different cars in the shop, he told me that if I promised not to rob him or kill him in the middle of the night, I could stay in the garage at night and help him with his work. I assured him I wasn't a murderer and was definitely not a thief; I was just hungry and looking for food, so if he wanted, I could stay and help him with work as long as I got to sleep in the garage every night and got a bowl of soup and a piece of bread to eat each day. That was all I wanted from him, and I promised I wouldn't cause any trouble for him. He accepted my offer, and that turned the page to the second chapter of my life.

"After I ran away from the orphanage, they didn't bother looking for me. Maybe it was because I was getting older and they knew I would only cause more trouble from now on. Whatever their reasons, I was happy that I finally had my freedom. I had an agreement with the old man, and he allowed me to stay as long as I was honest and trustworthy. He didn't ask much from me except for my help around his shop, and I was happy because I was out of the orphanage.

"I demonstrated a strong interest in cars and a desire to learn everything, which made the old man so happy that he taught me how to change oil, fix engines, and everything else I needed to know about auto repairs. Together, we built a small room in his garage, and he told me to decorate it any way I wanted to, as long as there were no pictures of naked women on the walls. He was a religious man—a man with real faith, not like those bastards I had to deal with at the orphanage. Throughout those first few months away from the orphanage, I used to wake up in the middle of the night and expect to see the old man standing beside my bed. I would wake up drenched in sweat and afraid of the door opening, as I expected him to walk in with his pants down, wanting me to jerk him off. The slightest of noises used to make me jump out of my bed. I would watch the doorknob for hours to see if it would move. However, I slowly realized that that part of my life was over. I was safe. Regardless, I could never forget the faces of those monsters.

"It's funny, you try so hard to run away from your painful past, and you think to yourself, 'Finally, it's over,' but with a small trigger like seeing a similar face or smelling a familiar scent, it all comes back to you like a strong wave and knocks you down. But for the time being, I was healing. I was trying so hard to catch up and live a normal life, and that old man was helping me without ever knowing just how much. He never asked me where I came from or what I was running from. He just gave me shelter and my own space to breathe.

"For the first time, I had a safe place, my own bed, and my own door that I could open or close at night. I had a table and a lamp, and he even gave me an old radio and told me, 'Fix it and it's yours!' Oh my God, it seemed that I had won the biggest lottery ticket ever. I had no idea how to fix the radio, but I was so happy that it was all mine. It took me two weeks of looking at some old gadget magazines and asking anyone who came to the shop if they could help, then one day I got it to work. I jumped around and screamed, 'It works! It works!' Laughing, I just hugged the old man without thinking twice about it.

"He told me, 'Okay, son, it's just an old radio.' It may have been small, but for the first time, I felt really happy. That radio and that small room in that rusty old shop in the middle of nowhere became my sanctuary. Every night after work, I would place my radio on my chest, put my arms behind my head, and lay down on my bed to just listen to music. I would close my eyes and fly far away beyond the sky and just let my soul be free. Those nights are the best memories of my entire life."

A loud knock on the door interrupted Ray's story, and a guard walked in to say, "Time's up." He began to unlock the chains restraining Ray's feet.

Ray and I looked at each other, and I said to him, "Thank you, Ray."

"Are you coming back soon?" Ray asked.

"Sure, if you want me to."

"Yes, I would really like you to come back. I think we can finish the story in no time." He disappeared through the doorway and left me with a million thoughts and questions.

On the way back home, all I could think of was Ray and what he had been through. I started to feel something—admiration, infatuation, or maybe I simply felt sympathy for him. I had yet to figure him out. One minute he could be childlike, then the next he could get so angry and aggressive, then the next minute he was such a charming man with calm mannerisms.

I was not going to let myself get too deep. I was a professional, and this was just an assignment. A great story, but that's all it was. I repeated to myself, "Stay focused, Lilli."

I was home before I could even realize that I'd already been driving for four hours. It was eleven at night and Alex was in bed, but my mother was in the living room, waiting for me.

"Sorry, Ma," I said.

"How are you? I was getting worried about you," she replied.

"I'm okay, Ma. I just had to drive all this way, you know?"

My mother nodded. "How was he?" She knew everything about my job and how excited I was about this new project. I think that was why she was still awake. She wanted me to tell her about my meeting with Ray.

"Ma, I'm too tired and can't think straight. Let's go to bed, and we can talk tomorrow." But she insisted, and I didn't want to break her heart or upset her; besides, she had been waiting all this time for me to come home, so I could at least tell her a little bit about my day. I sat on the sofa with a glass of red wine in my hand and told her about my visit with Ray.

When I had started to interview him, my only perspective was that he was a criminal who had committed a horrible act and needed to be punished; however, as time passed and I listened to his story, I was realizing that it was too easy to judge someone without looking deep. Now, all I wanted to know was how he got to that point. I mean, who was this man, really? So far, all I could see was a child abandoned by his parents and abused by the hands of those who should not be capable of such evil.

As I was telling the story, my mother looked at me with tears in her eyes. I took her hand and gave her a hug.

"I'm sorry, Ma," I said. "I shouldn't tell you all of this. It will upset you."

She wiped away her tears and shook her head. "No, I want you to tell me. I want to know. Please, promise me that you'll tell me everything."

"Okay, Ma, I just don't want to upset you, but if you are really interested, I promise I will let you know everything. But now, please go to bed. You look tired."

I took her hand and helped her to her bedroom. She sat on her bed and looked up at me, and I suddenly realized how much my mother had aged over the past couple years, especially since my brother and my father passed away.

The next few days passed so slowly. Finally, I got a phone call that Ray wanted to know if I would visit for another session. Without any hesitation, I agreed to another meeting.

Our visit was on Friday, and by the time I arrived at the prison, it was already one in the afternoon. I waited almost an hour till he showed up.

Ray wasn't himself. He was so pale, with dark circles around his eyes. He walked toward me very slowly and sat in his chair with a faint smile on his face.

"Are you okay?" I asked.

"I'm okay," he replied, looking at me with those sharp eyes, but this time there was some kind of lingering sadness in them.

"Ray, if they are mistreating you, please let me know, and I can help you," I whispered to him.

He looked at me with that odd, subtle smile and told me, "Trust me, they are not mistreating me. I'm okay, but thank you for caring. It means a lot. I'm just not feeling well, that's all. Let's get back to the story. I'll get better."

I knew he didn't want me to carry on any longer, so I told him, "Okay, then let's continue from where we dropped off last time. You were at the old man's shop."

He combed his fingers through his curly hair and started to talk. "My life was going somewhere; I was healing, day by day. Having fewer nightmares. One day, the old man asked me to stop by his house after I closed up the shop. He said he needed to talk to me about something. I had a bad feeling. Had I done something wrong? Was I not good at my job? Maybe he was sick of me and wanted to throw me out. Maybe my happy days were over. I had no idea how those hours passed, but it seemed like years or even centuries.

"Finally, at seven that evening, I closed the shop, went to my room, and washed up. I tried to look clean so that maybe he would feel sorry for me and perhaps change his mind. I knocked on his door and heard his voice saying, 'Come on in, son. It's open.' I walked in, took off my shoes, and followed his voice to the kitchen. He was cooking something. There was a small table in his kitchen with two plates on it and a bunch of fresh flowers in a small jar. There was also one gift-wrapped box sitting on the table.

"I said gently, 'Can I help, Baba?' That's what I use to call the old man. It is Turkish for 'Dad.'

"He looked at me and said with such enthusiasm, 'No, you just sit, and dinner will be ready soon!'

"I asked, 'What's going on? Do you have a guest or something?'

"He put the food on the table and looked at me with those old but kind eyes and said, 'No, it's just us, son.' He put some food on my plate first, then handed me the gift box and said, 'I don't know when your birthday is, where you came from, or who your parents are. All I know is that you are like the son I never had but always wanted. So, I just wanted to think that today is your birthday, because it has been exactly a year since you came to my garage. You have brought nothing but joy and happiness into my life. I was a lonely man, but ever since you came to this shop, everything changed. I knew you were a good kid. I never asked you anything, but it seems to me you were running from something or someone, so I just let you be. Some nights, I could hear you screaming in the middle of the night, and sometimes you called someone's name. I just prayed for you, son, because I knew that all you needed was time, and maybe all I could do was just give you time. We all have a past, and it's yours to keep, but if you want, I can be part of your future. I'm old, and I have nothing besides you, my old shop, and those two old dogs. I want to legally adopt you so that when I'm gone, you can have this shop and the house.'

"I didn't know what to do except listen and be grateful for everything that was coming my way. The old man continued, 'You don't have to run no more, son; this is your home. Build your life here. Sometimes in life, we get a second chance. Let this be yours, as you are mine.' There were no words to describe how I felt in that moment, so instead of speaking, I jumped out of my seat and put my arms around him, hugging him so tight. He was the only person I'd ever hugged voluntarily out of love and admiration. I was finally close to someone who didn't want something from me.

"I just couldn't stop crying. He gently rubbed my back and said, 'It's okay, son, it's okay. You're safe now. Everything will be okay.' I just let the tears come. I didn't know if they were tears of joy or the pain of my past, but it was my first time feeling that someone loved me without any expectations. I told him everything from my painful past, from the darkness that I'd been trapped in for many years. He listened without saying a word or moving. I talked, I cried, and I screamed while pouring my heart out in front of him, and he just listened in silence until I had no more words, no more tears, and no voice left to scream anymore.

"Once I stopped, he put his hand on my shoulder and shouted, 'Happy birthday!' His whole face was streaked by tears, as was mine, but after that loud declaration by him, we both started to laugh like two crazy kids. He put some music on, and we danced like there was no tomorrow and we were the only people on earth who knew it. That night, I felt something that I'd never felt before. For the first time, I felt that I was home and was truly happy, and guess what? I had my first birthday! The old man asked me, 'I've never known your real name because I always call you "son." Don't you think it's time that I know your name?'

"I told him that until that night and that moment, I hadn't truly been living. I hadn't been alive, but his kindness just gave me life. I said, 'Choose my name, whatever you want, and I will be your newborn son from this moment on.'

"He said, 'All right then, I'll call you Ray, as you brought a ray of sunshine into my life.'

"I replied, 'I am Ray from now to eternity.' We spent the night dreaming about our future and how we would expand this small garage and how I'd find a nice girl to settle down with. A few days later, he filled out some legal documents and I legally became his son.

"Years passed, and I was practically running the shop, which had grown much larger as we had dreamed. I was a dedicated mechanic, doing everything from the paperwork to the hands-on garage work. Baba told me I had to educate myself, but I told him he could teach me whatever I needed to learn, which he did. Sometimes, he would question me about finding a nice girl and settling down, but I would just brush it off by telling a joke and then leaving it there. I didn't want to think about girls, because I still felt fear when I thought about being intimate with another human being. Living in that house of horror and going through what I'd gone through made me so confused about everything, especially my sexuality. Some nights, I used to dream about getting intimate with men. Every time I woke up after having those dreams, I hated myself for having confusing feelings, and there was no way on earth I wanted to tell Baba about those thoughts and feelings. I had a dark side that I hid from him and even from myself. From the earliest time I could remember, I used to hear voices and see scary images, and I still don't know if any of it was real or not. I had been living with shadows around me for a long time, and since I was living with Baba, I tried so hard to avoid them, to not listen to what they were whispering all the time. Many times, I built up the courage to tell him about it so that maybe he could help me out, but I didn't know how to tell him. I was sure he would have hated me if he found out I was a freak. So instead, I used to laugh and tell him, 'Sure, why not. You find me a nice girl, and I will marry her.' We just joked about the whole thing, but being with him was more than enough for me anyway.

"However, good times never last forever, and I knew something would eventually go wrong. I couldn't be that lucky, right? Baba was getting sicker as time passed, and every time I asked him if he wanted me to do something about it, he would just say, 'No, I'm fine,' but I could see in his eyes that he wasn't fine. I knew something was wrong. Most of the time, he stayed in bed or just sat on the porch and watched me work in the garage. Every time I asked him if he wanted me to call a doctor, he would say, 'I'm old, so what can they do for me, Ray? You're born, you live, and then it's time to go.' He used to talk about his inevitable passing with such a comforting smile on his face, but I knew that he was in pain and just didn't want me to worry. He always thought of me first.

"He would reassuringly say, 'I'm happy that I'm not going to die alone. You will be here.' Then he would smile at me and gently pat my hair. I loved him so much, and I didn't want to believe that one day he might die, and I wouldn't be able to see his face anymore. He was my reason to exist; Baba was my life, and I would have given my own life for him if only I knew how to make him live longer. I think he knew that.

"I think that when you fear something so strongly in life and dare to even think about it, it will get you. Somehow, someday, you finally have to get face-to-face with your fears, and I did. I finally lost Baba one sunny morning. I had moved into the main house with him after my adoption, and I used to go to his bedroom and check up on him from time to time to see if he was okay. I guess he died that night after I had already checked up on him. The doctor said he went peacefully while he was asleep, due to a heart attack. He never had any close relatives or friends except for a neighbor who used to play cards with him occasionally. The neighbor came over to help me with funeral arrangements, and in just a few days, it was all over.

"The house was so empty without him, and I berated myself for not taking better care of him and listening to his request to not call the doctor when I thought it was necessary. Then again, it was his last wish to be left alone at home and not stuck in some hospital room that he hated. He died just the way he lived—peaceful and happy. After he was gone, I did my best to be good, to walk in line with what he had taught me, and to keep my dark secrets in control. That old man was the white light that used to brighten my dark and stormy path. I never told him that, but I think he knew me well enough to see beyond my calm and collected demeanor and know that there was a deadly hurricane in my soul just waiting to emerge.

"Those cruel eyes that had watched me for so long from the dark shadows of my mind now showed themselves more clearly, and their whispers grew louder and louder. The shadows became darker, taller, and I just couldn't get away from them anymore. They were watching my every move, telling me once again that I didn't belong out there; I was not worthy, and that was why I killed the only person on earth who trusted in me and wanted to help me. The shadows wanted me back, but I fought hard to ignore the voices. Regardless, I began to believe them. For years, I had fought with myself. Even when Baba was alive, I used to get out of the house in the middle of the night and walk to the shadier parts of town, looking for men who wanted to be with young boys, hoping to lure them to the nearest dark corner, hit them as hard as I could, and run back home. Sometimes, I wouldn't be so lucky, and would receive a few punches in return before making it home. I would try to hide my face from the old man, and he never said anything. Even if he had, I was prepared to say, 'I was just working under the car and hit my head.' He was the reason I always wanted to come back home quickly and not do anything crazier. I didn't want to disappoint him. Now, the gate to hell was open, and there was nobody watching me. All I wanted was to just walk through that gate and let the beast inside of me walk free. It had taken me almost ten years to leash the demon inside of me, and now the chain was broken. Those urges inside of me were getting stronger."

Ray grew quiet now, and it seemed like he had just woken up and noticed me in the room for the first time. I didn't want to move an inch in case it distracted him just as the story was getting more intense. He looked at me without saying a word, and I began to grow uneasy with the awkward silence between us. I leaned forward and asked him very gently if he needed a break or a glass of water.

He very calmly replied, "No, I'm fine. Let's continue."

As I listened and observed Ray, I caught on to the change in his voice. A coldness crept into his voice now as he started to talk about those dark days of his life and the recollection of the "monsters" and "shadows." As he was opening up about his past, chills ran through my body, and I trembled just from being in the room with him.

Cautiously, I glanced over my shoulder to see if the guard was still sitting outside the room, and Ray caught on that I was looking for the guard.

My cheeks flushed with embarrassment. I hadn't meant to let him know that I was afraid of him, which might upset him and discourage him from finishing our interview. To my surprise, he had no reaction. He was lost in his own world and was hardly paying attention to me, but he still asked, "Are you afraid?"

I tried to be calm, so I raised my head very slowly, looked straight into his eyes, and asked him, "Why? There is no reason for me to be afraid. You are handcuffed, and the guard is sitting outside the door. Let's get back to your story, unless you have had enough for today."

Ray called out to the guard, "Open the door. I'm done for today."

I knew something had gone wrong, but I wasn't sure what. I told Ray, "You let me know when you want me to come back so we can finish your story. Okay, Ray?"

Ray didn't answer me as the guard escorted him away. Once again, he left me with thousands of unanswered questions.

On my drive back home, I was so angry with myself once again for upsetting him. Maybe it wasn't my fault—maybe it was just him and what he was going through—but still, if I hadn't been afraid and if I hadn't looked at the guard while Ray was talking, we could have stayed in that room and continued talking about his past.

His caseworker told me once that Ray was highly perceptive, and it was nearly impossible to fool him or get anything by him. She told me that trust was a very important issue with him, so I shouldn't do anything suspicious, because then he wouldn't open up to me as easily.

I had done the exact opposite of what I had been told to do. I had shown him that I was afraid of him and didn't trust him to be alone in the room with me. I smacked the steering wheel with my palm. If I wanted to gain his trust, I had to get my act together.

"Toughen up and get the job done, Lilli," I scolded myself out loud. The deadline was closing in, and I had to have the story or say goodbye to my job.

A week passed with no news from Ray. I couldn't wait any longer, so I called and tried to arrange a meeting to see Ray.

To my surprise, he had been asking about me too, so I jumped at the first opportunity that was offered to me. This time, I reminded myself, "Don't you dare blow it. This is your last chance. Be professional."

Before I entered the visiting room, a guard informed me that Ray's doctor wanted to see me. All he told me was that Ray didn't feel very well that day, so I shouldn't upset him or aggravate him in any way.

Pressing for more information, I asked the doctor what was wrong with Ray. The doctor acted surprised at the question, asking me, "Don't you know?"

"Know what?" I replied, wondering if I had somehow missed something.

"Ray has a terminal illness. He's dying."

When I didn't respond immediately, the doctor continued, "Ray has a severe brain tumor that is untreatable. He doesn't want anyone to know, but I thought that maybe one of the guards had already informed you about this. Anyway, I felt I should tell you because every time you visit him, it seems to have some positive effect on his condition. However, a guard told me that your last visit didn't go so well, which caused Ray and the guards some drama. So please, it seems that he likes you, and his last wish is to tell his life story. Also, the newspaper promised the head office that they would donate some equipment and medications to our hospital in exchange for the story, and I believe that is the main reason Ray wanted to do this in the first place. He still wants to do something good for everyone. That's our Ray. So, Ms. Lilli, if you guys want your story to have an ending, keep him calm. Don't stress him out. Also, just remember, not a word about our conversation to anyone, especially Ray. He doesn't want anyone to know about his illness until the end." The doctor looked at me rather sternly until I promised him that from now on, I would do my very best to not upset Ray. I left the doctor's office and headed to the visiting room to see Ray. I was shocked and saddened that this man would never again have a chance to live a normal life. When he had finally found his peace of mind here in this place, he was going to die.

I couldn't let anything cloud my judgment and take away my focus; I was there to get the story out of him and to the newspaper. As cold as it was, no one could do anything for him. The only silver lining was in letting people know the truth about him, which was Ray's last wish.

I stood outside the visiting room for a minute, closed my eyes, and took a deep breath just to collect my thoughts. The guard opened the door for me, and I entered the room.

Ray was already sitting in his chair, facing the window, seemingly swimming in the ocean of his own thoughts, as he didn't even notice me. I stood still for a minute or more and watched him, wondering to myself what had happened to that innocent child he had described.

What was so different about Ray and I, really? Who knew, maybe if I had been through what he had gone through, I could be the one sitting in that chair. What could turn a person into a monster? Is it in us from the beginning, or do the events of our lives create evil in us?

Who was I to judge? Why should I be so afraid of him?

As I was flooded with all those questions, Ray turned around and looked at me.

"Hi," he said, with a smile on his face. "Let's not waste time. What do you say?"

"I like that. Let's get to it," I replied.

He lit up a cigarette, inhaled deeply, and let his breath out slowly. A big cloud of smoke billowed around his head. He stared straight at me through the thick smoke. It was a beautiful, sunny day outside, and the small window let in a strong ray of light that covered one side of Ray's face, making his eyes appear light green with a hint of gold around the iris, just like the eyes of an African wildcat. For the first time, I noticed a black mark on the corner of his left eye, which made his eyes even more unique.

Ray continued his story, "After Baba's death, I started to go out more frequently, and not just late at night. Now I could freely choose how to spend my time without any second thoughts. I spent my time trying to find someone, trying to create a situation where I could beat up some poor bastard, and I gradually even thought about bringing someone home to do whatever I wanted.

"Honestly, I did everything I could to not give in, but controlling my urges was too hard, especially without the old man around to talk to me, calm me down, or at least be my motivation to never act on my sick desires. I remember one morning when he was still alive, I had bruises on my face from a fight that I'd had the night before, so I was hiding my face under my long hair, but while he was pouring tea for me, he looked at me and said, 'Ray, I don't understand what you are going through, but I can feel your pain. I'm telling you, son, we each carry our own demon inside of us, but the choice is yours to not let it control you. Instead, nurture your inner light and let it shine all over your soul. I have faith in you, Ray. I know you have good inside of you. I can see it every day. My only wish is for you to be able to see it too.'

"I did my best to listen to him and see the light inside me, but the shadows were stronger than the light, and they swallowed me completely. As long as he was alive, I thought I was safe, but now, who would be able to calm my soul when I needed it? Who could save me? I tried my best on my own to keep everything under control and to only get drunk once or twice a week, doing some crazy things now and then, always making sure I was home before midnight. That was the least I could do for the sake of my old man. I made myself crazy busy with work and started taking some pills to sleep better and stop the nightmares and voices. I honestly wanted to do the right thing, but you see, sometimes it doesn't matter how hard you try to change your path and get away from your destiny; destiny never lets you leave your path. It will keep following you until you give in.

"Two years had passed since Baba's death, and I was working nonstop. All I did was work, stay home, and occasionally drink. Gradually, I even stopped going out to cause trouble. I think my work kept me extremely busy, and besides, those pills were helping me get good sleep. I thought I was doing okay. Yes, I still had dark thoughts and confusion and urges, but the fight was still on. Temptations would come and go. As long as my life had a simple routine, I was okay with it. I never had any friends or any visitors to the house, but I never felt lonely apart from missing my old man from time to time. I wanted peace of mind, and as long as I stayed in that garage, working on cars and doing my own thing, I was okay. Day by day, however, the shop became quieter and fewer customers showed up. Most of the time, I would close the shop around six in the evening and just stay in, or I'd wait until it was late to get out so no one would notice me. I thought I was happy. But I guess happiness doesn't last forever.

"It was the middle of a cold winter night, and while I was working, I kept the garage door open so the freezing cold breeze could help me stay sharp, focused, and awake. I wanted to keep my mind occupied. The house was so empty without the old man, so I was working late to fix the engine on a customer's car. After Baba had passed, I'd stopped listening to music while I worked. The silence was loud enough for me. I used to drown myself in my own thoughts and do my work.

"As I was working under the car, I heard the sound of tapping shoes beside my head. *Tap, tap, tap.* The person tapped three times with the right foot, then switched to the left foot. All of the sudden, it felt like my memories were pulling me back to the orphanage at a hundred miles an hour. What was happening to me? I was shocked, confused. Blood rushed to my brain. My heart started beating so fast that for a second, I thought I was going to have a heart attack. I stayed under the car and listened carefully as the person said, 'Can I talk to you for a second?'

"I was frozen. I didn't know what to do. I couldn't stay under the car forever. I had to come out eventually, but what would happen if it was who I thought it was? What if he recognized me? No, how could that be possible, after all these years? It had been almost fourteen years, and I had changed. I wasn't that fourteen-year-old kid anymore.

"Despite my hesitation, I replied, 'I'll be out in a second. Wait in the office, please.' While I was still lying down on my back, I told myself to get it together. It was just a coincidence. Nothing was wrong. Be cool. Be calm. I was safe. I went to the bathroom, splashed some cold water on my face, fixed my hair, and returned to the office.

"The man was facing the whiteboard, which I used to keep track of my work schedule and customers' names. I said hello, and he turned around. For a second or two, I was speechless, staring at him with my eyes wide open. Stepping forward, he asked, 'Are you okay? Hey man, are you okay?'

"I nodded my head, took a deep breath, and told him, 'Yes, just a bit dizzy after working under that car all day. What can I do for you?' I couldn't even look in his direction.

"He smiled and said, 'My car broke down about half a mile from here, and I just walked all this way until I saw your garage. And guess what? You were open! I guess it was fate, or my lucky night.'

"With every word that came out of his mouth, my rage grew more and more. It was him, Brother Joseph from the orphanage. I pictured myself at seven years of age, standing in the basement, naked. Standing in the middle of the room, looking down at Brother Joseph's shoes. *Tap, tap, tap.* The sound of his shoes tapping was a sound of horror to my ears. Every night, I knew there was no way out. I had to endure the torture. All I could do was be motionless and force myself to feel nothing. Each time, I would die a little more.

"Now, after all these years, he was standing in front of me and had no idea who I was. I could never forget that tapping sound, though. It was burned in my head forever, along with those eyes, those cruel blue eyes. I had been terrified of those eyes for years. They were always bloodshot because of his excessive drinking.

"Now all I could feel was rage, anger, and hate. Not fear. I walked closer to him and asked him, 'You don't remember me, do you?'

"He looked me over and very casually said, 'I don't think so, why? Should I?' He laughed and stepped closer to get a better look at me, then he asked, 'Who are you?'

"I looked down, walked toward the door, and told him, 'I'm nobody. Let's go get your car and bring it to my shop.' It was already past eleven, it was a cold, snowy night, and no one was around. I could have killed him right there and buried his body, and no one would have ever known.

"He wasn't looking healthy at all. I guess the years of drinking and using drugs finally put some heavy miles on his body. He sat beside me in my car and looked over at me with a smile. 'Thank you for doing this, man,' he said.

"With a bitter smile, I replied, 'No problem. I'm sure if you were in my shoes, you would have done the same, right?' I don't think he got my sarcasm. I could have smelled the alcohol on him from miles away. I asked him, 'Still drinking?'

"He looked at me with puzzled eyes and asked, 'Do I know you? Who are you, man? It's freaking me out.'

"I laughed and said, 'You're drunk, man. I can smell it on you.' I didn't want him to get suspicious, at least not now. He laughed and said nothing in response to my observation, but I could see that he was relieved.

"I don't know why I didn't confront him right then and let him know who I was, but I guess I was looking for the right time, the right moment, because for years I had blamed myself for all those nights. Maybe I was still afraid and trapped in my past. Or maybe I was acting like a lion, playing with my victim and getting a bit of excitement out of it first. Whatever it was, I just let him be so I could watch his every move and then see what happened.

"We drove for a few minutes until he said, 'You can stop right here. This is my car. I told you it wasn't that far.' We got out and walked to his car. I tried to start the engine, but it didn't work.

"I asked him, 'When was the last time you checked the oil in your car?'

"He crossed his arms and answered rather aggressively, saying, 'I don't know anything about this forsaken car, man. I usually take it to my friend and he does all those things, but that son of a bitch ripped me off. I guess I should give him back this piece of junk and find something else, or maybe you can get me a cheap deal. What do you say, man?' He put his dirty hand on my shoulder. In that moment, I just wanted to jump on top of him and break his arm for touching me, but I controlled myself and pulled away. I think he was a bit offended, because he quickly said, 'Can you fix it or not, man?' He still had a short temper, and it was starting to resurface right then.

"I looked him in the eyes and told him, 'Yes, I can fix it, but I'll have to tow the car to my shop, and you'll have to leave the car with me for at least a few days, and it's not going to be cheap. The whole engine is damaged now. I can't do anything for you right now.' I don't know why, but without waiting for his response, I said, 'I can give you a ride home, if you want.'

"He seemed to have calmed down a bit. He asked, 'You sure? It's far, maybe ten or twenty miles from here.'

"I shook my head, saying, 'I'm almost done for tonight. Just give me a few minutes, then we can go.' We towed his car to my garage and then I walked toward the house. I could hear his footsteps behind me, following me. Without looking back, I told him, 'You are more than welcome to come inside and have a drink before I take you home.' I knew that if I offered him a free drink he wouldn't be able to refuse it. Without a word, he followed me into the house, and for the first time, I was the one walking in front of *him*. I felt in charge, and it made me feel powerful."

Ray stopped talking for a minute or two, and he squirmed in his chair like an excited little boy. In his eyes, I could almost see the demons that he had been talking about. That darkness was coming alive right in front of my eyes. I knew he was about to reveal something terrible about his past, and it was starting to scare me, but I knew that this time I was not going to stop him. I wanted the whole story, and there was no way back for me. I had to know everything. Tonight was the night! I leaned closer to him so I could hear his voice more clearly.

Ray lit up a cigarette and continued, "I walked to the living room, and Brother Joseph came in and sat on a chair as I went to the kitchen to make him a drink. I mixed his vodka with a few of my sleeping pills to make him drowsy. I could see him looking around the room, looking for some clue about who I really was.

"I walked back to the living room with two glasses of vodka in my hand, and I gave him his drink. He didn't wait for me to say a word but just poured the drink into his mouth in one go, then said, 'God, I needed this so much. Can I have another, please?' I returned to the kitchen, poured him another glass, and went back to the living room. Suddenly, Joseph asked me, 'Where is your family? Do you live alone like me? A lone wolf.' I figured he was getting drunk, and my memories of his drunken days were coming back.

"I looked at him with disgust and said, 'I live alone. No kids, no wife, just me, only me.' There was a silence between us as he looked around, and I just watched him. The silence between us started to grow uneasy, and Joseph was getting tipsy. He sat back in the chair and just stared at me. I sat in the chair across from him and asked, 'Do you want to hear a story?'

"He said, 'Sure, why not. I'm too drunk to go anywhere, and I always love to hear a good story.' Joseph made himself comfortable in his chair and tried hard to keep his eyes open.

"I started my story by saying, 'Once upon a time, there was a little orphan boy living in a boys home. There was a big monster that used to live in the basement of the place. The monster used to be so mean and scary, and all the boys at the orphanage had to call him Brother Joseph.' I stood and walked toward him, handing him his second drink. He looked up at me as I was towering over him, forcing me to look into his repulsive eyes. Now Joseph was looking at me in fear. I told him, 'Be careful, Brother Joseph, don't spill your drink.'

"Trembling, he dropped the cup, and, with a shaky voice, he quickly said, 'Ah, look at me, I'm so clumsy. Look, it's getting late, and I need to get back to my family or they will get worried.' He got up from the chair so fast that I thought he might not be drunk anymore.

"I laughed and told him, 'I thought you said you're a lone wolf and you live by yourself.'

"Joseph inched toward the front door and said, 'Okay then, when can you fix my car? Because I can come back tomorrow, or if you just tell me how much it will cost to fix the damn thing, I'll pay you right now and then you give me a call when it's ready.' His shaking hand grabbed the door handle, and I could tell that he was simply babbling and trying to get out of that room as soon as possible. I just laughed. He had no ride, and it was almost midnight.

"With a smile on my face, I told him, 'It's already late and it's snowing. You won't find any car to take you home. Let's just finish our drinks. Besides, my story is not finished yet, so let's hear the end and then I'll take you home. What's your rush?' He'd realized that I knew something about his past, and it must have scared him to death. As he stood there, powerless and shaking from nerves, I felt powerful with rage and excitement because I knew I had the upper hand this time. Here I was, young and six feet tall, and there he was, a weak, drug-addicted, alcoholic, middle-aged man.

"Joseph sat back down in the chair opposite me and took a packet of cigarettes from his pocket, his hand still shaking like a leaf. He tried to use his lighter, but he just couldn't stop shaking. I stood and took his lighter, helping him light up his cigarette. He looked at me and mumbled, 'Thank you.'

"I had to control my temper, as I didn't want my anger toward him to cloud my judgment or allow me to make any mistakes. I knew it was a cold night, and snow had covered the whole road, so any loud noises would disappear into the night. I sat in front of him once again, scooted my chair closer to his, looked into his eyes, and told him with a steady voice, 'Look at me, Brother Joseph. Do you remember me? Take a good look and go back to a long time ago. To the cold basement with no light, no windows, and no bed or blanket, just the cold, wet concrete. Can you remember now?' I moved closer and whispered in his ear, 'Can you remember me now, Brother Joseph?'

"He let a tear slip out, and in a shaky voice, he muttered, 'Oh, God . . . Oh, God . . .'

"I jumped up and began to yell at the top of my lungs. 'It's just you and me, Brother Joe. God has left the building!' I laughed, hoping to make it obvious just how much I was enjoying this. 'Remember? Every time I cried and prayed that you would stop, you used to say what?' I shouted at Joseph, 'You used to say *what*? Say it to me now like you used to scream it at me years ago!'

"He trembled visibly and started to cry like a little baby, begging me, 'Please, I don't know what to say. What do you want me to say?'

"I looked at him and said, 'I want you to tell me what you used to tell me every time I cried and called to God to help me. What did you used to tell me? Tell me, Brother Joe, what? *What?*'

"All of a sudden he screamed, 'God has left the building! God has left the building!' He covered his ears and kept screaming those words at me. I sat back in my chair and let him sob; let him remember everything. As I sat and watched him, I knew what I had to do. There was no way I would let him leave this house. Something inside of me was changing, coming alive. All those thoughts that I had tried so hard to escape from were all crawling back into my head. The voices and the memories that had been caged somewhere in my mind were breaking free. Suddenly, I felt no fear, no anger, and no rage. There was a calmness that was emerging from inside. The shadows came alive, and I welcomed them with pleasure. I unleashed the beast inside of me; no more fighting, no more struggling to stay on my path. That night, I found my path to vengeance. I was going to take judgment into my own hands.

"I walked toward Joseph and said to him, 'Now that you have your memory back, let's talk. Let's drink, because I know you need it, especially now.' I handed him his glass and took the other for myself, as I was going to need a drink too.

"He started to drink it straight up then reached his hand out, asking again, 'Can I have another one, please?'

"I had brought the bottle into the living room with me, so I just poured him another glass and asked him, 'There were three of you at the orphanage, as I remember. What happened to the other two? You guys used to share us like a piece of lamb, remember? Those two mutants used to like much older boys, but you, you liked yours too young to fight back. I guess I was your favorite, right? Brother Joe?' He stared straight at the ground and didn't look at me while I was talking. I asked him again, 'What happened to them? You were best buddies. I'm sure you guys still get together for a sick reunion or something, right?'

"He looked at me and said, 'Mathew was my best friend, and we still see each other from time to time. As for Brother Yusif, he moved to Australia.' He shook his head and continued, 'We were a bunch of drunk, doped-up idiots. We were stupid. We had no idea what we were doing. In our minds, we were trying to toughen you up, make men out of you all.' He was trying to explain away their actions, and it made my blood boil. I jumped out of my chair and threw my hardest punch in his face.

"He covered his bleeding nose as I screamed at him like a wild animal, 'You had no idea what you were doing? You wanted to make men out of us?' I couldn't control myself as I clasped my fingers around his throat. 'Tell me, Brother Joe, at what time exactly were you trying to make a man out of me? Do you have any idea how you changed our lives? Because of what you guys did to Reza, he couldn't take it anymore and he finally killed himself. You, Brother Joseph, made me believe that it was my fault, that I deserved everything you three did to me. Every night, we used to pray that by morning we could all be dead so you guys couldn't hurt us any longer. That was our prayer every single night. Don't you dare ask your God to help you now. Right now, I own you! Beg me for mercy. Sit on your knees and beg me, Joe, as I am your only salvation.'

"While standing over him, I briefly looked out the window and noticed that his car was in front of the house. I had to be quick and take his car into the garage before the sun came up, so I decided to tie him up in the chair, cover his mouth with a rag, and deal with his car as soon as possible. I tied up his arms and legs with a rope so he couldn't fight me, although he was too drunk anyway and the sleeping pills had also started to take effect. He was half asleep now, but I still couldn't trust him, and I had to be sure that he wouldn't be able to run away. I went outside to push his car into the garage. I knew I had to do something with it. I would hide it first, and then when the time was right, I'd get rid of it so that nobody could track him to here. I had to get rid of the evidence. I figured that maybe in the next few days, I would take it to the junkyard.

"That night, I had crossed a line, and I knew there was no way back. Not only was I not going to let him go, but I was also going to find those other two bastards and give them what they deserved. I raised my head to look up at the dark sky, took a deep breath, and closed my eyes, letting the snow fall on my face. The cold air woke me up a bit and helped me think straight. I looked around; there was nothing but darkness and snow as far as the eye could see. Something whispered in my head, 'Get inside, Ray.' Something buried deep in my soul was rising, and I was ready for it. I went inside and looked at Joseph. He was unconscious. He was bleeding from his nose and the corners of his eyes, and his left eye was swollen and bruised because of my punch. I cleaned him up a bit.

"There was a basement in which the old man used to keep all of his memorabilia and homemade wines. It was dark and extremely cold, even in the summertime. There were no windows to the outside, and, quite frankly, if you were locked in there by accident, no one could hear you or find you. I dragged Joseph to the basement. All I needed was a blanket, a chair, and chains. By the time he gained consciousness, he was tied up to the chair with the chains secured around his ankle. He started to move his body violently, trying to loosen the chains. While he attempted to scream for help, I told him, with a sarcastic smile on my face, 'Welcome to your new home, Joe Bro. Remember? You used to tell all the boys to call you Joe Bro. You loved American movies, remember? When you were drunk and high on drugs? You wanted to be cool. So come on, Joe Bro, why do you look so sad now?' I taunted him, 'Look at you now. All your teeth are rotten, and you look pathetically weak. You are nothing but an alcoholic, a drug addict, and a child molester. And you used to tell us we were little bastards, that we were nothing and would always be nothing. Do you remember, Joe Bro?'

"I reminded him about all those nights and days when he used to crush our spirits with all his cruel words, but now I had the power, and he was nothing but a piece a trash sitting in my basement. I could do to him exactly what he did to me and the other boys so long ago. 'How does that make you feel, Joe Bro?' I asked. Joe just listened and watched me in silence. His eyes were swollen, but I was certain that he could still see me clearly and could understand every word I said because he shifted his gaze down and began to cry. I think that deep down, he was so mad at me and probably wished that he would have killed me when he'd had the chance. I walked toward the stairs, but I looked at him one more time. His hands were tied behind him and his mouth was covered.

"I told him, 'Hey Joe, use this time to think about everything you did to us, or maybe you can talk to your God and see if he can save you now. But if I were you, I'd try to get some rest, because we have a big day tomorrow.' I turned off the basement light and locked the door behind me."

Ray stopped talking to once again light up another cigarette. His eyes still had a flame of excitement as he recalled that night with Brother Joseph. There was no remorse evident.

Ray's eyes quickly turned to me, and he said, "You know, Lilli, something deep in my soul was rising. I think that on that night, I figured out what I was looking for. I found my purpose in life. Finally, I knew who I was and what my mission was. I knew I had to find all of them, one by one, and give them what they deserved. I knew Brother Joe would be the first but definitely not the last. I knew I was just getting started." Ray stopped talking again. He stared at me, but I just couldn't think of anything to say.

The silence between us was surprisingly comfortable, but I could only wonder why. He was exposing what he had done, and it was the most chilling story I had ever heard, so why did I feel extremely relaxed, not wanting him to stop talking?

All of the sudden, Ray was telling me, "Time to go home, Lilli."

"Okay then, see you later?" I replied.

He simply smiled and said, "Goodnight."

That evening when I left the prison, I was drowning in my thoughts about Ray and his story. On my drive back home, a strange feeling rushed through my body. In some way, I was feeling what he felt. I felt his motivation for revenge and the need to take justice into his own hands, and somehow I didn't feel sorry for Brother Joseph.

What was wrong with me? I shouldn't let the emotional aspects of the situation get to me. I was a reporter. I couldn't throw emotions into the mix and expect to provide an unbiased take.

By the time I got home, it was late in the night. My son was already in bed, but Mom was sitting in the living room, waiting for me again. I looked at her with a smile on my face, kissed her forehead, and said, "Thank you, Mom, for everything."

"How was he?" my mother asked.

"Who, Mom?" I feigned cluelessness, knowing exactly who she was asking about, because I just didn't feel comfortable telling her everything about Ray and what he had told me. I didn't think my mother could handle hearing the entirety of Ray's story. It was too much for such a fragile woman.

She clarified, "You went to interview the prisoner. How was he?"

I knew I had to tell her something; otherwise, she just wouldn't give up. "Oh, you're talking about Ray. He was okay, Mom. Sorry, I didn't know you were so interested in his story." I tried to brush off her curiosity by walking away toward my room and pretending that I wasn't in the mood to talk about it anymore, but she wouldn't give it up.

She followed me to my room and persisted, "Tell me what he said. What did you talk about? What did he tell you about his past?"

I looked at my mother and sighed. "Mom, I'm tired, and you must be exhausted too. How about I tell you everything tomorrow? I'm going to bed, Ma." I started pulling out my pajamas to get ready for bed. She finally accepted my answer and said goodnight before disappearing into her own bedroom.

Before I went to sleep, I wanted to see my boy. I opened Alex's bedroom door very slowly to just get a glimpse of his face before I went to bed. With the moonlight sneaking in through his window, I could faintly see his face. He was sleeping like an angel, peacefully, breathing so calmly. For a second, I thought of Ray. Would he have been the same person if he could have had a safe place to lay his head every night? I imagined that if what had happened to Ray a long time ago had instead happened to my child, maybe I would be behind bars right now instead of Ray. Or maybe Alex would have become a murderer just like Ray.

There was something about Ray that I couldn't explain, but I tried not to think about him or work anymore that night. All I wanted was to close my eyes and get some sleep.

The next day was Saturday, so I woke up late. As soon as I went to the kitchen, my son gave me a big hug and kisses. My mom had just made an omelet, her specialty, accompanied by a cup of her special chai ready for me. This moment with my family made me feel safe and happy.

I knew Mom was going to start questioning me about last night's conversation, so before she could open her mouth, I told her, "Mom, not now. I'll tell you later." I nodded toward Alex to indicate that we shouldn't talk about it while he was in the room.

Mom kept quiet, but I knew she wasn't happy about it. I just gave her a hug and told her very gently, "I'll tell you everything when Alex is taking his afternoon nap. Okay, Mom?" She just smiled at me and shook her head with anticipation. Why was she so interested in Ray's story? I had no idea, but her curiosity and interest in anything made me hopeful that she was getting better.

The house was quiet while Alex was taking his nap. Mom made her signature Turkish coffee and her delicious baklava, and we sat at the kitchen table. I knew she wouldn't leave me alone until I talked about Ray, so I started to tell her about yesterday.

"I don't know, Ma. Ray is a troubled soul. I know he's a killer, but at the same time, I feel so sorry for him, you know? He had a miserable childhood. I mean, they found him in a dark alley when he was less than a week old. Think about it, Ma. What kind of a heartless mother would do such a thing to her own child? I don't understand, Ma. I mean, if something happened to Alex, God forbid if I lost him in a shopping center or something, I would never rest until I found him. I will do anything to keep him safe, but there are some people who will just abandon their infant child. What kind of a monster does such a thing?" I was so emotional about this subject that I began to tremble as I explained Ray's childhood.

My feelings about my own son took over, so my mother just took me in her arms and comforted me, saying, "You can never judge anyone. We all do things that make sense to us at the moment, but when we look back later in life, we would say to ourselves, 'What was I thinking? What have I done?'"

My mother comforted me with her words of wisdom. I guess she was right. None of us really know how something will turn out when we make certain decisions, especially as a mother trying to do the best for her child. Who knew what kind of situation Ray's mother was in when she made that decision?

As she held me in her arms, she asked, "So how has he lived his life until now?"

"He didn't have an easy life at all. He escaped from his orphanage, and, to cut the story short, he practically raised himself. This man has been abused emotionally and physically since he was a little boy. He was rejected by everyone, from his parents to the system. They all failed to protect that innocent child, and when he became a killer, they got him, and now he's going to be punished. I am trying so hard to make sense of it. He's sick and is going to die soon from some sort of brain tumor. His doctor told me he might have less than a few months to live. I think that is why they wanted me to get as much as possible from him. To be honest, I think he wants to do this more than anyone else. Maybe he wants to have a clear conscience, and believe me, whatever reason he has, I will do my best to let people know the truth behind what they heard about him in the news."

After that, I didn't want to go through the details of my interview with Ray, because I knew how emotional and sensitive my mother was. If I told her everything that Ray had told me, I knew she wouldn't be able to handle it emotionally. I stopped talking about him, intending to change the subject.

All of the sudden, my mother said, "You just find out what his favorite food is so I can make it for him, and you can take it to him." My mother had such kindness in her voice, and I didn't want to break her heart.

I kissed her forehead and gave her a hug, but I had to say, "Aw, Ma, that's so sweet of you, but it's not possible. This is a prison, not a summer camp."

She desperately tried to convince me. "It doesn't hurt to ask, okay? Promise me you'll ask."

"Okay, Mom, I promise," I told her.

The next day, I got a call from my boss at the newspaper, informing me that my deadline for this story was the end of next week. I contacted the prison and scheduled as many hours with Ray as they would allow. I was able to set a visiting time nearly every day the coming week, but I guessed that they were being generous because they knew he had very little time left to live. Now, all I had to do was to find accommodations in town, close to the prison so I could easily get to Ray without having to drive back and forth every day. This way, I could spend more time with Ray and finally finish this project.

I would have to explain the situation to my mother and let her know that I wouldn't be able to come home for a whole week. She wasn't so happy about it, but when I told her it was about Ray, she changed her mind and simply told me, "Good luck, honey, and don't worry about us. We are going to be just fine."

I was a little surprised, but since I knew she felt sorry for Ray, I thought that maybe her interest in him was why she was being so supportive about my decision. Whatever it was, I was happy to have her support and know that Alex would be in good hands. This was the first time since Alex had been born that I was going to be away from him for such a long time, but I reminded myself that whatever I did was for his future. Having a job meant a better income and better opportunities for all of us.

That night, I stayed up on my computer and found a motel close enough to the prison. I had taken a week off from my studies and told everyone at work where I was going to be for the next week, so they could reach me whenever they needed to. I packed my small suitcase, said goodbye to Mom and Alex, and began my journey.

On the way to the prison, I said to myself, "Look at you, Lilli. Where is life taking you?" Parents from two different parts of the world got together, and their union created two children. I grew up with three different cultures under one roof. I had hardworking parents, and life seemed too perfect until tragedy hit me so hard that I didn't even have time to realize what had happened. First, losing my brother, my best friend. Then my father, the rock of the family, the one person I could always count on, knowing that no matter how bad life got, he would be there for me. Then my marriage fell apart. I felt like nothing but a robot, waking up every morning, doing the same things over and over and over again. I had no choice, because now there were two innocent people depending on me, and I just had to put myself together every day, pretend everything was okay, and carry on. My heart had started to get used to being alone. For a while, I thought it was just a cruel way for fate to tell me that this was it, that this was my life's destiny. The emptiness inside me grew bigger day by day, but time changed everything.

Then, I found an opportunity to open a door to a different side of life. I had come face-to-face with the reality of misfortune through Ray. All of a sudden, I realized just how lucky I had been all this time without even noticing it. Ray had opened my eyes more than I ever could have imagined. He helped me find what I'd been looking for all this time. I was a mother, a daughter, and a woman who was blessed with good fortune. Ray opened my eyes to the real world. Now, it was my turn to tell his story to the world, with honesty, humanity, and compassion. That was my mission from now on, until his life story was published.

I didn't notice how deep I was in my thoughts until I arrived at my destination. By the time I got there, it was almost five in the afternoon. In such a small town, everything closed around five or six in the evening.

Thankfully, my motel was still open for check-in. I checked in and took the key to my room. It was a small room with a twin bed, a tiny refrigerator in the corner, a small desk beside the window, and a painting depicting snowy Australian mountains.

My mother had packed me so much food that I thought it might just last me the entire week. She had also sent a box of her famous Baklava, but I knew that was meant for Ray. I didn't want to disappoint her, so I would do my best and see if they would allow me to give Ray her gift.

I decided to take a quick shower and go to bed so I would have no problem waking up early to gather my thoughts.

The next day, I woke up to the sound of my alarm, got myself ready, and went downstairs to see if I could find a decent breakfast or coffee. To my surprise, there was a full breakfast buffet.

I asked the lady at the front desk, "What's going on? Is every day like this around here?"

She told me, "Actually, today is visiting day at the prison, and a lot of families come a long way to stay here overnight so they can go visit early in the morning. That's why we serve a full breakfast buffet, love. We serve breakfast, lunch, and dinner. You see, this small town mostly gets families and loved ones visiting the prison, which is just two blocks from us. We take care of our guests, no matter who they are or what path of life they come from." She took my hand and asked, "Are you visiting someone special, love?" She squeezed my hand gently.

I told her, "No, I'm actually a reporter."

"Well, good luck, love. You take care," she said, walking away from me.

Before she made it very far, I noticed several different people eyeing me from their tables. I caught the front desk lady as she was walking away and asked, "What's wrong? Why is everyone giving me looks?"

She simply shook her head and replied, "I guess they don't like reporters, how should I know?" She laughed to lighten the mood. "Are you the reporter who is writing about that priest killer? If that's who you are, then you should know why no one wants you in this town."

I was shocked. How on earth could they know about my visits with Ray? Just before I opened my mouth to ask another question, the lady took my hand again and whispered, "It's a small town, you know? Everyone knows everybody's business. So be careful."

My appetite was gone, so I took my cup of coffee and walked outside to my car. How could we judge someone just by looking at the surface? In everybody else's minds, Ray was a monster who had killed a saint, a man of God, an innocent priest. I had many questions for Ray, and over the next seven days, I'd receive the answers to all my questions.

I arrived at the prison and was led straight to the warden's office. He had been expecting me. I told him that I was staying at a motel in town so I could spend more time with Ray and finish my article by the end of next week.

The warden nodded and said, "That's all the time you will have and not a day more. We started getting complaints from the town hall people. They don't like seeing a young reporter coming to their town, trying to snoop around our prison and write about a priest killer." His voice was low and he deliberated on each word as he calmly expressed disapproval. At the start of this endeavor, he had been perfectly okay with me being here, but I gathered that the pressure from other people and the mayor was getting to him. The mayor was related to Ray's victim, the priest, so I could completely understand the pressure that was put on the warden and why he was so upset.

Without any hesitation, I reassured the warden that I only needed seven more days with Ray, then I'd be out of there. I shook his hand and left his office to go see Ray.

Ray was waiting for me in the visiting room. He looked a bit pale, and I observed that he'd lost a little weight. I told him about the dilemma and how we only had this next week to finish up.

He took it lightly, saying, "They must hate you with passion." We both laughed.

I told him, "I'm not the only one they hate; you are the first on their list."

He grew more serious, and he clasped his hands together, leaned forward against the edge of the table, and stared down at his handcuffs.

I quickly attempted to recover the situation. "I'm sorry, I didn't mean to upset you. I just—"

He didn't let me finish, as he abruptly said, "Let's get started and not waste any more time."

I leaned forward and tried to make eye contact. "Hey, Ray, I am sorry, okay?"

He shook his head, smiled, and said to me, "I know you didn't mean anything bad. It's just that all my life I was searching for shelter, a safe place, and looking for love and acceptance from people. I ended up where I began. No one likes me. To them, I'm just a monster who killed a holy man. So what's changed in my life? Nothing. Born into hate and I'll die by hate." His tone didn't convey anger but rather melancholy.

"I don't think so, Ray. When your story comes out, they will know the truth. They will know who the real monsters were, the men of God who were supposed to protect the innocent but instead abused their power and position. They will get to know the real you. I will do my best to reveal the truth," I said, with such passion and conviction in my voice that I even surprised myself.

Ray looked at me with eyes wide open, taking in every word that came out of my mouth. I caught a glimpse of that once-innocent boy in his eyes.

"Let's get started," I said, hoping to use the momentum to fuel the story. I opened my notebook and turned on my tape recorder. "Okay, what happened next?"

Ray began, "The next day, I woke up with the perfect plan in my head. First, I had to destroy Brother Joseph's car so that nobody could track it to me. Then, I had to keep him alive until I figured out what happened to his two friends from the orphanage. I was sure they were still best buddies; he'd even told me that he still kept in touch with them. I knew he had no family or anyone who would miss him, but I still had to be sure. I made breakfast and took a plate down to the basement. Joseph was awake, and the blood on his face was dried up, but he didn't look good at all. He was a drug addict, and I knew by now he was in bad shape without a fix. As soon as he saw me, he started to cry. The pathetic look on his face made me mad, so I kicked his chair and told him, 'Stop looking at me, or I'll cover your eyes!'

"Joseph looked down, and I removed the cloth from his mouth. I gave him some water then started to feed him, offering him little pieces of bread and some tea. I felt nothing for him, no sympathy or remorse. After I fed him, he said to me, 'I need to use the bath-room, please.' His pants were wet with his own piss. He smelled so bad. I removed the chain and told him that there was an area in the basement where he could wash himself, and there was also a toilet. I told him to go clean up but reminded him that I would keep an eye on him like a hawk.

"I warned him, 'Hey, one wrong move and you're dead.' He didn't say anything, just walked to the bathroom. I could hear the sound of running water. I wasn't worried at all. There were no windows in the bathroom, and to be honest, this basement was basically soundproof. After a few minutes, he came out, and I gave him some new clothes to wear.

"He sat down on his chair and asked me for a cigarette and some whiskey, then asked, 'Now what? What do you want from me? As you can see, I'm a drug addict. I need my stuff or else my body will go into shock. I can't talk like this. I need a drink first, please. I'm useless to you like this.' Joe begged me for drugs and alcohol, and I knew that he was right; I could see his body shaking. He was a junkie experiencing withdrawal, but I wanted him lucid enough to talk to me and understand what was happening.

"I went upstairs and brought him back a packet of cigarettes and a whole bottle of whiskey. I set them down in from of him and told him, 'Now we are going to talk, and you are going to tell me everything I need to know.' I took his wallet out of his pocket and looked at his address. His house was about twenty miles from my place. I asked him, 'Who lives with you?'

"Joe answered, 'No one. I live by myself. My parents died some time ago, and they left the house for me. I have never been married. No kids, nothing, man. I have no money. What do you want from me?'

"I overplayed my surprise so he could catch on easily. 'You think I'm after your money? I don't give a damn about your money. I want justice for myself and for all of those innocent kids you bastards tortured.' My voice grew louder and louder with each sentence as a rage built up inside of me.

"He was once again trembling and sobbing, and he began begging me, 'I am sorry, man. I'm so sorry. What do you want me to say?'

"I told Joe, 'You could tell me how to find those two assholes. You guys used to be like the three musketeers. Remember?'

"Joe finally started to talk. 'In the beginning, I used to just help out at the church, but then I was kicked out because I was using drugs, and a family had also reported that I'd touched their kid inappropriately. There were several complaints about me, so they were finally forced to kick me out. Mathew and I were partners in crime. We did bad things together, so when they threw me out, he lost his job too. We hated those kids, and I think that after that, we both wanted to take revenge and just do whatever we wanted without consequences. This time, we were going to do it right, and what better place than an orphanage, right? Those kids didn't have any parents. They were unwanted kids who had been found on the street or outside the church's door, so no one would care. It really wasn't that difficult to get a job there as long as you had a recommendation letter or someone from your community could say that you were all right. It was then that we met brother Yusif, and we got him to vouch for us. From the moment we met, the three of us became inseparable. We were all in our early twenties, and we had no idea what we were doing. All three of us came from the roughest neighborhoods, and our families were extremely poor. My father used to hit me with his belt until I passed out, just for disobeying the simplest demands. Some nights, he would get drunk and ask me to go to our backyard and wait for him, and I knew exactly what he meant and what he was going to do to me. I think that even my mother knew what was going on those nights, but she chose to close her eyes and never once asked me how I got the bruises on my face or why I was sick and didn't want to go to school. In our house, my father was everything, and the rest of us were nothing but trash that he could kick around. I grew up hating everything and everyone until I met Mathew and, later on, Yusif. I realized that I wasn't the only one who had been through all that hell. We bonded over our pain, hatred, and revenge in a sick, twisted way.'

"Joe was describing his life to me in the way that was intended to make me feel sorry for him, or perhaps he thought it would justify all of his actions toward us. I could sense that he was trying to leverage his situation, and that was making me furious. He finally got to the point of bargaining and asked, 'If I give you all that you need to know about Mathew and Yusif, then you'll let me go, right?'

"I decided to entertain the idea just to get more information out of him, so I said, 'Okay, Joseph, we'll see. As long as you tell me everything I need to know, okay?'

"Joe's eyes widened with the slightest bit of hope that he might be able to get away from me after all. He quickly replied, 'Okay, no problem. I can tell you everything. Just tell me what you want to know, and I'll start from there.' Joe waited for my command, eager to tell me everything he knew for the sake of his freedom.

"All along, I was thinking to myself, 'Poor bastard.' I had no intention of letting him go, but that was the only way to get Joe to talk. As long as he believed I would set him free, he would talk. This was my chance to get all the information I needed to find those other two monsters.

"Joe continued his story by telling me, 'As I said before, we were a bunch of sick bastards. When I was a teenager, I started drinking a lot and would run away from home often. Finally, the last time I escaped from home, I didn't go back because of my father. As I said before, I stayed at the church for a while. I met Mathew then Yusif, and we all found ourselves with jobs at the boys home. From then on, it was nothing but a sweet ride for the three of us. In that place, no one questioned us. We could act superior toward this group of young, unwanted kids. We became gods to them. They were afraid of us, and no one ever investigated what was happening or why they had cuts and bruises on their face. Even if it had been investigated, we would have said they were just a bunch of young boys who played rough or got in fights with each other. We would brush it off, and that was the end of the story. Seeing the fear on those boys' faces used to give us such pleasure and power to act however we wanted. None of us had a wife or a girlfriend, and we couldn't afford to pay for sex. Whatever money we made was put toward alcohol and drugs, so all our frustrations, anger, and hate had to go somewhere. You poor bastards were easy targets, and we thought that in some way we were doing you guys a favor making sure you boys were prepared for real life outside of the orphanage. We were toughening you up a little bit, just the way my father made me tough, so we didn't think we were doing anything wrong. I went through the same thing as you, and Mathew also had a similar childhood, so we thought that you boys could use some of our experiences to become men too, you know?' Joseph paused and looked up at me, probably hoping that I would understand and accept his excuses.

"I didn't want to hear any more of his nonsense and excuses. He was attempting to justify his cruelty in raping children, as though he was doing all of us a favor, like it was the most noble act of kindness they could do for us. He expected me to understand that bullshit? What was he trying to say, that it wasn't his fault? That the three of them were the true victims? I knew there was no way he would ever admit that what he did to us was his fault or that he could have made a different choice. He could have stopped what he was doing at any time if he had wanted. Even after all those years, Joseph was still defending his actions without any remorse or regret. He felt sorrier for himself than for what he did to us in that hell house. He wanted *me* to feel sorry for *him* and just accept that what had been done to him gave him every right to abuse, torture, and rape young boys. All because his father did the same thing to him when he was a child?

"I didn't want to listen to any more excuses, and before he could continue, I threw an elbow in his face and shouted at him, 'Stop giving me those bullshit excuses, and tell me how I can find your friends!' Finally, he gave me Mathew's address. I was surprised to see that he lived only a few blocks from my garage, and the fact that I had never once seen him is still a mystery to me. Joe told me that Mathew was married once, but he was divorced now. Apparently, he was a horrible husband and a father, and his wife divorced him after he almost killed her. She took their kid and moved back to her father's house. Mathew was also a drug addict, just like his best friend Joe. Now that I knew Mathew also lived alone, that would make it much easier for me to find him and bring him here. No one would really miss him. To be honest, I was doing everyone a favor—his family and the city of Izmir.

"I also learned that those two losers still got together every Friday. They would go to a public bath house, which was for men only. Joseph told me that it was easy to find young boys for sex, especially poor, homeless boys in there. The way he smiled and talked about it made me realize that he was getting aroused remembering their Friday night meetups. I was reminded of the face he made while raping me down in that cold, dark basement. Before I knew what I was doing, I lost control and hit his head with a shovel I stored in the basement. I don't know how many times I hit his head with that shovel, but once I stepped away, the entire basement floor was red and I was covered in Joe's blood. I was breathing so fast that I thought I was going to pass out any second.

"As I looked around, reality sank in. I'd killed Joe, and now I had to do something with his body. I took off all of my clothes, dropped them on the floor, and ran upstairs. I needed to breathe and make sure I wasn't dreaming. What happened in that basement was real. I went outside. It was overcast, and the air was cold. There were no sounds or anybody else in sight. I took a few deep breaths and let the fresh air bring me to the present.

I knew what needed to be done now, so I went back in, took a shower, and stepped outside to check that the garage door was locked. I went back inside, sat on my chair in the kitchen, and made a cup of tea, telling myself, 'It's going to be fine, just let it be for a while.' I didn't want to go to the basement yet because I didn't want to believe that what I'd done was real. Surely he was still breathing down there. I desperately wanted to believe that. That day and the next day, I went on with my life. I opened up the garage and did a few small jobs as though nothing was wrong. I did my grocery shopping as usual, watching everyone else go about their days. Everything was the same. Nothing was out of the ordinary, and I realized that I was safe and still invisible, which was a good sign. I wanted to be invisible, a nobody, unnoticed. It gave me freedom to carry out my mission.

"That night, I sat on the couch in the living room, and the voices in my head were whispering, 'You have to go downstairs; you have to bury his body before the smell gets out of control. Bury the bastard and get it over with. Brother Joseph can't hurt another soul. His clothes and all of his belongings should be burned, and then you can just dig a hole in the basement and bury him right there. That way, you can spit on his grave any time you want to.'

"I knew that burying him was the right thing to do anyway. I had killed a monster, a demon, a soul killer. All that Joe had done to me came back into my mind like I was watching a horror movie. His voice, his heavy breathing, the sound of his belt, and those shoes tapping . . . I jumped up from my chair and turned off all the lights in the house, gathered my tools, and headed down to the basement. From the stairway, I looked down at the room. It was most certainly real. His headless body was crawling with rats, and the smell was sickening. I locked the basement door behind me. That night, I lost whatever was left of the innocent soul that my old man had tried so hard to save in me. I finally gave myself completely to my demon, and it felt good.

"All I could hear were the voices of all those boys begging, crying, and pleading with him to stop, including Riza and my eight-year-old self. The hate and rage I felt that night gave me the strength to dig a hole as deep as I could and bury Joe's body as far from me as I could, as if he might come back one night and hurt me again. I had to make sure that couldn't happen. I threw all of his belongings into the fireplace in the basement. I also dumped his car in the poorest area of town, where I knew people would disassemble every piece of it in no time. In the end, no one would even be able to tell what kind of car it was to begin with. I was witnessing Joe's existence disappearing in front of my eyes. No more reminders of him would exist. I cleaned up the basement floor and went upstairs, and after that night life was as ordinary as it could be.

"For a while, I busied myself with work. I didn't want to rush anything. After all, I had all the time in the world. I even thought about letting go and moving on with my life, but every time I wanted to let go, the headaches, nightmares, and voices kept coming back. I couldn't let go, even if I wanted to. Something inside of me was telling me that I had to finish what I'd started, and I knew that if I wanted to end all my nightmares and pain, I had to carry on with my original plan. I waited until one Friday evening, then I decided to visit the public bath, the one that Joseph had talked about. It was a few miles away. I knew I would recognize Mathew if I saw him, but just to be sure, I found his house first and watched him leave his apartment. Poor bastard, he looked ancient. With his big belly and his aging face, he looked like he could be in his seventies or eighties. He was walking alone and saying something to himself. According to Joe, Mathew was a junkie too. I reckoned he also still he had his bad temper like his buddy Joe.

"I watched Mathew from the other side of the street as he walked and talked to himself like a madman, and then kicked over a trashcan as he crossed the road. He got into a very old car, and I followed him to the public bath. I didn't go in, but I watched him as he went in. After about two hours, he came out. He had a young boy with him, and they drove away together. They went back to his place that night. The young boy was probably around fifteen or sixteen years old. By the looks of him, he was either homeless or a drug addict, which would explain why he was desperate enough for money to go home with Mathew.

"That night, I couldn't go home. Instead, I sat in my car just across from his apartment, and all night I watched his apartment window. I wanted to know his routine, particularly who he saw during the day, if anyone came to visit him or not. Would anyone even miss him if he disappeared? What about his child? These were the questions I had to answer before moving ahead with my plan.

"After a while, this pastime became an obsession. After I closed the garage each day, I would follow Mathew wherever he went until he returned to his apartment and turned off the lights. I would sleep in my car until dawn and then drive home to do my work. Then I'd repeat exactly what I'd done the night before, until I finally figured out that he was a loner. Nobody ever came to visit him, and he never went to visit anyone, even his own child. Except for his Friday night routine, he didn't have a regular job or any sort of structure to his life. Mostly, he spent his time drunk. He made his living by selling drugs and picking up odd jobs painting cars in a mechanic shop next to his apartment building. He lived in a shabby part of town. The population was mostly drug-addicted homeless people, especially young boys who were easy targets, just looking for some cash to feed themselves. In his twisted mind, I knew he was having the time of his life, but I was going to make sure that it wasn't for long.

"One Friday afternoon, I decided it was time to meet him. I chose to meet him at the bathhouse, the one he went to on Friday nights. I followed him there, then I walked with him to the locker room, where we changed into nothing but towels around our waists. It was warm and steamy, so nobody could see clearly. I sat just opposite him. He was relaxing, his eyes closed and his head resting against the wall. I watched him closely, staring at his face and thinking to myself, 'Look at him. Same face, same body language.' As I watched him, my mind wandered back to when he was younger and we all used to be afraid of his temper, especially the way he used to beat up Riza and me after we disobeyed him. I remembered some nights when he would come to our bedroom hall and scream, 'Tonight, when I call your name, make sure you are ready for me! Now get some sleep, my little dogs, because you're gonna need it!' Then the three of them would laugh loudly and leave us trembling in absolute fear. We used to huddle in a group and just hold on to each other till one of those monsters came and called our names.

"Now, he was sitting in front of me as I watched him through the steam. He opened his eyes, looked straight at me, and asked me, 'What are you looking at?' His voice pulled me back to the present.

"I shook my head and said, 'Nothing. I thought you looked familiar, that's all.'

"Mathew accepted that answer, and he smiled before saying, 'I've never seen you here before, and I have been coming here a long time.'

"I told him, 'I'm from out of town. I just moved here, and to be honest, I'm kind of lonely, you know what I mean?' I smiled playfully to get my point across.

"Suddenly, he felt comfortable enough to move and sit beside me. I could see that he was sizing me up from head to toe. He leaned closer and asked, 'What do you need? I can get it for you. It would be my pleasure.' Then he gently rubbed his shoulder against mine.

"I also leaned closer so I could whisper in his ear, and I said to him, 'I want you.'

"He looked at me with eyes wide open, clearly startled by my directness, and said, 'Are you sure? I'm not much to look at.' I laughed along with him.

"I put my hand on his hand and told him, 'I like what I see. Besides, it won't be just the two of us. We will have some company too. I have a party to take you to.' I pulled back a little, leaving him wanting more.

"I think I had the right approach, because he got impatient and told me, 'It's getting too hot in here. Let's talk outside.' I knew my bait had worked and he was hooked deep; now, all I had to do was carry it on just a little bit longer so he couldn't get away. I'd let him swim a little bit longer then yank back as hard as I could.

"I told him, 'I'm busy tonight, but we can meet up tomorrow tonight. How about I pick you up around eleven tomorrow night?' He was so thrilled that he didn't want to know anything more, especially when I told him we would get high. I already knew his address, but I pretended that I needed it, so he gave me his phone number and home address.

"When he wanted to say goodbye, he took my hand and squeezed it hard, then rubbed my shoulder and said very slowly, 'I can't wait until tomorrow night.' For a second or two, he kept my hand in his and stared straight at me, like he was remembering something.

"I panicked a little bit, but I didn't want to make him suspicious, so I quickly asked him, 'Are you okay, man? I don't even know your name yet.'

"He said, 'I'm sorry, forgive my manners. I am Mathew, and your name?' I told him my name was Ray. He asked me, 'Ray, have we met before? Because you look familiar.'

"I laughed it off and told him, 'I don't think so, Mathew. How could I forget such a handsome face like yours?'

"I think my compliments distracted him, because after that, he told me, 'See you tomorrow night, and make sure you aren't late, Ray.' He walked off toward his car, and I waited little bit longer so he wouldn't see me getting into my car.

"The next night, I waited outside of his apartment for a while, somewhere that he wouldn't be able to see me. Exactly at eleven, he stepped outside to wait for me. After a while, he became clearly agitated and kept punching the palm of his hand and lighting one cigarette after another. He kept looking up and down the street then checking the time. I watched him from the dark alley on the other side of the street, but he couldn't see me. An hour passed, and all he did was wait, walking up and down the street. Then he started talking to himself and kicking the empty trashcans into the street. Finally, he gave up and went back into his apartment. I could tell how angry he was, but I needed to make sure he was going to be alone. I had to be sure no one was going to be there with him. I saw his apartment light turn off, and I was sure that he was done for the night. I waited a little bit longer, and then knocked on his door. I wanted to catch him off guard.

"He screamed, 'Who is it?'

"I told him, 'It's me, party boy.'

"He opened the door and, like a little boy missing out on a play day, asked me, 'What happened to you, man? I was waiting out in the cold forever, and you didn't show up.' He folded his arms and pouted his lips like a little kid, and I was sure he was high already. His behavior made me sick to my stomach, but I knew I had to control myself.

"I told him, 'I am so sorry, Mathew, but my car was stalling so I had to fix it, and it wasn't easy to get here.' I thought that maybe I could convince him I was high too, so I started mimicking his behavior. 'But, if you still feel like going to the party, we can leave now,' I said with excitement.

"A big smile crossed Mathew's face, and he said, 'You mean we can still party this late?'

"I laughed and replied, 'Late? They're just getting started, and I wouldn't go there without my buddy Mathew.' We both laughed, and I told him, '*Shh*, keep it quiet. We don't want to wake up your neighbors, do we?'

"He hugged me and said, 'No way, let's be quiet then. But really, it's only me on this floor. The rest of the apartments are empty. They are renovating the building or something.' We walked out of the building. To be honest, it was a relief to know that the whole floor was empty, so no one would even notice him leaving with me that night.

"I told Mathew, 'Let's go in my car. Besides, I won't let you come back tonight, because we are going to party all night long. And I have a big surprise for you.' Mathew jumped up and down a couple times and even started to dance, but I told him to calm down, once again saying that he was going to wake up all the neighbors. It was like trying to control a kid.

"On the way to my place, Mathew kept telling me how lucky he was to find me and how he'd been lonely for such a long time.

He told me about the one close friend he had and how he would love for me to meet him, but he'd just left town without a word. I knew who he was talking about. I just stayed quiet as I listened to him. I wanted him to talk and not focus on anything else, such as where we were going.

"We arrived at my place. It was pretty obvious that all the lights were off and there were no other cars parked outside my house, so before he had the chance to say anything, I told him that I'd asked everyone else to park behind the house so no passersby would get suspicious. I reasoned with him, 'With what we're about to do all night long, we don't need any police snooping around this old house. You know what I mean?'

"Mathew seemed to ponder what I'd said, but then he asked, 'But why there are there no lights on?'

"I lied again. 'Everyone is in the basement. You know you don't want to have that kind of party in the house where there are lots of windows and nosy neighbors, right?' I moved the car into the garage so no one could see us getting out.

"He nodded his head enthusiastically and said, 'You're too smart for me, man. You're right.' I closed the garage door and we went inside. He was looking around and listening very carefully. I told him we should go to the basement where the party was and have some fun.

"He followed me like a kid in a candy store. As soon as he stepped in front of me to walk down to the basement, I smacked him hard across the head, and he rolled all the way down to the bottom of the stairs. I walked down to the basement and looked at him. He was unconscious, which gave me enough time to tie him up and gather my thoughts. I wasn't ready to finish him off right away. I had to get as much information from him as possible. He had to know who I really was. He had to face the consequences of his actions, of what he did to us. I was going to be the judge, jury, victims' advocate, and prosecutor. It was judgment day.

"I sat down in the chair across from him, watching him until he finally opened his eyes. He glanced around and then realized that he was all tied up. His body jerked as he tried to loosen the bonds. His wide eyes met mine. 'What's going on, Ray? What is this? What happened to our party, man?' He asked quested after question, voice quavering as he tried to untie himself by moving around in his chair.

"I moved closer to his face and told him, 'Mathew, look at me and tell me, can you recognize my face? Do you think you've ever seen me before last night? Maybe a long time ago when you were younger, perhaps?'

"Mathew stared at me first with confusion, but then the strangest thing happened. He was much sharper than I had expected. Underneath that drunk and drug-addicted body lived a demon, still alive and well. He looked at me with disgust and said, 'You are that little, pathetic orphan boy, right? The one who was always begging and crying?' He laughed and began to mimic my voice, 'Oh no, sir, please. No more. It hurts. I remember you now, so what? What are you going to do now? I'm already screwed up, and I got nothing to lose except my crappy life, so go ahead, do whatever you want to do. You can't do anything; you're still that scared little bastard who used to pee his pants whenever someone came for you, crying and asking for God to help you, right? You gutless little prick. We thought we could make men out of you little bastards, toughen you up, but I guess it was useless. You're still the same coward I remember.' He continued to hurl insults my way, and I soaked up every word and recalled every single hurt he had caused me when I was a child. With every word that left his mouth, my logic and sanity began to slip away. He continued to verbally abuse me until he got so mad that he spat on my face.

"The next thing I remember is being upstairs covered in blood. I wasn't sure what had happened, so I went back to the basement and found Mathew's dead body. I walked up the stairs and straight outside to catch some fresh air. The cool breeze of the night calmed my soul, and I looked down at my two hands, which were covered in Mathew's blood. Under the moonlight, though, the blood looked dark blue. I smelled my hands, and the scent of blood made my heart race from adrenaline. I'd killed the second monster. Now there was only one left.

"By dawn, his body was gone from my basement floor. He didn't exist anymore, and a piece of me was gone with him too. The part of me that was good and decent, I guess. Every time I killed a monster, they also took a piece of me, but I didn't mind. It was worth it."

Ray paused abruptly. "Lilli, I knew what I was doing was wrong, killing another human being. But define a human being for me. To me, a human being is someone with morality, decency, integrity, and compassion, and those monsters had none of that. So I felt nothing but relief. They got what they deserved."

With such calmness in his voice, Ray continued his story, "After I killed Mathew, everything went back to normal once again. I was working and living as I had before, and I honestly thought that from now on, I would find my peace of mind. I thought things would get better for me. However, those dreams, the night sweats, and the midnight panic attacks were all still there. The only relief came in knowing that those two monsters were buried deep down in my basement. Still, the third one was alive and well somewhere far away from me. My obsession became finding out where he lived and learning as much as I could about his life. As long as long as I had something to look forward to, I could distract myself from the emptiness, fear, and pain that I felt inside. I thought that when I finished my mission, then I would be okay. I could start fresh, and I could finally figure out who I really was. Maybe by then, I could really settle down.

"Then I thought about my old man and how he'd wanted me to have a life of my own. I told myself that I just had to finish my mission, and then I could have my real life. These thoughts raced through my head every second of every day. I had no idea how I would find Yusif. The only piece of the puzzle that I had so far was that he lived overseas, somewhere in Adelaide, Australia. Over the next eight months of my life, I felt so alive because I was working hard to figure out how I could migrate to Australia. I worked sixteen to eighteen hours a day, saving money and doing everything in my power to get my visa to start my new life in Australia. Finally, I made the right connections, and because I was the best mechanic in town, one of my frequent customers found a company in Adelaide that wanted to hire a top mechanic for their factory. My customer passed along my name, and after my second phone interview, the interviewers told me they were certain that I would be able to get my working visa. The day I received the letter confirming my visa, they phoned me for my final interview and let me know they accepted me for the position.

"I was shouting and laughing in my garage and doing a victory dance. My customers were excited for me too, and they all wished me luck. If only they knew who I really was and the real reason I wanted to go to Adelaide. I don't think they would have been so supportive of me. Almost one year after I killed Mathew, I finally had my working visa in my hand. I had to make a decision about what to do with my old man's house and garage. I mean, it was practically mine, but I didn't have the heart to sell it. Besides, how could I with those bodies buried in the basement? I could never sell the house, so I ended up just selling the garage and keeping the house for myself.

"The day finally came. I was ready to pack up my life and move on to the next chapter. The night before I moved, I went down to the basement and looked at those two spots where I had buried the bodies. I decided to make that night special, so I slept down there with those two. I drank a little, and the three of us had a big conversation. I told them that I was leaving them for a while and that they shouldn't go anywhere until I came back. They deserved a proper goodbye."

Ray stopped and reached for another cigarette, chuckling to himself. Was I looking at a madman? Was he damaged beyond what anyone could ever repair?

After a moment, Ray continued, "I came to Australia with a working visa. Got a job as a top mechanic for the biggest automobile company in Adelaide. I specialized in European cars. Received a good salary, and they also got me an apartment near the factory. For what I had in mind, though, I knew I needed to find my own place, somewhere quiet and far from people. The first few months, I stayed in the apartment that they'd provided for me, and when things finally settled down, I got to know my way around town. I decided to look for an old house suitable for me. Finally, I found what I was looking for. It looked just like my old house back in Turkey, and it reminded me of my old man, my best friend.

"I rented the house and moved in as soon as I could. I worked five days a week, and the weekend was my research time. I spent every weekend researching different orphanages, churches, and boys homes in town. I knew Yusif would be working in one of those places, and it was only a matter of time until I found him."

Ray stopped talking again, and I realized it was getting really late. Ray was looking pale, and I figured he could use a break anyway, so I asked, "How about I come back tomorrow, and we'll continue our session then? What do you think, Ray?"

He nodded his head once, and I took that as a yes.

"Goodbye, Lilli," Ray said, just before I left the room.

Worried about Ray, I called the guard and asked if they could check on him and make sure he was okay.

The guard answered, "It's okay, he just needs his medication. That's all. You can come back tomorrow." He was so calm that for a second, I wondered why they couldn't be more concerned about Ray's health. But I knew I couldn't say anything. I was just a reporter, and to be honest, I didn't want to jeopardize my position in any way. I was already walking on thin ice with my boss, and one mistake could cost me my job. Besides, this story meant much more than just an article to me. I wanted to help this man in any way I could, so for Ray's sake, I decided to keep my mouth shut. I left to get some food then head back to the motel to work on the story.

I arrived at the motel around eight at night, and I went straight to my room. All I wanted was to call Alex and say goodnight to him, because just before I'd left home, I'd made a promise to him that no matter what, I would make sure to call and say goodnight each night this week that I wasn't at home with him. By the time I called, though, my mother told me that Alex was in bed and wasn't feeling very well.

My stomach sank. I told my mom that I had been working until now, but I would make sure to call him right on time tomorrow night.

She told me not to worry, that he would be okay. "It's just a cold. You don't have to worry, Lilli. I'll take care of him," my mother said, with so much love in her voice.

Just before I had the chance to say goodbye, my mother asked about Ray and how he was doing. I told her that everything was fine and I'd talk to her later, but she insisted that I tell her about my interview. I didn't want to break her heart, but I also just wasn't in the mood to talk about Ray in that moment.

All I said was, "He's sick, Mom, and doesn't have much time left. He has done so many bad things, but I don't think he deserves to die like this. I think people need to know the truth about him. Maybe we can all open our eyes and not be so judgmental. Maybe he can find some kind of peace in his heart by telling his story. I wish I could find his parents, but I know that's impossible since he was born overseas. Also, I'm sure that if they don't want to be found, it would be impossible to track them. All I can do is let his words tell the story. That's all, Mom."

Right before I said goodnight to hang up the phone, I thought I heard her crying.

"What's wrong, Mom? Are you crying?"

I was certain she was crying. Her voice trembled as she talked, but I could hear her perfectly. "Lilli, I'm a bad mother, and I did a horrible thing."

I had no idea what she was talking about. As long as I had known her, my mother was an angel who could never even kill a fly. What on earth was she going on about?

I told her, "Ma, you are tired. Just go to bed, okay? We'll talk tomorrow. You are a saint, and you've never done anything wrong as a mother. I know you better than you know yourself. Goodnight, Mom."

I was ready to hang up the phone when she hit me hard with just a few words. "Lilli, listen to me, please. Ray might be my son. Your brother."

The phone was still in my hand, but I was motionless, speechless. I didn't know what to say.

My mother continued, "I was eighteen years old and from a very strict and religious family. Your grandfather was an army man, so I grew up in a military family. None of us kids were allowed to make any mistakes, especially their golden girl, me. I was the oldest of three, and I had to be an example for my siblings. I was in love with the boy next door, Arda; he was four years older than me and already attending a university, studying to become a doctor. We used to see each other secretly from time to time. I was madly, crazy in love with him. He told me he was going to marry me, but I had to be patient until the time was right so he could talk to his family. Those days, if a boy liked a girl, he had to send his parents to ask the girl's parents for permission to court. Well, one day I told him that I was late and thought I might be pregnant, so he'd better hurry up and send his parents over, because my father would kill me if he found out. I was about six weeks late. He told me he would tell them that night, but I had to promise not to say anything to anyone until his family came over and we got engaged. I jumped into his arms, over the moon with joy. Thinking about it kept me smiling all day, and my mother was so surprised by my behavior, because I was normally in a bad mood or nagging about something. I waited eagerly for Arda and his family to come over the next afternoon. I cleaned our house, set up the table with fresh fruits and sweets, and made a fresh pot of tea. My mother asked me, 'What's going on, Belgin? Who's coming over?' I told her it was a big surprise, so she just had to wait and see."

My mother paused her story, but I didn't want to interrupt, so I waited while she collected her thoughts. She soon continued, "The afternoon turned into the next day and then into the next week. I went to our usual meeting spot to see what had happened to him and why his family hadn't shown up. I was sure something must have happened to him; otherwise, they would have come.

I waited for an hour, but he didn't show up. I didn't know what to do, so on the way back home, I decided to knock on his door and ask some unrelated question to see what was going on. I was sure that once he heard me talking to his mother, he would run to me. I knew how close he was to his mom, and I thought that maybe she would invite me in so we could set up a day for them to come over. I knocked on their door. My heart was racing so fast, my palms were sweaty, and my mouth was dry. Every second felt more like an hour. Finally, his mother opened the door, and she was all smiling and happy. I said hello, then I asked her if I could borrow a book from Arda to help me with my studies.

"She responded, 'Oh my God, you didn't hear the good news? Arda left for America to stay with his uncle and his family! He's going to continue his education in medicine over there. He has already been accepted into one of the top universities in America.' She was talking so fast and I couldn't believe what she was telling me. How could this have happened? I was with him at least three or four times a week. All those promises, those passionate moments that we shared, were those all a lie? I told his mom I had to go. She acted surprised and asked, 'Are you okay? I knew you two liked each other, but he always assured me that it was nothing serious.' To add more salt to my wounds, she told me, 'Also, you know that Arda is engaged to his cousin in America, right? They have been writing to each other for years now, and they saw each other last year when we went to America on family vacation.'

"I was enraged at him and at myself. How did I let him make a fool of me like that? How on earth did I allow myself to trust him the way I did? I felt tiny, unworthy, and less than nothing. I felt so much pain and anger that I didn't know how to stop my body from shaking. I ran home and went straight to my room, closed the door, and started to cry, hiding my face in the pillow and hoping to die soon. My mother noticed my behavior, so she came after me. She stood by my bed and asked, 'Belgin, what's wrong?' as she started to pat my hair. I didn't know how to look her in the eyes and tell the truth. How could I tell her that her golden girl, the one she called the apple of her eye, the one my father had such high hopes for, was not only pregnant but the guy didn't even want to marry her?

"Our family reputation, our good name, and my father's years of being such a respectable man in our town would go to ruin because of me. I looked at my mother and whispered, 'If I tell you something, you have to promise not to say a word to Father.' She promised, and she kept her promise till the day she died. That day, I told my mother about how I fell in love with Arda, and how he'd led me to believe he was in love with me and wanted me to be his wife. I told her about my pregnancy. I'd never seen my mother's face filled with such pain and sadness, and I had no words to comfort her, so I grabbed her hand and kissed it.

"She pulled her hand away from mine, and before leaving my room, she looked at me and said to me, 'Belgin, today you broke my heart, and I will never forgive you for that.' Then she turned around and left my room. She was a wise woman, and I knew there was no way on earth that she was going to let my father know the truth, because then he would blame her for not being a good mother and for not teaching me to be a decent girl. I knew my mother would also blame herself for my mistakes. Now she was as guilty as I was in her own eyes. A few days passed so slowly, and I tried hard to avoid my parents, especially my mother. She didn't even look at me once. Finally, one afternoon, she came to my room, and without even looking at me, she told me I was going to live with my grandmother for several months. Once I gave birth, then I could come back home, and life would go on. I was so ashamed and afraid to even ask, but what about the baby? I knew there wasn't a chance in the world they would let me keep my baby or even see my child's face. In our culture, to have a child outside of marriage was the worst thing a woman could do. Now imagine a young girl who was supposed to be a virgin until marriage got pregnant, and the worst part was that the father of the child had run away. He didn't even honor her enough to marry her.

"Without anything else to do, I obeyed my mother and was soon moved to the village where my grandmother lived. My mother told everyone that my grandmother was sick and needed help, so

I was going to take care of her. My father told me how proud he was that I was sacrificing my lifestyle and time with my friends to do such an act of kindness for my grandma. But my mother and I knew the real reason, and I felt terrible about the whole situation, especially being dishonest to my father. Grandma lived in a small village, which was basically like a convent or jail, but I thought I deserved what was happening to me.

"My grandmother was so kind and understanding, and I think that those six and a half months were the best time I ever had with her. She opened my eyes to the reality of life. Every night, while she brushed my hair, she talked about her life and how she made the same mistake that I made. Her family introduced her son as her brother to the whole neighborhood. She was only thirteen when it happened, and not even her own daughter, my mother, knew the truth. The bond between my grandmother and I became so strong that I didn't want to go back home even after I had my child. Eventually, the time came that I went into labor and gave birth to a beautiful baby boy. He looked like an angel. He had dark brown hair and the most beautiful green eyes. But I knew I had to give him up. The night I gave birth to him, my mother was by my bedside. I was in pain, but she didn't want to take my hand. My grandma rubbed my forehead and said a prayer in my ear. As soon as the baby was born, my mother let me look at him and feed him once, then she wrapped him in a blanket, took my boy, and left my grandmother's house. I screamed, I begged, and I cried my eyes out, but it didn't change anything. For the next month, I did nothing but cry from depression. My milk dried up, and it was time for me to go back home.

"Finally, I accepted reality and realized that my mother had no choice. She did the best she could. That child couldn't have had a place in my life, especially with my culture and the family that I belonged to. My grandmother helped me forgive my mother's actions and told me it was tough love, not an act of cruelty or heartlessness. She was trying to save my future and my good name. 'You are young,' Grandma told me, 'and one day, you will understand her pain and what she sacrifices for you. After all, it was her first grandchild too.'

"As time passed, I forgave my mother and lived my life just the way my parents wanted me to. I finished my education, which was so important to my father. A respectable boy from a very good family came to our house and asked my father for my hand in marriage, and in no time, I was married to your father. It was an arranged marriage, and I never thought I would be happy, but God blessed me with your father. Let me tell you what a wonderful man he was. The night we got married, we went to the room, and it was the first time we had been alone together as a man and wife. I told him there was something I had to tell him, and if he couldn't forgive me or wanted to divorce me right away, I completely understood, but I wanted there to be no secrets between us. He sat beside me on the edge of the bed, took my hands, and very calmly said to me, 'Belgin, there is nothing you can say that will make me want to divorce you or hate you at all. I love your courage and bravery for wanting to be honest with me and build our life on truth.' So, with that, I told him everything. He took me in his arms and held me for a long time. Then he told me, 'I love you, Belgin, more than you will ever know.'

"The rest of our marriage was love, joy, and wonderful memories that we created together. We tried to find my boy, but my mother never wanted to talk about it, so day by day, I learned to let it go. Your father and I moved to Australia for you kids so that you and your brother could have a better future. Our life changed, and your father and I had to adapt to a new way of living and culture. We just thought about your future and how your lives would be different from ours, and that made it easier for us to cope. From time to time, I would get homesick, but your father was always there to comfort me. He became my best friend, my family, my lover, and my rock. I don't think I could find anyone else like him. He was in my destiny, as my grandma used to say. You and your brother came to the world and brought lots of joy into our lives, but the memory of my firstborn was always there; the guilt, the shame, and the sorrow were all still there. I decided to write a letter to my mother and ask her for the last time about that night when she took the baby from my arms. A month later, I received a package from Turkey. It was from my mother. I opened it, and there were a few gifts for you kids and an envelope with my name on it. My heart started beating fast because it was the first time I'd received an envelope with my name on it. I didn't want to open it until you kids were in bed, so once your father and I were alone, we opened it. It was my mother's handwriting. She explained what had happened that night after she took my baby from me. Apparently she gave the baby to her driver, who told her that he knew a family who wanted to have a baby boy, but the wife couldn't get pregnant. He was sure the husband would be more than happy to have a baby boy. My mother gave him the baby and went back home.

"From time to time, she would ask her driver about the child and how the family was doing, and he would tell her they were doing great, that the baby was a lucky boy to be in such a wonderful family. After that, she was happy to know that at least her grandson had a good and safe life. After all those years, though, she found out that her driver had lied to her. He had left the baby behind a restaurant and driven off, all because of the money my mother had promised him if he found the baby a good, safe family. He asked my mother for her forgiveness. She couldn't stop thinking about the poor child and what she had done.

"As I was reading this letter, I couldn't stop crying, and your father just held me and tried to comfort me. In her letter, my mother asked for my forgiveness. She wrote to me, 'Please, Belgin, forgive me. I don't want to die knowing you have hardened your heart toward me. God will punish me for what I have done to you and my grandson. That, I deserve and can cope with, but to know that you hate me will burn my soul forever.'

"A week later, I received a phone call that my mother had passed away from cancer. Apparently, she had been sick for a long time, but my parents decided to not let anyone know. My father was devastated. He relied on her for everything like a child, and my mother was his everything. I knew he had no idea about the letter. I knew my mom was capable of keeping my secret. There I was with a dead mother, and I didn't know how to feel about her anymore. Should I hate her? Love her? Miss her? Forget about her for good? None of those seemed possible for me anymore.

She was gone, and even in her death, she was still in control. She'd never allowed me to scream at her or argue with her. She was gone without letting me say what I'd wanted to tell her all those years.

"Time passed, and your father and I knew there was nothing we could do. We even hired someone in Turkey to find out anything about my mother's driver and the location of my child, but nothing was helpful. Finally, I gave up, and it became just an unhealed wound in my heart, and it used to bleed from time to time. When I lost your brother, it seemed like God was punishing me through his death. Your father knew how I felt, and he was always there for me. But a mother will always blame herself for everything that happens to her child, and when I lost your father, all I could think about was my firstborn child. I think that losing your dad and your brother made me relive the past. I didn't want to live any longer, and I even thought of killing myself, until the day you came to my bedroom and shouted at me to live again, to find happiness again, and you reminded me that I still had you and Alex. You were right, I still had you two, whom I love more than anything in the world. Then you told me about Ray, and it was like God was finally answering my prayers. I knew he was my boy, which is why I wanted to know more."

My mother started to cry again, begging me, "Please, Lilli, do anything in your power to help him. I want to see my son before he dies. I want to hold him in my arms and tell him that it wasn't my fault, that I've always loved him. I want to ask for his forgiveness."

That night, my mother opened up to me for the first time. That night, she told me her deepest secret, and I was overwhelmed with sadness for her, for all these years that she had to carry such a heavy burden in her heart. This was a lot of new information, and I didn't know what to tell her.

All I said was, "Mom, I'm sorry for everything, and I'll do anything I can to find out his true identity. Please let me go now, and I'll talk to you soon."

It was almost daylight. My mother and I had been talking all night.

I had to find out if it was true. Was Ray my half brother? And if he was, how could I confront him? How could I tell him that the same woman who gave him up a long time ago was a wonderful, caring, and nurturing mother to her other children? How could I tell him that while he was suffering and being abused in another part of the world, his siblings were sleeping in comfortable beds and had someone kissing them goodnight and tucking them into bed?

All those thoughts traveled through my head at once. I couldn't close my eyes for even a minute, so I just got ready and headed back to the prison. Once I came to my senses, I realized I was sitting in the visiting room in front of Ray. Words were lost in my head, and I was struggling to look at him. Could it be possible that the man sitting in front of was my brother? A serial killer? What should I tell him? Should I just deny the whole thing and carry on with my job, or should I tell him, "Guess what, Ray? I might be your half sister."

"Lilli, are you okay?" At the sound of Ray's voice, I jumped out of my stormy thoughts.

I nodded. "I'm fine, I just didn't get enough sleep last night. I was working late." I tried to avoid any eye contact, which I knew he would hate.

Ray asked me again, "What's wrong? You're acting strange today." I had to tell him something, anything but the conversation I'd had with my mother, so I lied. I told him that my boss was very angry at me and I was behind on my project and studies, and on top of that, my mother was also complaining about Alex being quite a handful. Wow. Those lies came to my mind so quickly that I was surprised, but he bought it, and we started our interview.

Ray started to tell me the rest of his story. "I moved to my new house, which reminded me so much of my place in Turkey. The only part missing in it was the old man's memories and memorabilia. For a while, I kept my mind busy by buying furniture and decorating this new place just like my previous house. The most important part of this house that convinced me to buy it was that it had a basement exactly like the previous house. Apparently, the previous owner was into making his own wine, so he'd built a room without any windows, and if you didn't turn any lights on, that room would be darker than a night without any stars or moon. Jet black. It was just perfect for what I had in mind.

"I spent hours and hours down in the basement to make it just the way I wanted it to be. Finally, it was done. I was ready to go on my hunting mission, to find brother Yusif, the last part of my puzzle, and then everything could be fresh and brand new. Finally, I could be free. No more bad thoughts, faces, nightmares—no more pain. The case would rest. Those were my thoughts and hopes for my future.

"Every day after work, I used to go through telephone books, the yellow pages, and anything that could give me a clue, but I found no leads. I was getting frustrated, and after a while, I thought that maybe this was a sign to put my dark past behind me and move on with my life. I began to think that I should just sell the house and find a small apartment to move into. I could take some serious medications for my headaches and nightmares. Almost a year and a half passed, and every day, I was getting more certain that I would never find him. Maybe he was dead. Thinking about Yusif being dead used to bring me some comfort, because even though I hadn't killed him, at least he couldn't hurt any more kids.

"It was Christmas Eve, and I was going to talk to someone about putting the house on the market, when I received an invitation in my mailbox. It was an invitation to Mass, a celebration at our neighborhood church. There was a picture of a middle-aged priest. I looked at the picture and then glanced down at the written description. It was him, Brother Yusif!

"All that time, I'd been searching everywhere else, and he was just two blocks away from my house, working in stuffy old church. His name was now Father Yusif, as he had become a proper priest. I just couldn't believe it. Just as I was ready to change my path, he had to resurface. I couldn't believe how destiny had a different plan for me. I think that even God wanted me to finish my task. It was as if God was telling me, 'Ray, I didn't want you to give up on your mission. Now is your chance, finish it!' "

Ray was getting worked up as he talked about his supposed message from God, and I could see how much he truly believed that this mission was from God. He was definitely delusional, I could see that now.

Ray continued, "The day of Mass, I was beyond excited. I dressed in nice clothes and was ready to face my destiny, to see Yusif face-to-face after all these years. I arrived early and sat in the end row in the back corner of the church. The church was peaceful; all the candles were lit, and beautiful flowers sat in vases throughout the church. The fresh scent of candles and flowers and the peacefulness of the church helped me relax a little bit. I looked at the statue of Jesus, which seemed to be looking straight at me with those innocent, suffering eyes. I felt something in my heart, like there was a message in his eyes telling me, begging me to stay. 'Don't move, Ray, don't move.' The voices that I could clearly hear inside my head were telling me to not back off, to stay put, and I would see him soon. I was drowning in my thoughts and listening to the voices in my head when I realized that there were now people all around me. I looked around. The church had filled with people, and I hadn't even noticed.

"I felt a hand on my shoulder and turned—it was Father Yusif. He greeted me, 'Hello son, I've never seen you in our church before. You've come earlier than anyone else.' I stood up, and he stretched his arm out to shake my hand. He asked my name, and I told him it was Ray. He smiled and told me, 'Well, Ray, welcome to your church, and please, you are more than welcome to see me any time you need. I'm here to help.' He started greeting other people and walked away. As he walked away, I watched him. He was much older than I'd expected him to be, and his face was much calmer than I remembered, but he couldn't fool me. He was still a demon inside. I knew that. It was just a matter of time until I unveiled his dark secret.

"It seemed that everyone at that church loved and respected him. If only they knew the truth about their Father Yusif. He was walking around, placing his hand on top of every young child's head and kissing their foreheads. I had to stop myself from jumping over the pew and choking him in front of all those people.

Touching those kids and kissing them in front of their parents, as if he was a holy man and he was blessing those children. They were happy and joyful that he was giving his affection to them. It made me mad and sick to my stomach, so I ran outside in rage. I had to. I just couldn't sit there and witness his charade. I was suffocating in there. I ran home to get away from him until I was ready to face him again.

"Now that I had found him, now that he had finally appeared in my life, there was no way on earth I would let him get away. I had to work on my plan, the perfect way to make him disappear from the face of the earth. A few days later, around seven in the evening, I was walking around my basement and thinking about Father Yusif, when I heard the doorbell. I wondered who that might be. I didn't have any friends, and even my neighbors didn't know me, so who would be ringing my doorbell? I tried to ignore the doorbell, but it went on and on. It seemed like they didn't want to give up, or maybe they knew I'd be home at this hour, so I decided to go upstairs and see who it was. For a minute, I stayed behind the door and tried to gather myself before opening the door. I peeked out from behind a curtain to see who it was. I was shocked to see Father Yusif. It took me a few seconds to gather myself, then I opened the door as he was just walking away the house. As soon as he heard the door open, he turned around and said hello with a big smile on his face.

"Brother Yusif told me, 'You left too early, and I didn't have a chance to talk to you, son! I asked around and finally got your address. Are you living by yourself? Please, don't be shy. I have been living in this neighborhood a long time and I know many people, so if you need anything at all, my door is always open to you, my son. I live behind the church, so come. Perhaps one day after work, you can come over and have supper with us.'

"I didn't invite him in, and I think he noticed that I felt uncomfortable, as he said, 'I'm sorry to bother you at this hour. I better go now, but remember, Ray, the invitation is open, so don't be a stranger, okay?' Brother Yusif smiled and walked away from my front porch. After a moment, he stopped and turned around, just before I closed the door, and said, 'Everyone is telling me that you are the best mechanic in town, so whenever you have time, come over and look at my old companion. It's an old Subaru, still working, but a few days ago I couldn't start the engine, so if—'

"I interrupted without thinking. 'Yes, yes, I can come look at your car now, if you want me to.'

"Brother Yusif looked at me with surprise and asked, 'Are you sure? I don't want to put any pressure on you. Besides, aren't you tired?'

"I assured him, 'Father, it's nothing. Just give me a minute, and I'll be right with you. Please wait here, if you can.' I closed the door and started to get ready. While I was walking down to the basement to pick up my tools, I thought about when he said, 'Come over and have supper with *us.*' Who was he living with?

"Quickly, I packed my tools and walked outside. He was sitting on my porch, waiting for me. We started walking together toward the church, which was two blocks from my house. He was telling me about his stupid car the whole way, and I wondered how on earth Yusif had just made the whole plan so easy for me. Before I planned anything, I had to know who lived with Father Yusif. We went to the back of the church where his car was parked. I looked it over and told him that I needed a few new parts, which I could get from work.

"He thanked me and asked if I would like to come in for a cup of hot tea, and I asked him, 'Can I have a glass of water instead?' I followed him toward his house, and we stepped inside. All of a sudden, two German Shepherds ran toward him. They growled defensively at me, but he told them to be quiet, saying, 'Ray is a friend.' Nevertheless, they planted themselves in front of him, guarding him from me. Supposedly, animals can sense danger, so perhaps they knew what I was thinking, because no matter how many times he tried to calm those dogs, they both kept growling and standing ready in attack mode.

"Yusif apologized, 'I am so sorry. I have no idea why they are like this tonight. Usually, they are very calm and obedient dogs.' I told him it was okay, and that I had to leave anyway. The next day was a work day, so I had to get some sleep. He nodded and told me to call him whenever I had the spare parts so he could bring his car over.

"I got home and realized that this was my chance—it was now or never. For the next few days, I kept busy with work and tried to keep a low profile. After all, I still didn't know how on earth he'd found my place and how he'd learned that I was a mechanic. I never even socialized with anyone, but the neighbors must have known who I was and what I was doing. I quickly grew paranoid about everything. I started having nightmares again, and the dark thoughts and headaches came back. I couldn't sleep, so I was up all night, mad at myself for not getting it over with. I needed to get the job over with as soon as possible.

"Since I couldn't sleep, one night I went for a walk around the block, particularly around our church area, to see if his light was on by chance. Maybe Father Yusif also couldn't get a good night's sleep, just like me. Monsters don't sleep at night. As I had guessed, his light was on. It was sometime between twelve and one in the morning, and I could see his shadow in the window. Father Yusif was walking around, doing something in the kitchen. I knew that if I knocked on his door or tried to sneak in, his dogs would attack me or, at the very least, wake up the whole neighborhood, so I decided to go home and give him a call. Even though it was late, he was still up. Besides, he had told me to call him any time I wanted to, so this was my chance.

"I dialed his number, and as it rang, I felt strangely uncomfortable calling him. I was about to hang up the phone when I heard his voice saying, 'Hello, this is Father Yusif. Can I help you?' For a second or two, I was silent, and I didn't know what to say. Suddenly, Father Yusif said, 'Ray? Is that you?'

"I was frozen in shock. How on earth did he know it was me? I replied, 'Yes, Father. I can't sleep, and I need someone to talk to. Can you come over to my place, Father Yusif?'

"He was quiet for a moment, then with such calmness in his voice, Father Yusif said, 'Of course, my son, I'll be there in a minute,' then he hung up the phone.

"I held on to my phone a moment longer, thinking to myself, 'This is it, Ray, you finally got him.' I quickly walked to the basement, turned on the light, and looked around to double-check that everything was in order. By the time I came back upstairs, he was at my door, ready to knock, when I opened the door on him. Father Yusif had a book with him. I asked him to come in.

"He handed me the book and a thermos. 'Nothing feels nicer than hot cocoa when you have a troubled soul and can't get a good night's sleep,' Father Yusif said, with a smile on his face. I agreed with him and closed the door behind him. Father Yusif looked around the place.

"I told him, 'It's cold in here, and I have a heater in my basement. It's much warmer and a lot cozier than here.'

"He responded, 'Okay then, you go ahead, and I will follow you.' He made everything so easy for me. I just couldn't believe it. He followed me to the basement. There was a single bed, a small TV, a bookshelf, and a table with only one chair and nothing else. There was no heater. Father Yusif looked around. He was quiet. I looked at his face to see the fear in his eyes, but there was nothing but calmness. All I could see in him was curiosity and concern. It was strange. Why? Why wasn't he afraid of me in that moment? I asked him to sit on the chair, and I gave him the cup of hot cocoa that he had brought for me. I asked him, 'When I called you tonight, how did you know it was me, Father?'

"He sipped on his hot cocoa as though this were just a casual visit, then started to explain, 'I am like you, Ray, a creature of the night. Tonight, I saw you walking toward the church and standing there for a while, but you didn't knock on my door. So, for some reason, when the phone rang and no one answered, I knew it must be you, Ray. I knew you would finally find the courage to call. For some reason, Ray, I think I can feel your spirit, and I can sense that you have a troubled soul, my child, so here I am. What is troubling you, my son?' Before I could process the question, Father Yusif continued, with such concern in his voice, saying, 'It is okay, Ray. No matter what, God will never abandon you. I am here for you, and I'll do whatever it takes to help you, son.'

"He spoke calmly, but my anger was building up. I didn't want him to talk. I didn't want to hear his voice or be a part of his act of kindness, as I knew it was all a scam; he was only pretending to be a holy man. I knew the truth about him. I wanted him to stop acting, stop being so nice, and just be the real Yusif I knew such a long time ago.

"Father Yusif stood up, reaching out to put his hand on my shoulder to calm me down, but I pulled back and shouted at him, 'Sit down! Don't you touch me.'

"He fell back in the chair, looking up at me with surprise and alarm, and asked, 'Ray, what is wrong? Why are you angry with me?'

"I stood in front of him, staring into his eyes, and told him, 'Tonight, you are going to pay for what you have done to me and to all of us. Say your last prayer, Father Yusif. Tonight is judgment night.'

"Father Yusif just stared at me with wide eyes and told me, 'Ray, I have no idea what you are talking about, but if you want, we can pray together.' Then he opened his holy book, and that was when I lost it. I started hitting him as hard as I could and screaming at him with everything in me.

"The last words that I told him were, 'You made a monster out of me, and tonight, the monster will kill his master!' Father Yusif just sat there, taking the blows, not defending himself. Maybe when he saw the rage in me, he knew he had no chance to do anything but surrender himself to my anger and vengeance.

"All I remember is that he kept repeating these words to me, on and on, 'Ray, you can make a choice. Son, you can stop. Please, Ray, you have to stop.' After that, I don't remember anything else except waking up in the basement next to Father Yusif's lifeless body. A loud noise from outside was making my headache worse. I looked around. Father Yusif was almost unrecognizable, but I had no idea how I had eventually killed him. I just remembered punching him hysterically, but how he ended up like he did is still a mystery to me. Don't get me wrong, I was happy that he was gone and I had finally finished my mission, but I only wished I could remember how it happened.

"Someone was knocking on my door without ceasing. I would have to walk upstairs and see who it was; otherwise, they might get suspicious once word got out that the priest had disappeared. I quickly fixed my hair and walked up to the main house to open the door and see what was going on. As I walked toward the door, I realized that quite a few people were gathered on my front porch, and their loud voices were growing stronger.

"I opened the door before realizing that I was covered in blood. The next thing I remember is the police crawling all over my place, and I was handcuffed, sitting in the back of the police car. Apparently, before Father Yusif came over to my place, he wrote a note stating the time, place, and my name, as a record of where he would be that night. One policeman told me that it was Father Yusif's habit to keep notes of his daily activities. He'd been missing for three days before they finally checked up on him."

Ray looked directly at me and shook his head. "It was then that I realized I had killed Father Yusif three nights ago, not that night. Or maybe I had finally killed him that night but had kept him alive for two whole days in my basement. But why? If I had only known that Father Yusif kept a daily journal of his activities, I wouldn't be sitting here in front of you, Lilli."

In that moment, I wasn't sure if he was really looking at me or if he was lost in his own head, imagining a different scenario for himself, one where he hadn't been caught. Ray stopped talking for few minutes, and we both looked at each other without exchanging any words. The silence between us was calm and relaxing. Ray began whispering something to himself and glanced over at the small window.

Then he finally spoke. "My job was done, and to be really honest with you, I knew I didn't have much life left in me. I mean, I always thought that when I had killed them all, I could start fresh. I thought my soul would be free, but as time has passed, I can see that no matter how hard I try to fix my life, the damage is done. I wasn't ever going to live a normal life. I am happy here. Some people need to be caged. I'm happy in my cage. It is safe; it is mine. The outside world was too big for me to handle. The only time I was truly free, happy, and safe was when the old man was alive. When he died, he took the good part of me with him. I don't know if you know or not, but I'm really sick. They said it's a brain tumor or something, but whatever it is, I'm happy. Maybe I can finally sleep without the headaches and those bad dreams."

Ray turned his gaze away from the window and said energetically, "So what do you think, Lilli? Is it worthy of publishing or not? I just want people to know that I didn't kill innocent men. They were all monsters and demons. Someone had to save the children; someone had to bring those men to justice. It was my duty. It was my calling." It seemed like he wanted to convince me to believe that he did the right thing.

I stared at Ray, and for a second, I wanted to tell him about my conversation with my mother, but I stopped myself. I just didn't want to give him false hope. Besides, I didn't know how he would react. It could make him angry or violent toward me, or maybe it wasn't the right move for his health to begin with. I had to talk to his doctor first.

I stood up and told Ray, "Thank you for everything, Ray. I will talk to you soon, and I will get to work on making your story known."

He shook my hand, handcuffs jingling, and said, "Different world, different place, and you and I could be best friends or even more." He smiled at me.

If only he knew who he might be, then everything would be different, but I kept my thoughts to myself. Instead of speaking, I smiled at him and left the room.

I had to speak to Ray's doctor about his condition immediately. I was waiting in the office when the doctor showed up, and I told him I had finished my interview.

The doctor asked, "So what is your observation about Ray? Also, tell me, what did Ray tell you about his victims?" The doctor waited for my response, but I needed to tell him about what my mother had told me the night before.

I evaded his questions and said, "Doctor, I need to talk to you about something very important, and I know I can trust you with what I'm going tell you. Until we are sure whether it's true or not, please, I don't want you to tell a soul about it."

The doctor reassured me, "Of course, you can trust me, Ms. Lilli."

I told the doctor about the conversation that I'd had with my mother the night before and that there was a possibility Ray could be my brother. Just as I was about to ask for a DNA test, getting excited at the idea of confirmation, he stopped me.

The doctor told me, "Look, Ms. Lilli, I am so sorry to interrupt you, but there is no way that Ray could be your brother. I am sure of that."

I tried to convince him otherwise. "But how can you be sure, Doctor? He is the same age as my lost brother, he's from Turkey, and he was abandoned by his parents. With all the evidence . . . how can you be so sure? At least let me do a DNA test."

The doctor put his hand on my shoulder and told me, "Ms. Lilli, as I told you, there is no way on earth that he could be your brother. The night they arrested Ray, he was almost in a coma. He had a very serious seizure and needed immediate medical care. That ended up being an early warning sign for his brain tumor. The police found the body of Father Yusif down in Ray's basement. The body was naked and had been stabbed more than sixty times. They didn't find Ray and the body for three days. Imagine being mentally ill and keeping a dead body in your basement, all alone in the house for three days. Ray was born in Australia. His father was a young Turkish immigrant who came to Australia a long time ago with his family. Ray's mother was Australian, and she was a drug addict who gave him up the moment he was born. We found out that an orphanage found an infant baby on their doorsteps the night Ray was born. Ray was a normal, healthy child, but what happened to him in his foster homes and orphanages pushed him to develop a split personality. That was how Ray managed to cope with abuse, rape, and torture inside those homes that he grew up in. Later on, we found out Ray was right about the mental and physical abuse, including the molestation. The men involved were convicted. One of them died in jail and the second one is still serving his term. Ray has never been to

Turkey, and he was never a mechanic. Ray is a very intelligent man, but because of his symptoms, he never even finished high school. Due to his split personality, he was in and out of hospitals for a long time, even if he doesn't remember those times. He was a mentally ill patient, so he was receiving a disability pension for a long time. The house he lived in belonged to his grandfather, who had tried to find his lost grandchild for years. Finally, with the help of a social worker, he found Ray when the boy was around fourteen years old. Ray lived with him, and they really had a wonderful relationship until his grandfather got sick and finally died.

"Apparently, Ray's old man was the only person he trusted and the only one who could keep him calm. The old man taught Ray how to drive and work as a handyman in the neighborhood. Back then, Ray had more control over his psyche. Having a routine and a good relationship with his grandfather helped him. I think the old man told him about his father and where he originally came from. Everything that you heard from Ray is the interpretation of his mind and the fantasy world that he created for himself, which is not uncommon for kids who have been abused. The only unfortunate outcome was for poor Father Yusif, which was actually Ray's real name. When he was found at the orphanage, there was a tag on his baby blanket that said, 'His name is Yusif.' But Ray changed his name once his grandfather found him. We think the old man knew how much he hated his past, and he wanted to give his grandson a new identity, hoping that would help him heal and move on with his life. After that, in Ray's mind, Yusif became one of his abusers. In Ray's mind, since he himself had allowed the men to do all those things to him, he was also a bad guy. The only way he could punish himself was through someone else. He couldn't stand the name Yusif. He couldn't stand being true to himself. Joseph, Mathew, and Yusif were all fictionalized men based on a true part of his past that he tried so hard to forget.

"Father Yusif was the only real victim, and that was just a sad coincidence. He was a wonderful priest from Egypt, and he had come to Australia with his family when he was a young teenager. Everyone loved him and respected him. He used to help the homeless and troubled teens, and his home and church were always open to everyone from different paths of life. When he met Ray, he noticed that he was troubled, and all Yusif wanted to do was help him. But unfortunately, he was with the wrong person at the wrong time.

"We agreed to the interview when someone from your newspaper contacted us and told us it might be a good idea to do a story on Ray. Father Yusif is dead, and Ray's life can raise some awareness about mental illness and how an innocent child's life can be crushed and abused and finally turned into a killer."

I was astonished. After a moment of silence, I managed to stammer out a few questions. "Why haven't you told me all of this from the beginning, Doctor? And why is he in jail instead of in a mental institution?" I was angry and upset about the whole thing. I felt like a fool for believing that he could be my brother. Maybe deep down I'd wanted him to be, because then I wouldn't feel as alone anymore, and my mother could have had a second chance to wipe her guilty conscience.

The doctor sighed and sat down at his desk. "I do apologize for not telling you from the beginning, but Ray has been with us for a few years now. He has been put through intensive treatments and psychological evaluations for a long time. He lives in his fantasy world, and the only way we could bring him out of it was with many sessions of electric shock, heavy medications, and therapy, but even that only lasts for a few days. He has always gone back to that safe corner of his mind. The real Ray is an extremely shy, insecure, and antisocial person. He would have sat in the corner of a room, looking for a way to hurt himself or commit suicide. Numerous times, we had to put him in an isolation room with his hands and feet tied to the bed for days. However, for some reason that is a mystery to us, he suddenly snaps out of it after a few days. He becomes Ray again—charming, outgoing, socializing with everyone, wanting to work in the kitchen and cook the most delicious food you can imagine. He will take his medications and follow the rules.

"Believe me, Ms. Lilli, we have tried treatment many times, but it just gave us the same result every time. He always returns to being Ray. Finally, we came to the conclusion that his childhood and what he went through as a boy must have been so horrifying and devastating that his mind tried to create a way to protect him. Ray is the answer. He is a brave protector and someone who can defend himself, unlike Yusif. That is why he goes back to the safety and security each time. Ray can give him that feeling of stability and happiness. Besides, he's very sick now and doesn't have much time.

"Ray deserves to be heard, and if I'd told you everything from the start, I'm not sure you would have wanted to be in the same room as him. He would have been just another mental patient to you. Ray is not a monster, Ms. Lilli. His past made him who he is today. We as a society failed him, and as a result, an innocent bystander like Father Yusif paid for it with his life."

When I left the doctor's office, I struggled to walk straight with my mind and thoughts so scattered. I went to my motel, packed my suitcase, and drove all the way back home. I didn't want to stay in that town a minute longer. I hated everything about my story and the way it had turned out. I started crying as I drove, wondering why I hated everything. I went to that prison to become a hotshot reporter and prove to everyone that I could do this. Maybe now I could create the best story of the month or maybe even the year. Perhaps, however, I needed Ray more than I could have imagined, and to have reality yanked out from under my feet like this was startling. Ray had helped me grow closer to my mother. She had opened up to me about her deepest secret. Before that, I didn't have much of a relationship with her, but now, because of Ray, I'd found out the secret behind my mother's sadness all those years. It wasn't just because she was homesick; it was the love of a mother who had been forced to give up her child. I found out how wonderful of a man my father was, that he'd known everything about my mother's secret but not even once tried to punish her or reveal her secret to anyone. I realized that not all men were like my husband, and I started to have more faith and be more open to love again. I finally realized that my son was so lucky to have a mother and a grandmother who loved him unconditionally and would do anything for him, so I shouldn't carry guilt about raising him without a father. I was a good mother, and Ray helped me love my life and myself again.

I wiped my tears and smiled to myself. I made up my mind in that instant that I was going to write this story to the best of my ability, not only to cherish the memories of Father Yusif, but also to let the world know that Ray was not a coldhearted, calculated killer. He was a child once, a ray of sunshine who could have warmed up many people's hearts and touched their souls with his kind and generous heart. Instead, what happened to him pushed him to live on the dark side of the sun.

I published my story, and it became the most-read story of the year for our newspaper, and it even went on to get national acclaim. It made me quite famous, so I got a promotion. Things couldn't get better.

However, in the back of my mind, I couldn't stop thinking about Ray. I wanted to see him one more time and let him know how his story had changed people's perspectives and opinions about him, and that as a society, we all should take responsibility for the forgotten children.

It wasn't that difficult, since I had actually become a kind of celebrity around the prison. As I heard, all the prisoners wanted me to do a story on each of them, which was surprising to me. I always thought they hated me, but it turned out they wanted the outside world to know that not all of them were monsters. Wrong choices had been made, and they were human just like the rest of us.

I called Ray's doctor and asked him if it would be okay for me to visit and bring a copy of the newspaper article for Ray. He said that would be great and that since Ray was very sick, this might cheer him up.

The day I was leaving to visit Ray, I got up early and went to the kitchen to have my usual morning coffee. As always, my mother was standing beside the stove, making me breakfast, even though she knew I never wanted anything except for a cup of coffee. Still, she would force me to eat, and she would always win.

There was a wrapped gift box on the kitchen table. I asked her, "What is this, Ma?"

Without even looking at me, she replied, "It's for Ray. You are going to take it, and I will not take no for an answer."

How could I argue with that answer? I hugged her from behind and kissed her shoulder gently.

I had told my mother the truth about Ray's identity, but somehow, she still kept a special place in her heart just for him. Maybe deep down, she didn't want to believe the truth. Whatever the reason, I never questioned my mother but just let her have these joyful illusions for herself.

"Mom, do you want to come with me and visit Ray today?"

She turned around, smiling joyously like a little kid. "Can I?"

I took a sip of my coffee then told her, "Well, what is the worst thing they might say? That you will have to wait in the car?"

She quickly replied, "No problem, I'll wait as long as it takes."

She hurried off to get ready, and I called the doctor and asked him if it was okay.

He told me, "As long as you don't mind your mother coming to the prison, then it's fine with me, but remember that Ray is in a special care unit and is very ill. The tumor hasn't left him much time to live. He's heavily medicated so he can cope with the pain. He might not even recognize you."

My heart was heavy from the news, but I still wanted to see Ray. I owed him that much.

We arrived at the prison. It was a very cloudy day, and a storm was brewing on the horizon. I took a deep breath, looked at my mother, and asked her, "Are you okay, Ma? Remember, if at any time you feel this is too much for you to take, just let me know and we can leave. Okay?"

She took my hand and told me, "My dear Lilli, I am so proud of you and thankful that you are doing this for me. I'll be okay, I promise you." My mother was just excited to finally be meeting Ray.

They took us to a new building, which was apparently the special care unit for critically ill patients. This building was dark and sad, and an eerie silence hung over it. The front desk lady told me to follow the corridor, and Ray's room would be at the end on the left side. It felt like the longest walk I'd ever taken. My mother walked behind me, and I turned to see if she was okay. There was sadness yet also anticipation in her eyes. She gave me a smile to make me believe she was doing okay.

I walked into the small room. It had one window, obscured by metal grilles. The window was partially open, and I could feel the fresh air. There was Ray. He was all skin and bone, and he had an oxygen mask on, along with a handful of IVs connected to his body. His eyes were closed, and he appeared to be sleeping. It was obvious that his condition was much worse than when I'd seen him a few months ago. I felt guilty for not coming and visiting him earlier. My mother touched my hand and brought me back from my deep thoughts of guilt.

My mother gently told me, "Silly of me to bring him baklava now." We both smiled and got teary-eyed at the same time.

"Oh Mom, I'm so sorry, I should have listened to you and brought it to him before, when you told me to," I whispered.

"It's okay. We are here now, and that's all that matters." My mother walked closer to him and just stood beside his bed for a few seconds. She put her hand on his chest, then she leaned forward and kissed his forehead. I was shocked and didn't know how to react. There was no one else around, only the three of us. She pulled a chair close to his bed and sat beside him. She took his hand and started to pray in her mother language. I just stood in the corner beside the window, watching her. Two strangers had just crossed each other's paths. Both had lost something precious. But somehow, my mother was calming her wounded soul by reaching out to Ray and showing him the kindness that he had never experienced from his own mother.

As I was watching, the doctor walked in. I wiped my tears and walked toward him, wanting to apologize for what he was witnessing. He put his finger to his mouth and shook his head, indicating that we should not interrupt what was happening between my mother and Ray.

Instead, the doctor pointed outside the room, and we both walked out to the corridor.

He told me, "Ms. Lilli, it is perfectly all right. Your mother is not doing any harm, and to be honest, I think it is comforting to Ray. He can feel the love, and he can hear your mother's gentle voice. You can stay as long as you want, and you are more than welcome to come back with your mother anytime she wishes."

I didn't know why, but all of a sudden, I put my arms around the doctor's shoulders and gave him a hug. He gently patted my back and said, "It's fine. I understand."

I pulled back in embarrassment and apologized to him.

"Please, Ms. Lilli, you don't have to apologize. We're all human, and I know your mother is still mourning for her lost son. Let them have this moment. I'm sure Ray is in peace right now. Let them comfort each other in their own way." The doctor left, and I went back to the room.

To my surprise, Ray's eyes were open, and my mother was still holding his hand. They both looked at each other, and she continued to pray for him. As I walked closer to the bed, I realized she was talking to him, not praying.

I heard my mother say how much she loved him and how she had been looking for him all these years but was never able to find him. How every year she had bought him a birthday present and saved all of them for him because she knew she would find him one day.

Ray had a tear running from the corner of his eye. He was nodding and smiling, believing every word my mother told him. My mouth dropped open from the shock of what I was hearing. Why was my own mother telling all those lies to Ray? She knew it wasn't true, that Ray wasn't her son. I had told her the truth the same day I heard it from the doctor.

Why? I just didn't know how to confront her. They were in their own world, and it wasn't my place to intrude and stop their moment. My mother was patting him, hugging him, and kissing his hand while she talked to him, and Ray watched her without any fight or struggle to get away from her. He was like a child listening to his mother while she told a story. He was in such a peaceful state that I had never seen him in before. He struggled to breathe even with the oxygen mask, but his eyes widened, and he tried to say something to my mother.

I didn't know what to do except run down the hall and ask for the doctor. By the time I got back to Ray's room, my mom's head was on Ray's chest, and her face exhibited such peace that I had never seen before.

The doctor looked at the machine monitoring Ray's heart.

"He's gone," the doctor said.

I didn't know what to say. I looked at my mother and Ray's lifeless body. He had a smile on his face, like he had finally found the peace he had always been looking for.

In that moment, I realized one important thing. Sometimes, a simple lie can set you free and give you closure and peace of mind. Even if you know it's not the whole truth, all you need is to hear what your heart has wanted to hear for a long time.

My mother never had a chance to say goodbye to her baby boy when he was taken away from her, and Ray never had a chance to hear a lullaby when he was a scared little boy. All he wanted was a safe whisper to put him to sleep. Two strangers came together in the most unlikely and unique way that I still can't explain, but all I can say is that my mother was not the same woman from that day forward.

I wasn't so much upset with her as I was shocked and confused. After all, who was I to judge?

If we'll only let it happen, love and compassion can find a way into our lives in so many different ways.

The End

MY GENTLE GIANT

Do you recall any stories that your parents told you when you were a child? I unquestionably do! My mother was a dramatic storyteller. Her sweet voice kept me on edge each time I tuned in to hear her stories. She always had several of her own childhood tales. These included a range of different genres and both fiction and nonfiction stories. Some of them, I later realized, were intended to be life lessons. Often, she would highlight how fortunate I was because I didn't have to go through experiences like hers. It was so captivating how she narrated stories; they were detailed, engaging, empowering, interactive, and authentic. All of her stories piqued my interest when I was a young boy.

One night, she had a new one to tell me about her childhood. She commenced her narration of the story, and, in suspense, I listened attentively.

She opened with one of her favorite introductory lines, "When I was growing up, we did not have much. As a child, my creative ability helped me design my own dreamland. Often, I would imagine myself as the main character in a story, having an awesome time at the playground with my toys. Unlike you, Michael, I had to work before I was allowed to play. Nowadays, kids just have basic chores, like an obligation to clean their rooms or take the trash out. What a joke! I had to cook in order to eat. Otherwise, I would go to bed hungry. It was a matter of survival then. It was my responsibility to take care of my younger siblings, as well as the neighbors' kids, should they ask. Toys and clothing were luxuries, not necessities. Having a fabulous time playing with other children on our street or going to their houses to play with toys were as good as going to Disneyland, should you contrast it with the present world.

"I stayed home more often than not because of a rare genetic blood disorder. This illness made me pass out often. On the days that I managed to attend school, other students regularly harassed me. The monstrous embarrassment the school kids subjected me to was truly excruciating as a child, unfortunately. This was all just because of my appearance. Indeed, even today, I just can't grasp why they made fun of me such a great amount, all because of the freckles all over my face and my curly, red hair. Envision my predicament. I felt that the illness was a gift from God. On my worst days, I didn't have to go to class, which I incidentally thought was God's gift to me, since I didn't have to deal with mortification from the horrendous bullying. In any case, I realized I needed to do something about it.

"At home, there was only contention between my parents. We were poor, and I mean truly poor. We had very little nourishment. I did not have an adoring family lifestyle. I did not have friends at school. I became a recluse, an outcast, and, as some kids used to call me, a weirdo! So, I chose to make a move. I made up my own companion in my own little world, somebody I could converse with, play with, and have a fabulous time with. I needed a companion who could protect me. Whenever my father stormed into my room to spank me, or when children at school pulled and made fun of my hair, I needed my warrior princess who was tall and strong. She was my closest friend, and I called her my gentle giant.

"Why gentle giant, you might ask? Well, I wanted her to be kind and thoughtful, yet at the same time strong and invincible like a giant! It would have been very easy to create a cruel and angry monster in my imagination, one that could destroy everyone who hurt me, especially the bullies at my school. Nonetheless, I was drawn to create a gentle and kind giant. Perhaps it was because I never experienced love and kindness as a child. Regardless, that was how my gentle giant came to be.

"My giant was tall, like one of the skyscrapers in New York, but not necessarily that humongous—it's kind of funny, but I didn't want the giant to have a sore neck due to constantly bending her head. My gentle giant was strong and steadfast, like one of those castles in storybooks, with big, bright eyes that shone like a lighthouse, so she could see far away. She had a tender heart, like a lioness caring for her cubs, and at the same time, she was brave and fearless."

Suddenly, the excitement in my mother's voice disappeared. Then she gazed at me intensely and said, "I hope that one day you will find your own gentle giant, Michael."

"What happened next, Mom?" That was all I could blurt out. I really loved it when she told me her life stories. Those were the only moments when her face would light up, and an aura of elation would radiate from her. This time, we were both just relaxing in the kitchen, yet I could sense deep emotion from her as her mind took a trip back to her childhood days.

She proceeded with the story, "My gentle giant impacted my life for the better. I soon discovered a happy atmosphere at school, living in my own world. My grades improved, and I became a member of the handball team. Previously, I was extremely shy and afraid of other kids making fun of me. Back home, my parents could see the positive change in me, and they were happy. However, they still struggled financially and in their relationship with each other. Having my gentle giant changed everything. I had someone to talk to and someone to look up to when things got tough. Other kids thought I was crazy for having an invisible friend, but I didn't care. It didn't matter to me anymore.

Ms. Brown, my English teacher, was my favorite. She looked like an angel to me, and she was always so kind and so patient toward everyone, especially me. There was this particular day that I can recall, when a few kids were making fun of me because I had this invisible friend. In Ms. Brown's defense of me, she told them that it was actually really cool. She said, 'Only a person with a special power and a great imagination can have an invisible friend, and I think Sue is a unique girl.' Then she smiled and winked at me. In that moment, I felt like I was on top of the highest castle, standing tall and waving to everyone who was looking up to see me. I felt a super power inside of me."

My mother's eyes became watery as she narrated that beautiful moment when her English teacher had showed her support. She stopped the story momentarily, gazing out the kitchen window. There was a momentary silence between us.

"Why did you stop, Mom? What happened to your invisible friend?" I exclaimed, after a minute or so of silence.

She looked back at me, then she lowered her eyes and said, "I lost her as I was growing up. Maybe I lost her when I was trying to discover myself as a teenager. Whatever it was, I changed. I started to act like other kids. I tried to act 'normal' to blend into a crowd, hoping that no one would notice me. I guess I wanted to be invisible." She looked at me with her teary eyes and said to me, "We are all capable of having our own gentle giant inside of us. If you find your own, promise me that you'll never let it go, no matter how old you get. Try to keep it alive inside you."

I promised her that I would do my best not to let it go. I knew in that moment the one thing that could make her feel better was a hug. I embraced her tightly, and then walked to my room. That night, I kept thinking about my mother's story. How cool would it be if I had my own gentle giant?

I had a very close relationship with my mother at this point in my childhood. We talked openly about anything and everything. I will forever remember the moment she first opened up to me about her heartaches. She had been through so much, and it was heartbreaking to learn that my father never tried to understand her or love her the way she deserved to be loved.

My father was a one-man show. He was a legend in his own mind. He thought he was the most perfect man on this earth, and the rest of us were just there to please him. My mother and I were never good enough for him. We never had a loving or emotional relationship with him, and that was all his own doing. He was not happy with us, I guess. I think that deep inside he was just a miserable and unhappy man.

Over time, my relationship with my mother changed because of my father. I hated the way my mother let him take advantage of her. Why couldn't she see how wonderful she was? She was a beautiful woman with amazing talents. There was nothing that she couldn't create with her own two hands, but for some reason, she was always begging for my dad's love and affection, and that son of a bitch never gave it to her. He could talk to other women at gatherings or parties for hours, yet when it came to his own wife, he was always busy or not in the mood to talk. The only thing he would do whenever he wanted to show her some kind of attention was to take her to the movies. Obviously, the choice of movie was always his. They would spend two hours in a crowded movie theater, not speaking to each other, watching whatever he wanted to see, and then they'd come home. There was nothing in it for my mother. It was all about him.

Whenever she would object, a fight ensued. Then there was drama, and ultimately, for no apparent reason, I would receive physical punishment. He would take his frustrations out on me and show us who the boss was, I guess. After many years, since my mother didn't want me to go through the pain, she stopped complaining or objecting to whatever he wanted and ultimately let herself die on the inside.

As I grew older, everything got worse, especially my relationship with my dad. We didn't talk much, except if we had to. The only time he wanted to talk to me was when he wanted to criticize me or if I'd done something wrong. Otherwise, silence was normal in our house. My mother was lost in her own world. She became a woman not capable of remembering something simple like someone's name or phone number. She couldn't talk on the phone for more than a few seconds. She had no friends to go to, and she wouldn't do anything for herself. I started to hate her with a passion.

To be honest, I didn't even like myself, and I think I hated myself more. All I wanted to do was finish high school and get away from those two, as far away as possible. I held so much pain inside of me. Finally, I found an escape, a way to release and numb the pain. I started hurting myself. The first time I did it was when my dad slapped me so hard that I was dizzy for a while. I quickly rushed to my room and sat there, not knowing what to do. I wanted to scream, punch the wall, hit myself, anything to release the anger inside of me. I started to bite myself and scratch my skin so I could see blood. I wanted the pain to get out somehow, but I wasn't sure how that was possible.

One day, I was sitting at my desk, pressing a pencil into my skin. I kept pressing and it hurt more and more. Strangely, this made me feel good. The pain made me unable to think about anything else except for this moment, and seeing the red color of the blood flowing from my arms was strange yet relieving.

From that day on, I used to get home after school and immediately go to my room, lock the door behind me, and lay on my bed. I'd use a safety pin or a sharp pen that would break my skin and just let the pain, frustration, and anger fade away with each drop of blood that dripped from my wrist. Most of the time, I would get up and look at my arms, and even if they had stopped bleeding, I still felt good. I would go to the bathroom, wash my arms, and put some bandages over the cuts. No one could ever see anything. Neither of my parents ever checked up on me to see if I was alive or what I was up to in my room for such a long time.

From that day on, it became my dark little secret. It was something that helped me release my anger. This was my body, and no one could tell me what to do. I was in control. At school, I was not doing very well. I used to be an honors student, but gradually my grades dropped, and I started to hang out with the wrong crowd.

I thought that maybe this was the way I could get back at my dad, because he was so proud of himself and kept telling everyone that I was just like him, smart, and sharp. I hated when he spoke about me like I wasn't in the room. I didn't need his approval about how smart I was and how alike we were. To be honest, I hated the idea that I was going to be just like him. He was miserable, a control freak, angry, and emotionally empty.

For a long time, nothing changed in my life. I became skilled at hiding my cuts from everyone. I would wear long-sleeve shirts all the time. I stopped taking swimming classes. Football was my only other resource to release the anger in me. If anyone ever saw me naked, then they would figure out what was going on, so I tried to be very sneaky about it when I took showers after our football games. Even around the house, I had to make sure that no one ever saw me shirtless.

As for my mother, I could see the sadness in her eyes from miles away. I felt sorry for her, but I was angry at the same time. She didn't know how good she was and that he didn't deserve her. Sometimes, she would talk about her childhood and how her parents never gave her love, so now she was trying to give her family the things that she'd never felt. She wanted to give us love and a sense of security. Maybe that's why she put up with my dad's cruelty. He was killing her day by day and minute by minute by ignoring her, neglecting her needs, and just waiting for her to drop dead. As the years passed by, she became even more forgetful, and she used to get sick more often.

She started to pass out frequently, most likely due to her blood disorder, and that bastard not even once called an ambulance or took her to the doctor to see if there was some way to help her. The only things she was still good at and he let her do were house chores and grocery shopping. She adjusted herself to being a simple housekeeper and a nanny, and whenever he felt like it, she could warm up his bed. He abused her without even putting a finger on her and was slowly killing her without pulling a trigger, and I witnessed the whole thing. I didn't know what to do. I think that's why my rage and anger toward her grew stronger.

Finally, one day, I think God took mercy on us, because my father left us for another woman. There was not a word or anything to indicate that he loved me or even cared for me a little. He just packed his suitcase and disappeared from our lives.

What he left behind was a fifteen-year-old boy full of anger, confusion, and fear of uncertainty, and a woman who was emotionally and mentally crippled. Until now, all I'd witnessed in my mother's life was that she was capable of taking care of the house, cooking, and cleaning. How on earth would she be able to support me and care for me now? My father had been in charge of everything else around the house. I was afraid and uncertain of what would happen next.

Somehow, I had to find a way to cope with all these feelings. I had always suspected something like this would happen. Often, I was left at home with my mother while my father was away on business trips, doing this and that, really just about anything to escape from the house and us. Now that he was gone for good, I wasn't sure who was going to take care of me.

I vividly remember the day that man left the house without a word to either of us. I heard my mother crying in her bedroom. I went to check on her, and she was sitting on the floor, hugging her knees and crying like a child. She was scared, and it looked so pathetic. It just made me so angry in that moment, and I didn't know what to say to her. Should I put my hand on her shoulder and comfort her, or should I just scream at her? I mean, for God's sake, did she even consider the impact this had on me? How on earth was I going to believe this weak, puny woman could handle everything from now on?

I began to scream at her, "For God's sake, Mother, what's wrong with you? You should be happy that he finally left us. Now we can breathe! What did you expect, for him to change? Do you seriously think he cares for us? He never has, and he never will. Wake up, Mom. Stop crying. Be a normal mother, as you should, and act like a normal human being for once. I hate you, and I hope you leave me alone too." I ran to my room and slammed the door as hard as I could. I was worried about our future but somehow relieved too. There was only one way that I knew to handle my pain, fear, and anger. The only truth was in those moments when I could feel nothing but the pain, and it was great.

In my room, I started to cut myself, then I lay on my bed, thinking about my father and what life would be like going forward. Whatever lay ahead, however daunting, at least I could thank God that my father had finally left us. In my mind, I revisited the time when he still lived with us, remembering how I used to pray daily after my mother picked me up from school. Praying that he wouldn't be home, that maybe he had gone out with his lady friend or somewhere else. This prayer was a yearning for some tranquility every time I stepped into the house after school. The trauma from his angry outbursts had emotionally damaged me for years, so I loved getting home while he was away. It was truly a blessing to me.

My dad was a very smart man, especially when it came to ideas for generating income. He was a brilliant engineer by profession. He spent most of his time at home in his office, working. On other occasions, though, he spent his time at home either talking to his friends on the phone or emailing his girlfriends. It was as though we were nonexistent in the house, and he had built his own world apart from us. Even though I was young at the time, I could still sense that whatever he did for me was just out of obligation. My mother used to beg him to spend time with me. Even when we had time together as father and son, it always ended up with him verbally or physically abusing me.

I grew up to be angry all the time. There was an unspoken, deep hatred in my heart toward him that was so dark and confusing. At the same time, he was my father, and I loved him too. Now that he was gone, I had to become a man. I had to do something with my life and help my mother too. After all, she was my mother, and I had to live with her since I was a minor.

A couple months had passed since he'd left, and at least it was peaceful in the house. My mother was busy looking for a job, and I started to feel a little less afraid about my future. Still, nothing changed at school in terms of behavior. I was still the same troublemaker, not focused on schoolwork. However, my life changed when I met Coach Tony.

It was an autumn morning. I went to school with the same bad attitude and a big chip on my shoulder. I was always angry with everyone at school. Throughout my school years, I had developed this well-known, disrespectful, fierce look that used to just annoy all my teachers. During the first period of math class, I received a note requesting that I go to the gym after class to meet our football coach.

"Oh man, what have I done now?" I blurted out loud in class. All my classmates started laughing, and this infuriated my teacher.

"Stop disturbing my class and leave now, Michael," he shouted firmly.

As I entered the gym, I spotted my old coach talking to someone I didn't recognize. The stranger was a tall, muscular black man with the deepest voice. He looked like he belonged in an action movie. For a moment, I nervously wondered if I was in trouble and they were going to send me to prison or something.

As I was deep in my own thoughts and fears, trying to figure out some bullshit story to tell them and contemplating whether I should just turn around and run, I felt a hand on my shoulder. I froze and looked up to see my old coach standing beside me.

"Hi, Coach," I uttered.

Coach nodded toward the stranger and said, "This is Coach Tony. He wants to interview each player privately. As we all know, you have an amazing athletic ability, and all you have to do is fix your attitude. Otherwise, I can't have you on my team, and you know that."

Coach Tony shook my hand with his huge hand and said, "Michael, I'm so happy to meet you. Coach was telling me about the incredible talent you have. Looking forward to coaching you, son!"

It was the first time that someone had talked so kindly to me and expressed that much confidence in me.

I looked down at his feet, avoiding eye contact, and said to him, "I'm sorry to disappoint you, but I am not all that good, Coach. Besides, I just want to finish high school and then I'm out. Football is just passing the time for me while I'm here."

He folded his arms across his chest and asked, "Out where, Michael? You can't always choose to run away from yourself and everything else. One day, you'll have to stop and make a decision about what to do with the rest of your life."

I looked up at him, wondering what on earth he was talking about, but I had no idea that this mountain of muscle was about to change my life forever.

Coach Tony smiled at me. We walked out of the gym and proceeded toward the football field. He talked about his childhood, and how he came from the worst area of Chicago. He grew up with five siblings. They shared a one-bedroom apartment. Furthermore, his single mother worked three jobs just to support the family.

He continued, "You see, Michael, the world is enormous for a reason. Nevertheless, we always think our problems and our lives are bigger than this world. At times, it feels like we are alone on this gigantic planet. We are not. Whenever things get out of your control, pull yourself away from the situation you're dealing with. Like an eagle, let your mind and body fly away to the highest mountain, then look down at everything. Only then can you see how everything is so small and insignificant, even your problems. Life is like a maze; you can't remain stationary in one corridor and let everything pass you by. There might be a better life or a better opportunity waiting for you around the next corner. Don't be afraid to let go and try something new. Be excited and be hopeful about your life instead of just numbing your pain and not dealing with your situation."

I froze, wondering how he knew what I was going through. It was as though someone had told him my life story. After that conversation, I felt different. Something happened that I couldn't explain. Whatever it was, I was so excited, and I wanted to tell my mom about it. Usually, by the time I got home, my mother would be in the kitchen preparing dinner. I would come home in a bad mood and just say a quick hello before hiding in my bedroom. I would slip into my routine of cutting myself, thinking that I was numbing the pain.

This day was different. I walked straight to the kitchen and hugged my mother. She was taken aback to see me this joyful and in high spirits. She looked me over in wonder and immediately asked if I wanted something to eat. Then she asked why I was in such a good mood. I told her about my time with the coach and what had transpired. That afternoon, I hung out in the kitchen with my mother, talking and talking. This was the first time in a long time that I enjoyed my mother's company, and I also managed to finish my homework. That night, I went to bed without a fight with my mother or any angry outbursts. I couldn't even find the urge to hurt myself to feel better. Usually, I would lock my bedroom door, but that night I left it wide open, because when I was younger, my mother used to come to my bedroom, kiss my forehead, and pray with me. When I got older, I stopped allowing her to come into my room. On this night, I called for her and asked if she could come into my room so we could pray together.

I struggled to sleep that night. I imagined that I was in a maze, and I visualized many rooms and corridors. I imagined everything that I wanted to be was just waiting in the next room. All I had to do was imagine flying like an eagle and seeing the world from a different perspective. I flew higher and higher until my house and the hurtful people in my life looked like ants. Within my imagination, I could see how small they were, and how they could not hurt me. The coach was right; I actually felt better.

The next day, I couldn't wait to go to school and see Coach Tony. Our team practiced every morning. What consumed my thoughts was the urge to learn more about him and how he survived all the problems of his childhood.

Maybe I was just selfish and looking for a way to help myself. Maybe I saw my pain and what I was going through reflected in his story. Whatever it was, I knew he had a solution to calm me down. Every school day, I talked with Coach for anywhere from five to fifteen minutes. Sometimes, I would quickly grab my lunch and head to the gym, where I would have my lunch with Coach Tony.

Coach talked about how his father was a troubled soul and a cruel man who used to abuse his family, and Coach got the worst of it. Oftentimes, Coach stood up for his mother to stop the physical abuse, which was why he experienced more torment from his father.

He told me, "One night, I asked my mom, 'Why don't you scream or stand up to him? Say something. Fight him back.' I can still remember the pain in her voice when she said, 'I know what you think, Tony, that your mother is just a pathetic woman. But I know that if he doesn't empty his evilness and anger on me, he will start to abuse my children. That's why I let him use me. I know it's wrong, but I can't do anything about it right now. I'm working on it, trust me.' There was a spark in her eyes all of a sudden! That was the moment I found out that my assumptions about my mother were wrong. Apparently, she was smart and had been working on a plan. All she was waiting for was the right time, the right moment to free us. It was then that I found out she was such a strong woman, and I just hadn't noticed it before. I underestimated her power. My mother was studying part time to become a nurse. She was saving money and planning to take us to a new apartment and a better neighborhood."

As I listened to Coach Tony's story, I noticed that he had the same look as my mother did when she talked about her childhood. Coach continued his story, "I was surprised and proud of her. Suddenly, I felt safe and hopeful about our future. From that day on, I started to have secret meetings with my mother pertaining to the future of our family. She told me not to reveal the discussions to my other siblings, because they were so young and might talk to someone, and then our plans would be ruined. Every night, when all of us sat around the kitchen table while my mother cooked for us. She used to look over at us with a smile and then wink at me. This was a sign that everything was going to work out very soon. It was so moving for me to have my mom's trust at such a young age. It made me feel like the man of the house. I wasn't only her bodyguard but someone she could confide in. It made me feel special." Coach stopped the story, put his hand gently on my shoulder, and told me it was time for me to go home.

I was so drawn into the story that being told to go home felt like my inner self had just been yanked out of my body. The warmth, the comfort, and the safe atmosphere dissipated. I pleaded with Coach to just go on with his story for a little more time. He kindly reminded me that it was time to go home. He emphasized that I should honor the commitment I had made to my mother that I would arrive home on time.

Football practice became my life, all because I wanted to spend more time with Coach Tony. This gave me an opportunity to receive regular mentorship from Coach. The conversations with Coach impacted my life tremendously. Since he had shared the story of his childhood, I too opened up to him about my father. I felt comfortable enough to even open up about my darkest secret, self-harm. I had just gained a best friend. Coach never judged me. He continued to encourage me to work hard in school and improve my grades. I couldn't let the cruelty of my father get the best of me. I had to believe that for every problem, there was a solution.

He didn't criticize me at all when I told him about my cutting. I told him that I thought I was a freak. On many occasions, I was so ashamed about doing this to my body, but at the same time, it kind of made me feel so good. Stopping this dangerous habit was an uphill struggle for me.

Coach shook me by my shoulders and stared at me sternly but with much care. He reiterated that what I told him did not make him think that I was a freak. "We all deal with our pain in our own ways. Sometimes, all we need is to trust the right person and open our heart to them. Let me tell you about my painkiller, Michael. I used to pull out my eyebrow hair whenever I had issues at school or at home, or whenever I didn't know how to cope with my problems." While Coach explained, I just couldn't control myself, and I chuckled.

"I'm sorry, Coach, I didn't mean to laugh at you." I clapped a hand over my mouth.

His response was comforting. He knew it was kind of stupid yet funny at the same time, the idea of plucking out one's eyebrow hair. "If you want to really laugh, now imagine me with no eyebrows. Oh man, I looked so weird, and let me tell you, it was so freaky that even my own mother couldn't stop laughing at me whenever she saw me without eyebrows. I used to tell my friends that it was a hormonal thing causing hair loss, just in my eyebrows. Strangely, they used to believe this made-up story."

Coach and I just burst out in uncontrollable laughter. My other teammates who were in the vicinity glanced at us, and I am sure they were wondering what all that laughter was about.

That afternoon, when I repeated the story to my mother, we both laughed hysterically, even up to the extent of tearing up a little.

As the days went by, my mother would wait eagerly at home to hear the latest story from Coach. She acted like she was following a TV show, just waiting for the next episode. One of her favorite lines to say immediately when I arrived home from school was, "What happened next?"

Just the curiosity about Coach's childhood stories was phenomenal. It seemed to renew my mother and restore her superb individuality. That was my mother as I knew her. She resumed running every morning. Occasionally, I would see her working with her camera. She was back! She began taking pictures again, rather breathtaking pictures, I must say. Oh, what an amazing photographer she was. I guess the many years of abuse from my father caused her to shelve her photography talent temporarily. I would just roll my eyes at the way she danced while cooking. It was like seeing a new person compared to the depressed mother I had grown accustomed to.

Our house was so peaceful. No one had to walk on eggshells anymore. I could run, scream, and just be a kid! It was thrilling. Coach was changing my life, and at the same time, he unknowingly impacted my mother for the better.

The imaginary maze method that Coach had first introduced to me seemed so promising. Sometimes, I would imagine being in an empty corridor, a place where I felt pain and fear, then I would remind myself that all I had to do was run to another corridor to find my peace. Coach used to tell me that things would always work out if I could only see everything from higher ground. All these wonderful visualizations made me stronger.

Sometimes, after our football practice, Coach and I would walk around the football field with some other teammates who had different life issues. Coach used those walks to mentor us, relating to us through his own troublesome teenage years. However, he had reached a point in life when he decided to make good choices for his life.

There was one particular story I recall from those walks, as Coach narrated it. "After my mother told me about her plans and how she was going to move us away from that life with our abusive father, I thought that this was it. We were going to be okay. My grades improved, and I also started to actually take care of my siblings. Little did I know, life can easily turn upside down in the blink of an eye.

"One day, I came home from school. There were police cars outside, lights flashing. Policemen walked in and out of my house. It looked like a scene from the *Criminal Minds* TV show, if any of you kids have watched that before. My heart was pounding so fast, as if it would pop out of my chest any second. My legs became numb, and I couldn't walk. I knew something horrible must have happened. Tears overwhelmed me. Anger began to build up, and I ran toward our house like a wild animal, screaming, 'Mom! Mom!' As soon as I reached our doorway, a police officer blocked my entry. This enraged me even more. I kept crying, punching, and screaming so I could free my arms. Finally, I fought my way free, and I rushed in. I couldn't believe what I saw. My mother lay on the floor, covered in her own blood. At that moment, everything played in slow motion. I couldn't blink, I couldn't breathe, and my mouth hung ajar. It seemed as though not an ounce of oxygen made it to my brain. The heavy weight of emptiness overwhelmed me at that moment.

"I stormed over to my father and screamed from the top of my lungs, 'He killed her! He killed her!' The wave of anger grew larger and larger. All I wanted to do was run out of that house and never look back. I didn't think about my siblings or my mother. Nothing made sense. I was confused and angry with everyone, especially my mother for letting him destroy our plan. I blamed my poor, dead mother for everything.

"I freed myself again from the police officer's arms and ran out into street. I don't know how long I ran, and I didn't know where I was going; all I knew was that I had to get away from everything and everyone. All I could see were my mother's kind eyes looking over and winking at me while she cooked in the kitchen, letting me know that we were going to be okay. That image was so painful, and I had to block it out forever. I couldn't run anymore, I was so exhausted. Once I realized it was dark, I knew I had to go somewhere for the night. I couldn't sleep outside. I saw an old YMCA building, which was more like an old, smelly gym. It didn't look open except for one room that had its lights turned on. I walked toward the door and pushed it open gently. It didn't make any noise, so I thought I could sneak in and sleep somewhere and maybe find something to eat too."

Coach stopped the story abruptly, then he looked around at all of us and said, "Okay guys, go back to your classrooms." We were so engrossed in his story that we had lost track of time. Regardless, we pleaded that he would just tell us what happened next. He wouldn't oblige. "Go back to your classes, and I'll tell you next time," he said.

The rest of that day, I thought nonstop about Coach Tony's story. If something happened to my mother, how would I react? How could he overcome such a tragedy and pull through in life to get where he was today? There were so many questions I was itching to ask him, and the next day felt like an eternity away. By the time I returned home, my mother was in her little garden, doing some gardening. I had a hunch that something was wrong. I could see that she was in a bad mood. She didn't respond to my greeting, even though it was my usual cheerful greeting. Then I asked her if there was something wrong.

All I received was a sharp, piercing look, followed by, "Nothing, I'm just sick of you and your behavior. I am sick of doing everything around this house." All of a sudden, she was screaming and yelling at me. This was so out of the blue. We had been doing well lately, or so I'd thought. Her tempers and lashing out at me had been kind of common when my father was around. During that time, I sometimes tolerated it. I was sure it was her way of releasing her frustrations.

This time, I kind of snapped and yelled back at her too. I screamed a few profanities at the top of my lungs, grabbing things around me to throw at the wall. It was as though I were possessed, because I just could not stop. "What do you want from me, you crazy woman? No wonder you are alone! You keep pushing me and pushing me! You want me to study, want me to be the best all the time! Telling me to do this, do that! I'm going nuts! Just leave me alone!" I yelled and cried at the same time. She just stood there and looked at me with exasperation. Then I ran to my room.

Contemplative thoughts and questions flooded my mind. Oh, how I wished I had a normal family like other kids—a normal home with normal parents. I despised my father so much, but I missed him at the same time. Have you ever hated yourself because you can't help but love someone you hate? This is some kind of oxymoron, yet we often encounter such circumstances that are so perplexing, like my family dynamics.

It didn't make any sense, but in that moment, nothing made sense in my life or in my mind. I felt bad for my mother too. She was doing everything by herself, and she was under a lot of pressure.

Afterwards, I was so remorseful of my behavior, and I really wanted to go to her room and apologize. Maybe I'd give her a big hug and let her know that I understood her loneliness. Maybe she was scared, possibly unsure about her life and our future. But I was too angry at her to do something about it. While I was thinking about all of this, I dozed off and fell asleep until I felt my mom's gentle hand on my head. She apologized for losing her temper and said she needed to be strong for us. In a calm tone, she reminded me that every family had these moments some-times. Nonetheless, in such tense moments, we needed to do something about it. I was just so humbled when she said that she needed to do something to manage her anger. She was right; her temper was like a tornado. It could happen so suddenly and just about destroy everything.

It was a beautiful, sweet atmosphere as we reconciled.

The next day, I went to school in such a bad mood. I didn't want to see Coach at all. Unfortunately, I couldn't hide from him since I had to go to football practice. Although I tried to avoid any eye contact with him and used just about every trick in the book to stay away from him, my attempts alone seemed to expose me.

I guess he sensed it, as he approached me. Calmly, he said, "Hello stranger, are you okay?"

"No, Coach. Please forget about talking to me today, okay? You can't fix it."

He put his hand on my shoulder. "No, I don't want to fix anything. You will do it all by yourself. Fly to a higher place, Michael, remember that? Then you can see clearly. Remember, nothing is really that bad if you choose to let it go and make it insignificant. It's all in your head. No matter what, you can choose how your day will be." Then Coach looked straight into my eyes. "Don't you want to know what happened with the rest of my story?" He softly punched my chest. I smiled and nodded to indicate that he could proceed with his story. It was amazing how this man could change my whole mood with a few simple words. He was my hero, my gentle giant!

We started to walk together, and Coach continued his story, "That was a dreadful night. After seeing the horrific, lifeless body of my mother lying in a pool of blood, I had rushed out of the house aimlessly. I slept in that tiny YMCA building that night and several nights after. It wasn't totally empty, but I took careful measures to avoid everyone else. Each night, I would stay in an empty storage room and just crawl into a corner. I was such a mess that it took me a while to understand that nothing was ever going be the same. My mother was gone, and with her, she took her big plan. Now what? I was alone. The avalanche inside my head kept rolling, getting bigger and bigger. The thoughts inside my head frightened me.

"Revenge, hate, and rage toward my father were my motivation. I stopped going to school. I started selling stolen goods to make quick cash. It was like a mini cartel, because I was working for this 'boss' guy. He had several other kids doing his dirty work for him too. In return, he gave us food and a place to stay. That was enough for me. Some nights, while everyone else slept, I would just sit beside a window, gazing into the quiet night and thinking about my mother and my siblings. I knew deep down that I wasn't happy, and this wasn't the life I had imagined for myself. It especially wasn't the life my mother wanted me to have. I was too young, angry, and confused, though, to think straight and do something about it.

"The days turned into months then into years as I continued in a downward spiral. My lifestyle was all about sex, drugs, alcohol, and stealing. Thank goodness, I did not degenerate into killing. I was miserable inside. It finally dawned on me when I turned twenty years old that I had to do something about my life. The only other option was to just end my life. I had to make a change, not only for myself but also for my mother's sake. I knew it wouldn't be easy to change, but the change had to start from somewhere. Taking one step at a time became my motto. I created simple goals for myself so that I wouldn't get discouraged. I knew I could do it. Often, I would visualize my mother's face while she was cooking. I'd recall the image of her in the kitchen, when she looked at me and winked. That was a sign to me that everything was going to be okay. I knew that as long as I had that picture in my mind, nothing could stop me.

"We are all gifted and talented in different ways. There is an intrinsic value to each of our unique gifts. In my case, I was always very athletic, and I loved football. This love for sports urged me to go back to my old school. Surprisingly, my old football coach was still there. His name was Coach Abraham. The guy still loved coaching. The moment he saw me, he recognized me. He gave me a hug and told me he had been looking for me for a long time. He asked if I knew what had happened to my brothers and sisters. I was ashamed that I had no idea. I was mortified by my selfishness. I told Coach that I was 'lost' and wanted to restore myself back to normalcy. All those years, I had been angry with everyone, especially with myself. Remaining angry at the world didn't get me anywhere except into more pain and more rage. Coach Abraham was the only person I could trust, and I told him that I needed help.

"His response was only more reassurance that he was the correct person to help me. 'Son, you were never lost, but your path was foggy, so you couldn't see where you were. Now that you have realized it, you are ready to see the truth. I promise you that I will do anything in my power to help you, though it won't be an easy road. I want you to know that as long as you believe in yourself, you are going to make it, and I'm here for you. Please promise me that you won't give up, even when the road gets bumpy and hard. It's a tough life. Remember, there are going to be obstacles in your way. You should keep the faith in yourself and in God, knowing that anything is possible.'

"Coach Abraham became my friend and mentor. He took me to his home and introduced me to his family. He welcomed me into his home with open arms. It was really comforting to have a safe place to lay my head every night. This was a home where we all sat at the dinner table for meals. Not once did his family make me feel like an outsider. Coach helped me locate my siblings, and we found out that they were in a foster home. Luckily, they had been able to stay together, and their foster parents were such kind, decent people. I promised them that one day, we would all be together again. I promised them I would be the big brother they deserved to have, and one day I would get a big house so we could all stay there together. Until then, though, I visited them almost every day, helping them with anything they might need.

"With each passing year, I got closer to fulfilling my goals. With Coach's help, not only did I manage to graduate from high school, but I also received a scholarship to a university. Finally, I was able to honor the promise I'd made to my mother a long time ago. I also honored the promise I had made to my siblings that someday we would live together under one roof. I managed to obtain a home for my siblings and myself. It was surreal to be able to live together under one roof. I will never forget the first night that all of us sat around the dinner table in our own place. We talked about our mother, how beautiful and kind she was. They were too young to remember everything, but I told them all about her and how she sacrificed her life to save us all. I told them she would have been proud of all of us. We cried, we laughed, and we all realized how precious our time with her had been. Our mother had wanted all of us to be happy and successful in our own ways. We reminded each other to honor her wish that we would love each other and cherish her memories. It was a magical night that none of us will ever forget. Years went by so fast, and as each of my siblings grew up, they went on to fulfill their own goals and dreams. I made sure to let them know that I was there for them if they ever needed me, and this was their home too. If they ever needed to come back and stay, the door was always open. They all turned out to be decent human beings, thank God!"

Coach Tony laughed in relief, then he continued, "Maybe they were just too young when all those horrible things happened, so perhaps I was the only one who witnessed the cruelty and abuse that our mother faced each day. I think I was the only one who saw her on the kitchen floor in a pool of her own blood. I was happy they didn't have to experience any of those atrocious things in our home. I still thought about my father often. I was still angry with him, and I couldn't forgive him for killing my mother and putting our family through so many hardships. Even though I was now an adult and living by myself, I would still talk to Coach Abraham often, because he'd become family to me. I recall one evening after dinner, Coach and I sat outside on the front porch of his house, and I told him that I still carried the anger and hate toward my father. He told me that I had to confront this anger head-on. Otherwise, it would create a demon inside of me. He encouraged me to find my father and confront him, then let it go. It was the only way I could set myself free. Otherwise, I would never be truly healed, and that hate and anger inside of me would damage my soul. Coach was right; I had to face my father once and for all and actually let him know how I felt about him.

"It wasn't difficult to find my father, because I knew he would still be in jail. He was in prison for killing my mother and for a few other felonies. Deep down, I was afraid to see him face-to-face. Coach was correct that I had to do this for my own sake and for the liberty of my soul, because no matter how successful I was in life, I was a prisoner of my own memories of him. They haunted me. For years, I had carried this anger and this frustration inside of me. I wanted to be free from him and from my past. I wanted to let it go and move on with my life. I had to face him and tell him all those things that I had kept inside of me for the past nineteen years, ever since he killed my mom.

"Finally, I told Coach that I was ready to see my father. Coach made a phone call to the prison and found out that the poor bastard had a heart attack and was in the hospital's intensive care unit. I decided to go see him there, and as I was waiting in the hospital, they told him that his son was there to see him. To my surprise, he agreed to the visit. I was nervous, and I didn't know what to expect, but I didn't want him to see me all nervous and shaky. He would have thought I was still afraid of him or that he had power over me. I calmed myself with deep breaths. Coach wanted to tag along to offer moral support, but I told him I had to do this on my own. I had to face my father and say what I had to say, let him know that he destroyed our childhood. He had no idea what we'd been through all these years. I wanted him to see how successful I had become in spite of him. I wanted to let him know that his cruelty didn't turn us into people like him, but that we actually turned out okay. I dressed so elegantly, putting on my best appearance. All I wanted was to burn him, to just look into his eyes and say, 'I forgive you because you are not worth the effort of carrying all that hatred inside of me.'

"I entered his room. There were no windows. It had one single bed, a side table, and some medical equipment, I guess to monitor his cruel and empty heart. I stood beside the doorway, feeling confused, angry, and revengeful. I hadn't seen my father for the past nineteen years. All I had in my mind was the image of the drunk, angry, violent monster that I'd been horrified to even make eye contact with. All that lay in front of me was a little, frail, old man. He was nothing but skin and bones wrapped up in an old blanket. He had his back turned to me, so I couldn't see his face. I don't know how long I just stood in the doorway, watching him. Then, all of a sudden, he turned around and looked at me. We both stared at each other until he recognized me. 'Anthony,' he said, with such a weak, broken voice. 'Son, is that you?'

"I responded in anger and hate, 'Don't you dare call me your son. I'm ashamed to have you as my father. All I'm here to do is let you know that I forgive you, but I will never forget what you did to my mother and to all of us. I want to forgive you because I want to move on with my life. I want to forgive you because this way, I will be free from all my nightmares. I am not doing this for you but for my own peace of mind. I will forgive you, so now you can burn in hell.' I turned around to leave the room. I didn't want him to see that I was shaking and that a flood of tears was about to rush down my face.

"I didn't want him to see me crying, but then he called my name. 'Anthony, please, you waited nineteen years to tell me all of this, to make peace with yourself. I don't blame you for hating me. I hate myself more, but please, at least give me only nineteen minutes of your time, that's all I ask. I beg of you.' His frail voice was full of pain, nothing like the threatening voice I remembered. He was weak, in pain, and crying out in desperation. I turned around and took one step toward his bed.

"He tried to move his body toward me, but I think the pain and the IVs connected to him stopped him, so instead he just tried to talk. Let me tell you, the person in front of me in that room was far from the evil person I had known so long ago. He was pitiful. Those eyes that used to always be bloodshot and strike fear into me now begged me to give him a moment of my time. That mouth that used to scream at my mother and us every night was now only an old man's mouth without any teeth. He had a tiny face, full of deep wrinkles and old wounds scattered across his face. Who was he? This couldn't be the man who had terrorized us for years. This couldn't be the man who killed my mother, the one I'd wasted years of my life hating. He was not the same person.

"As I stared at him in disbelief, he started to talk. 'I was an evil man. I had a beautiful family and a wonderful wife, but I never knew how lucky I was. My life was consumed by drugs, alcohol, and gambling. To make it worse, I spent most of my time with the wrong crowds. My father abused me, and his father abused him. It was a vicious cycle that I didn't think I could escape. In my mind, you all had to pay for my own abusive childhood. I blamed all of you for my pain and miserable past. I don't blame you for wanting me to burn in hell. Believe me, I have been living in hell for the past sixty years, and I don't complain, you know why? I deserve every minute of it. I don't wish to die, because that's the easy way out. I want to be alive and suffer for eternity. What I have done to my family, to all of you, especially your mother—there is no way on this earth that I can justify any of my actions. I don't deserve your respect, your kindness, or your pity at all.

I need to pay for what I have done to you all. All I am now is a broken man without any kind of redemption. Take a good look at me, and forgive me truly from the deepest part of your heart. Forgive me so you can move on and live a peaceful life. Don't you think for a second that your forgiveness will set me free, because I will never allow myself to feel forgiven. All I need to do before I die is to know that I did at least one thing right by getting your forgiveness, for your own sake. I can know that from now on, you will be free from me and all the pain I caused you. Release it, move on, remain upbeat. Be the best father you can be. Never say my name to your children, and change your last name. Carry on with your life without limitations. That is all I need from you.'

"My father endeavored to pull all the cords off of his arms and chest in an attempt to move toward me, and he grasped my hands. He kissed the back of my hand then placed it over his heart. He said, 'Your heart is excessively beautiful, making it impossible to keep hate in there. Let me go, and forgive me. Disregard yesterday, since all it will do is wreck your tomorrow.' He pivoted back toward his little bed, and at that time, the nurse came running into the room to help him.

"I told the nurse, 'That's all right, let me do it. He is my father.' I lifted him up into my arms; he was so fragile. He wrapped his arms around my neck, and I pulled him nearer to my chest. This time around, I looked at him differently, kind of like any son would look at his debilitated father, with empathy. At that point, I put him tenderly on the little bed and covered his body with a blanket. He grasped my hand and whispered gently, 'One son was conceived, turning a man into a father. After that, the father turned into the son, and the son turned into the father.'

"Both of our faces were streaked with tears by this point. I fixed his white hair, brushing it from his brow, then I whispered into his ear, 'I forgive you.' I kissed his head and left the room. As I walked toward the exit of the hospital, I could hardly understand how extraordinary I felt. A couple of days after that, he passed away. I figured he had come to terms with God. Above all, I had made peace with him.

"Coach Abraham was right. After that day, I moved on with my life. I felt lighter, and something in me was brighter and different. I think that the heavy weight of anger I had harbored in my heart for years finally disappeared. I was ecstatic about my future. I was ready for the next chapter of my life. I was ready to have my own love nest and family. I met a nice girl, and after a while, I told her about my dark past. She is a wonderful woman, and till this day, I love her like I did when we first fell in love. We have a son, and my family means everything to me. Every day, I remind myself how lucky I am to be alive and to have a second chance to make things right.

"When I look back and think about my dad, I am amazed that the person who tormented me for so long, the person I abhorred for so many years, became the person who helped me make peace with myself. He opened my eyes to the truth of genuine living. The significant lesson I learned from all the tragedy in my life is that it doesn't make a difference how rich or well-educated you are. If you don't relinquish the hate in your heart and let go of your past, you are genuinely the poorest individual alive. It's like being trapped in a virtual jail. Life is a mystery. The man who murdered my angelic mom turned into the person who spared my life. I suppose he turned into my own gentle giant, isn't that so?" Coach Tony grinned and said to me, "Now I'm here, attempting to reveal to you that regardless of what's occurring in your life, you have a decision. You are alive, and that is the best blessing from God. He will give you opportunities to make good choices and acknowledge that you have splendid future ahead, if only you choose to strive for it."

Then Coach Tony left. He was correct that life is a maze with many unexpected turns. At some point, you'll pick the correct one and get the astonishment of your life, and other times, you simply hit a stopping point. Regardless of what happens, we must continue onward and figure out what we're searching for in life. The person who is constantly prepared for the twists and turns of life will be the person who lives without limitations.

At that point, I went straight home. My mom was in the kitchen as usual, cooking for us. I ran into her arms and pressed my head against her chest. Right then and there, I didn't know what or how to say I was sorry for all that I had done. Rather, I stayed in that hug for as long as I could. I was certain she comprehended what was happening.

She pulled my chin up so she could see my face. "I love you, Michael," she said.

After that, my mom and I no longer fought like we used to. Our life improved. I moved on from high school and went to college to be a physical therapist and youth counselor. I stayed in contact with Coach Tony. He was a dear companion and pretty much like family to me. He eventually stopped coaching because of his health, and he invested his energy into his grandchildren and a newfound enthusiasm for gardening.

At last, my mom carried on with the life she had once longed for. She had the dauntlessness to follow her heart and passion for painting. This brought about her opening a little art school.

One day, as I swam in an ocean of memories, past recollections, and considerations about the future, I heard my mom's voice calling me. I was brought back to the present. I opened my eyes, and there she was before me, still wonderful, with her long, white hair perfectly braided. She wore a flowing, green botanical dress. She never attempted to be something she wasn't. When I was a kid, I used to call her a hippie mother, and she still resembled that.

I grinned at her and said, "Hello, Mom."

There was such fervor in her voice that she could scarcely breathe. "Michael! Are you ready to see your boy?"

I jumped up, pulled back to the reality of where I was—the hospital. Here was my opportunity to be the best father I could be. I must simply remember to love my son. Having a family was a blessing from God. The ball was in my court, and this was my opportunity to be a gentle giant for my son.

"Hurry up, your wife needs you!" my mom shouted. At that point, she began to jog, leading the way. I grabbed her hand, and she glanced back at me with those kind eyes.

"What is it, honey, are you all right?" she whispered.

"Truly, I'm all right, I simply needed to say thank you for being my mother."

She stopped and kissed my cheek, holding my hand firmly. This was the beginning of another chapter in our lives, and we ran toward a promising future.

The End

EPILOGUE

As I put my pen down and stop writing, I realize that I was writing through the whole night. I close the notebook and step outside onto the balcony of my apartment. All I can hear is the peaceful silence, and a soft breeze of fall brushes over my skin. I take a deep breath and imagine all those faces from my past, remembering a man who sacrificed his life and dreams so his children could dream bigger and have a better future in a faraway land; a woman who never gave up belief in the power of faith and love and didn't allow the actions of one man destroy her faith in herself and in humanity; a mother I met a long time ago who told me that she once had nothing to feed her infant child for almost a month except for a loaf of bread, a few cans of beans, and eggs, so she starved herself so that her child could live; a woman who escaped with her nine-month-old baby across one of the most dangerous borders on earth in the hope that she could someday find happiness for herself and her child on the other side of the world.

Walking down memory lane, all those faces smile back at me—Mama Jee standing in her kitchen with her famous tea, trying to hand me a glass; Eldana holding her grandson in her arms, watching me with those beautiful lavender eyes, full of love; Anouk sitting behind her café, smoking her cigarette; Ray holding on to the good inside of him in spite of everything that happened to him; and brave, innocent Michael looking up to the compassionate coach who became his real gentle giant and led him from a life of confusion, anger, and pain. May their stories be my guide and hope that no matter what, life is precious, delicate, and beautiful. At the same time, life can be cold, cruel, and empty if we don't make the right choices or if we let the darkness in us take over our souls.

I close my eyes and let their memories and faces be captured forever in my heart. I let the accumulation of their life stories of bravery, sacrifice, courage, and faith become the torch I use to light up the path to my unknown future.

ABOUT THE AUTHOR

Shahla Shahmiri was born in Iran. At an early age, her parents sent her to live in a small town north of Iran with her grandmother who was an herbalist with a vast knowledge of nature, herbs, spices, and the healing power of nature. Her grandmother taught all she could, and Shahla learned how to use those powerful tools to create the perfect dish and later become a chef.

After escaping Iran, Shahla lived as a refugee for many years. Eventually, Australia became home. It was there she finished her higher education while holding tightly to many lifelong dreams, three of which came true. One dream was to have her own café where she could interact with people, cook the perfect meal, and just be herself. The second was to become a photographer to capture moments in people's lives, nature, or anything beautiful in her surroundings. The third was to become a storyteller to celebrate the many people who influenced her along the way.

Shahla currently resides in Flowermound, Texas, where she operates her own catering company called Saffron Girl (www.saffrongril.com). Local patrons and special groups enjoy participating in her cooking classes to expand their knowledge of food and bond over elegantly prepared dishes. *Tears of Onions* is her first novel.

Made in the USA
Columbia, SC
04 May 2019